COWLES COMMISSION FOR
RESEARCH IN ECONOMICS
Monograph No. 13

COWLES FOUNDATION
For Research in Economics at Yale University

The Cowles Foundation for Research in Economics at Yale University, established as an activity of the Yale Department of Economics in 1955, has as its purpose the conduct and encouragement of research in economics, finance, commerce, industry, and technology, including problems of the organization of these activities. The Cowles Foundation seeks to foster the development of logical, mathematical, and statistical methods of analysis for application in economics and related social sciences. The professional research staff are faculty members with appointments and teaching responsibilities in the Department of Economics and other departments.

The Cowles Foundation continues the work of the Cowles Commission for Research in Economics founded in 1932 by Alfred Cowles at Colorado Springs, Colorado. The Commission moved to Chicago in 1939 and was affiliated with the University of Chicago until 1955. In 1955 the professional research staff of the Commission accepted appointments at Yale and, along with other members of the Yale Department of Economics, formed the research staff of the newly established Cowles Foundation.

MONOGRAPHS

Orders for Monographs 3, 7, and 8
should be sent to
THE PRINCIPIA PRESS, INC.
Evanston, Illinois

Orders for Monographs 10 to 17
should be sent to
JOHN WILEY & SONS, INC.
440 Park Avenue South, New York 16, N. Y.

ACTIVITY ANALYSIS OF PRODUCTION AND ALLOCATION

Proceedings of a Conference

Edited by

TJALLING C. KOOPMANS

In Cooperation with

ARMEN ALCHIAN   GEORGE B. DANTZIG

NICHOLAS GEORGESCU-ROEGEN

PAUL A. SAMUELSON   ALBERT W. TUCKER

JOHN WILEY & SONS, INC.

NEW YORK · LONDON · SYDNEY

PRINTED IN THE UNITED STATES OF AMERICA

CONTRIBUTORS TO THIS VOLUME

KENNETH J. ARROW, *Stanford University and Cowles Commission*

GEORGE W. BROWN, *The RAND Corporation*

YALE BROZEN, *Northwestern University*

ANSLEY COALE, *Princeton University*

GEORGE B. DANTZIG, *U. S. Department of the Air Force*

ROBERT DORFMAN, *University of California, Berkeley*

DAVID GALE, *Brown University*

MURRAY A. GEISLER, *U. S. Department of the Air Force*

NICHOLAS GEORGESCU-ROEGEN, *Vanderbilt University and Harvard Economic Project*

MURRAY GERSTENHABER, *Cowles Commission (formerly), The University of Chicago*

CLIFFORD HILDRETH, *Cowles Commission*

TJALLING C. KOOPMANS, *Cowles Commission*

HAROLD W. KUHN, *Princeton University*

OSKAR MORGENSTERN, *Princeton University*

STANLEY REITER, *Cowles Commission (formerly), Stanford University*

PAUL A. SAMUELSON, *Massachusetts Institute of Technology and The RAND Corporation*

HERBERT A. SIMON, *Carnegie Institute of Technology and Cowles Commission*

HARLAN SMITH, *University of Minnesota*

ALBERT W. TUCKER, *Princeton University*

MARSHALL K. WOOD, *U. S. Department of the Air Force*

CONFERENCE PAPERS NOT INCORPORATED
IN THIS VOLUME

W. DUANE EVANS, *U. S. Bureau of Labor Statistics*, "Similarities between the Concepts of Capital, Consumption, and Maintenance in Dynamic Models."

MERRILL M. FLOOD, *The RAND Corporation*, Discussion of Problems in Transportation and Location.

MURRAY A. GEISLER, *U. S. Department of the Air Force*, "Nonlinear Aspects of Air Force Programming."

DAVID HAWKINS, *University of Colorado*, "Linear Models in the Study of Competition and Monopoly."

MARVIN HOFFENBERG, *U. S. Bureau of Labor Statistics*, "Inter-Industry Relations Data Collection and Classification Problems."

LEONID HURWICZ, *University of Illinois and Cowles Commission*, "Business Cycle Stabilization as a Problem in the Theory of Games."

ABBA P. LERNER, *Roosevelt College*, Discussion of "Market Mechanisms and Maximization" by Paul A. Samuelson.

PAUL A. SAMUELSON, *Massachusetts Institute of Technology and The RAND Corporation*, "Market Mechanisms and Maximization."

C. TOMPKINS, *George Washington University*, Discussion of Mathematical Problems in Programming.

OTHER PARTICIPANTS IN THE CONFERENCE

ARMEN ALCHIAN, *University of California at Los Angeles*
GEORGE H. BORTS, *Cowles Commission (formerly), Brown University*
JEAN BRONFENBRENNER, *Cowles Commission (formerly), University of Illinois*
OSWALD BROWNLEE, *The University of Minnesota*
LOUIS COURT, *Rutgers University*
EVSEY D. DOMAR, *Johns Hopkins University and Operations Research Office*
FRANCIS W. DRESCH, *U. S. Naval Proving Ground*
MELVIN DRESHER, *The RAND Corporation*
DONALD FORT, *Federal Reserve Board*
WALTER JACOBS, *U. S. Department of Commerce*
NORMAN KAPLAN, *The RAND Corporation*
WALTER H. KEEN, *U. S. Department of the Navy*
CARL N. KLAHR, *Cowles Commission (formerly), Carnegie Institute of Technology*
JULIUS MARGOLIS, *The University of Chicago*
JACOB MARSCHAK, *Cowles Commission*
LLOYD A. METZLER, *The University of Chicago*
FRED D. RIGBY, *U. S. Department of the Navy*
DAVID ROSENBLATT, *Carnegie Institute of Technology and U. S. Bureau of the Budget*
TIBOR DE SCITOVSKY, *Stanford University*
WILLIAM B. SIMPSON, *Cowles Commission*
THOMSON M. WHITIN, *Princeton University*
MAX A. WOODBURY, *Princeton University*

ACKNOWLEDGMENTS

The conference on which this volume reports, and the research of all but one of the Cowles Commission staff members included in it, were carried out under a research contract with The RAND Corporation, Santa Monica, California. The contribution of C. Hildreth to Chapter XI was part of his research under a grant from the Rockefeller Foundation to the Cowles Commission.

Thanks are due to the participants in the conference for making their contributions available for this volume. The members of the Editorial Committee, and also Leonid Hurwicz and M. L. Slater, have contributed further as editorial referees.

Mr. Gerhard Stoltz gave valuable assistance in the preparation of the manuscript and drawings for the printer and in the compilation of the references and index. The main burden of proofreading was undertaken by Mr. Kirk Fox, and additional assistance was given by Miss Jean Curtis, Mrs. Mary Eckart, and Mrs. Lorraine Kirk. Thanks are due to all of these as well as to Mrs. Jane Novick, Editorial Secretary of the Cowles Commission, for general supervision of the preparation of the volume for the press and for seeing it through to publication.

PREFACE TO THE SECOND PRINTING (1956)

The ideas assembled and presented in this book have been extended and applied in many directions since its appearance in 1951. In particular, it is gratifying to see that the remarks made at the end of p. 4 below about the paucity of industrial applications have been superseded by subsequent developments. This is borne out by many articles in such journals as "Econometrica," "Journal of Farm Economics," "Journal of the Operations Research Society of America," "Management Science."

No attempt has been made to extend the list of references on p. 381. However, we mention here three subsequent publications somewhat similar in character to this book.

A. Orden and L. Goldstein, ed., Symposium on Linear Inequalities and Programming, Washington, 1952.

H. A. Antosiewicz, ed., Second Symposium on Linear Programming, Vols. I and II, Washington, 1955.

H. W. Kuhn and A. W. Tucker, ed., Papers on Linear Inequalities and Related Systems, Annals of Mathematics Study, Number 38, 1956.

The second printing of this book is identical with the first except for the correction of minor errors.

T. C. K.

TABLE OF CONTENTS

INTRODUCTION

By Tjalling C. Koopmans

The contributions to this book are devoted, directly or indirectly, to various aspects of a fundamental problem of normative economics: the best allocation of limited means toward desired ends. The central place of this problem in economic thought explains what otherwise might seem like a surprising fact: that the studies here assembled bring out affinities and connections between lines of thought and funds of experience developed in apparent independence by various groups of economists, mathematicians, and administrators. The volume thus testifies to the fundamental unity of the economic problem, even though the approaches and points of view may vary widely. An introduction to it should start by indicating some of the currents of thought here converging and interacting.

A specific historical origin of the work in this volume is found in discussions among Austrian and German economists in the thirties on generalizations of the Walrasian equation systems of mathematical economics. Neisser [1932] and von Stackelberg [1933] raised questions of existence and uniqueness of a solution to Cassel's formulation of the Walrasian system, with reference in particular to the requirement that prices and rates of production be represented by nonnegative numbers. In a mathematical seminar conducted in Vienna by Karl Menger, Schlesinger [1935] formulated a suggestion, made also by Zeuthen [1933], that economic theory should explain not only the nonnegative prices and quantities produced of scarce goods but also which goods are scarce and which are free (i.e., have a zero price). Wald [1935, 1936a, b] proved the existence and uniqueness of a solution to an equation system expressing this problem. His discussion concerned a static model of production in which each commodity in demand can be produced in one way (a given amount of production requiring the input of proportional amounts of primary factors of production). He assumed that the total availabilities of primary factors are given by nature and that there is a given static structure of demand (demand functions satisfying a monotonicity condition).

In a later contribution to the same seminar, von Neumann [1937, 1945] generalized this model of production in several directions. He introduced alternative methods of producing given commodities singly or

1

jointly, each method again involving fixed technological coefficients (ratios between inputs and outputs). Thus he derived not only which goods are free but also which productive activities (methods) go unused. Also, a commodity could appear simultaneously as input of one activity and as output of another. This circularity idea was extended even to goods demanded by consumers, through the somewhat forced concept of an activity producing labor by the absorption of consumption goods in fixed proportions. The model thus became a closed one, with no inflow of primary factors from outside or outflow of final products out of the system considered. Any nonconsumed "surplus" was assumed to be used for capital formation to obtain a continuous proportional expansion of all productive activities under unchanging technology. Von Neumann's model is therefore dynamic in the limited sense that change over time is described by one scalar coefficient of uniform expansion.[1]

Like Wald, von Neumann treated prices (including an interest rate) as determined in competitive markets so as to satisfy a zero profit condition on all activities engaged in. He further excluded positive profits on unused activities. Although his main concern was still with the existence of a solution (i.e., a set of nonnegative prices and activity levels meeting these conditions), the important observation was made at the end of the article that any such solution achieves efficiency of allocation in the sense of a maximum rate of expansion of production compatible with the given technology of production and consumption. This rate of expansion is uniquely determined by the technological coefficients, but there may be more than one solution achieving it.

We have dwelt on these discussions in some detail because even among mathematical economists their value seems to have been insufficiently realized. The second source of inspiration for the present studies, although still largely in the realm of abstract theory, is part of the common fund of ideas of "literary" and "mathematical" economics. This is the theory of welfare economics, particularly in its application to production. Bergson's [1938] concept of an "economic welfare function," employed also by Lange [1942] under the name "social value function," recurs in Dantzig's "objective function" [II], in a context where the distributional problem concerning individual welfare levels recedes to the background. Similar use is made of the idea underlying Pareto's "weak welfare principle" [Pareto, 1909, Chapter VI, Section 33], which regards a situation as maximal from the welfare point of view if no technologically possible reallocation or redistribution of commodities can in-

---

[1] The idea of a linear model describing an economy expanding at a constant rate is also contained in an earlier study by Leontief [1928].

crease somebody's welfare without decreasing someone else's welfare. Through the studies of Barone [1935], Bergson [1938], Hicks [1939], Hotelling [1938], Kaldor [1939], Lange [1942], Lerner [1944], and others,[2] this principle became the basis of what is known as the "new welfare economics." It is here applied by Koopmans [III], Georgescu-Roegen [IV], Samuelson [VII], and others to productive efficiency problems by substituting the outputs of desired commodities for individual welfare levels in the foregoing formulation.

Particular use is made of those discussions in welfare economics (opened by a challenge of L. von Mises [1922, 1935]) that dealt with the possibility of economic calculation in a socialist society. The notion of prices as constituting the information that should circulate between centers of decision to make consistent allocation possible emerged from the discussions by Lange [1938], Lerner [1944], and others. The underlying idea of the models of allocation constructed by them is that the comparison of the benefits from alternative uses of each good, where not secured by competitive market situations, can be built into the administrative processes that decide the allocation of that good. This suggestion is relevant, not only to the problems of a socialist economy, but also to the allocation problems of the many sectors of capitalist or mixed economies where competitive markets do not penetrate.

The third source of ideas is the work on interindustry relationships, initiated, developed, and stimulated largely by Leontief [1936; 1937; 1941; 1944; 1946a, b; 1948a, b; 1949] and given statistical expression by measurements and tabulations produced by the Bureau of Labor Statistics. One of the purposes of this work has been to provide an empirical basis for numerical estimation of the effects, on the levels of activity in individual industries, of given changes in the composition of final demand by industries supplying final goods. The theoretical concepts underlying this work have been adapted to the purpose of answering broad quantitative policy questions from an analysis of observable variables of a more or less aggregative type. The operations of an industry were regarded as one activity, and homogeneity of productive operations within an industry was aimed for by as detailed an industrial classification as was permitted by available data and computation methods and equipment. The method of measurement of input-output coefficients that has been used most extensively is the observation of the money value of all goods and services delivered by each industry to each other industry in a census year. This method, which precludes the separate measurement of alternative processes to produce the same commodity, or the recognition of joint production, can be and is being supplemented

[2] For further references, see, for instance, Samuelson [1948, Chapter VIII].

by the study of engineering information, which is not subject to these limitations. Substitution possibilities have not been explicitly introduced in his models by Leontief but are not incompatible with them, as will be explained further below. Present work by Leontief and his collaborators is directed to the dynamic generalization of the static models so far developed.

The fourth source of inspiration has been the study of equally practical but more detailed, less aggregative, allocation and programming problems that arose particularly in the organization of defense or the conduct of war. The most comprehensive work in this category has been the development of programming models by George B. Dantzig and other members of a group of officials of the U. S. Department of the Air Force, under the direction of Marshall K. Wood. Several reports on this work are contained in the present volume [I, II, XII, XIII, XXI, XXIII]. The models of this group were developed to deal both with the dynamic aspects of scheduling the interdependent activities of a large organization and with the choice of a best combination of activities toward the achievement of a stated objective. Although in practical elaboration the dynamic features have so far received precedence, the conceptual structure of the models also invites the comparative study of alternative ends attainable with given means.

In the same "detailed practical" category is work by Koopmans [1947] on a static model of transportation developed, in ignorance of an earlier study by Hitchcock [1941], under the stimulation of statistical work for the Combined Shipping Adjustment Board, the British-American board dealing with merchant shipping problems during the second world war.

There is, of course, no exclusive connection between defense or war and the systematic study of allocation and programming problems. It is believed that the studies assembled in this volume are of equal relevance to problems of industrial management and efficiency in production scheduling. They also throw new light on old problems of abstract economic theory. If the apparent prominence of military application at this stage is more than a historical accident, the reasons are sociological rather than logical. It does seem that governmental agencies, for whatever reason, have so far provided a better environment and more sympathetic support for the systematic study, abstract and applied, of principles and methods of allocation of resources than private industry. There has also been more mobility of scientific personnel between government and universities, to the advantage of both.

The foregoing references to the main currents of thought that have inspired the present studies may already have helped to characterize the intent of this volume. The immediate occasion for it is to report on a conference on "linear programming," held in Chicago at the Cowles Commission for Research in Economics on June 20–24, 1949. In this conference, scientists classifiable as economists, mathematicians, statisticians, administrators, or combinations thereof, pooled their knowledge, experience, and points of view to discuss the theory and practice of efficient utilization of resources. The mathematicians brought new tools of analysis essential to the progress of economics. The administrators introduced an element of closeness to actual operations and decisions not otherwise attainable. Those speaking as statisticians adduced data and discussed their limitations. The economists contributed an awareness of the variety of institutional arrangements that may be utilized to achieve efficient allocation.

The present volume contains the majority of the papers presented to the conference. A list of contributors to this volume, a list of papers presented in the conference but not reproduced, and a list of participants in the conference who did not formally present papers are given on pages vii–ix. A number of papers [III, IV, V, IX, XI, XIII, XIV, XX, XXIII] were rewritten and substantially extended after the conference, either because only an abstract was prepared for the conference or because additional material was found to be essential for a well-rounded presentation. Two mathematical papers [XVII, XVIII] were added. Other papers have undergone some revision or extension [II, VII, XX, XXII] or were abstracted [X, XVI, XXIV] because of plans for fuller publication elsewhere. The remaining papers [I, VI, VIII, XII, XV, XXV] are reproduced essentially as presented to the conference. Of the articles in the volume, the first two are reprinted, with minor [I] or more extensive [II] revisions, from *Econometrica*, Vol. 17, 1949. All other contributions appear here for the first time in print.

The name of the conference topic, "linear programming," requires explanation. In earlier phases of the work reported on in this volume, contacts and exchanges of ideas among its authors were stimulated by a common interest in the formal problem of maximization of a linear function of variables subject to linear inequalities. The term "linear programming" became a convenient designation for the class of allocation or programming problems which give rise to that maximization problem. The different title of this volume is intended to convey that the work has in part already outgrown the designation and may be expected to outgrow it further.

The term "linear" still applies to all the models discussed here. But to carry that term at the masthead would impede an understanding of the true intent of the work by emphasizing its present limitations.

Moreover, because of a semantic difficulty, its use would tend to over-state those limitations. To many economists the term linearity is asso-ciated with narrowness, restrictiveness, and inflexibility of hypotheses. We cannot pass such judgment until it is specified where the linearity assumption is made. In this book the adjective in "linear model" re-lates only to (a) the assumption of proportionality of inputs and out-puts in each elementary productive activity, and (b) the assumption that the result of simultaneously carrying out two or more activities is the sum of the results of the separate activities. In terms more familiar to the economist, these assumptions imply constant returns to scale in all parts of the technology. They do not imply linearity of the produc-tion function, only its homogeneity of degree one. Curvilinear produc-tion functions with that property, and with the continuity of derivatives suggested by the appealing smoothness of textbook diagrams, can be obtained from the models here studied by admitting an infinite set of elementary activities. The limitation to a finite basis of activities in most of the present contributions is a matter of mathematical conven-ience and is of little economic consequence. As long as the homoge-neity assumption is satisfied, the "polyhedral" production functions de-rived from a finite basis permit any desired degree of approximation in all applications and constitute a gain in realism in many. In particu-lar, the production functions so obtained fully express the phenomenon of decreasing returns to proportional increases in the inputs of some but not all primary factors of production.

Neither should the assumption of constant returns to scale, made throughout this volume, be regarded as essential to the method of ap-proach it illustrates, although new mathematical problems would have to be faced in the attempt to go beyond this assumption. More essen-tial to the present approach is the introduction of the method of pro-duction, the elementary activity, the conceptual atom of technology, into the basic postulates of the analysis. The problem of efficient pro-duction then becomes one of finding the proper rules for combining these building blocks. The term "activity analysis" in the title of this book is designed to express this approach.

In going down to idealized technological fundamentals in this way, a new freedom is won in the specification of institutional assumptions. These can be left blank in an abstract study of the criteria of efficient allocation. Alternatively, a centralized direction of allocative decisions can be specified. The term "programming" suggests the latter institu-tional setting, emphasizing in particular the problems involved in the time sequence of productive activities. However, it is also possible to specify decentralized decision making, through a market mechanism or through administrative communication. It seems, therefore, that the term "allocation" as the economist uses it is more suited to the variety of possible institutional arrangements envisaged, it being understood that this term includes the problem of best time sequence of activities.

Where so many diverse minds are at work on a problem area of common interest, a certain amount of overlapping in content between their contributions is inevitable and, indeed, wholesome. In order to preserve the diversity in points of view and methods of approach, editorial processes have left authors with considerable freedom to restate or enlarge other authors' results in their own terminology or context. Likewise, authors have chosen their own notations, subject only to mild editorial persuasion where differences in notation might place hardships on the reader.

It may be useful to give brief comments on individual articles in the book in order to help the reader find his way rather than to attempt a characterization of the various contributions, which can be left to speak for themselves. Therefore comments are apportioned only on the basis of the desirability of introductory explanations.

The four parts of the book follow the natural order of theory, application, and tools, the latter subdivided into mathematical tools and computational procedures. Those who find the theory somewhat abstruse may prefer to start their reading with some of the applications given in Part Two, in which the subject matter is more concrete and the style more expository.

The opening chapter of Part One discusses the allocation problem from the point of view of an organization in which a high degree of centralization in decision making is a strong tradition and in all likelihood a nearly as strong necessity. To von Mises' arguments [1922, 1935] regarding the unmanageability of the computation problems of centralized allocation, the authors oppose the new possibilities opened by modern electronic computing equipment. In Chapter II a model is developed to guide the study of this allocation problem. Dantzig's model, initially conceived independently of von Neumann's model already discussed, is similar to it in allowing commodities to be inputs as well as outputs, in introducing alternative ways of achieving the same ends, and in choosing stocks-at-end-of-period rather than flows-during-period as the output variables. It is, however, more truly dynamic in that it permits change over time in the relative amounts of various activities in order most efficiently to achieve a stated objective. Dantzig's model is an abstract allocation model that does not depend on the concept of a market. It does not introduce prices except implicitly (for final commodities) in the formulation of the objective, which is to maximize a given linear function of the amounts of certain activities or (equivalently) commodities. It utilizes the concept of an exogenous activity to introduce limitations on the amounts of primary (or initially available) resources and is therefore an open model, unlike von Neumann's.

The model developed by Koopmans [III] is a static flow model but in other respects builds on the work of von Neumann and of Dantzig. It is an open model in which, instead of specifying a single objective function, the class of all objective functions that do not exhibit saturation of demand for any of the "final commodities" is admitted. Allocative efficiency, in von Neumann's analysis a property of a solution of market equations, is here made into the main object of study. The production function is defined as the set of all points in the space of commodity flows that result from an efficient combination of activities. Substitution of factors in production is studied as resulting from such shifts in the levels of the combined activities as preserve the efficiency of the combination. While this model is again an allocation model independent of the concept of a market, a price concept applicable to all commodities is derived from the requirement of efficient allocation. These prices represent marginal rates of substitution whenever the latter are defined. They are related to the technological data in the same way as prices resulting from a competitive market structure and can be used as devices to decentralize allocative decisions.

Georgescu-Roegen [IV] discusses a production function concept similarly defined but using a somewhat different definition of the elementary activity. He then relates those concepts to von Neumann's model and gives an alternative proof, based on more elementary mathematical concepts, of von Neumann's theorem regarding the existence of a solution of expanding equilibrium.

The remaining articles of Part One deal with various aspects of the models utilized by Leontief. In Chapter V Georgescu-Roegen discusses a dynamic generalization of the static Leontief model for two industries, which also extends earlier discussions in mathematical business cycle theory. Smith [VI] discusses the uses of Leontief models for answering quantitative questions relevant to economic policy and the interpretation of the variables in these models appropriate to each use. Chapters VII, VIII, IX, and X all deal with the effect of introducing alternative methods of production into Leontief models. It was pointed out by Samuelson, and independently by Georgescu-Roegen, that, as long as each available method has only a single final commodity as output, and as long as only one primary factor of production is subject to a limitation on availability, then any bill of goods (set of final commodity flows) that can be produced in such a technology can be produced efficiently by utilizing only one particular production method for each commodity (this method being the same for all bills of goods). A proof of a theorem stating this property more precisely is outlined by Samuelson [VII]. This proof assumes that the alternative methods available for each commodity can be summarized in a differentiable production function. An alternative proof using the properties of closed convex sets has been developed in order to show that this assumption is not necessary for the theorem. Koopmans [VIII] gives such a proof for a three-industry model. Arrow [IX] generalizes this method of proof to the case of n industries, at the same time introducing an alternative, still weaker, set of assumptions. An abstract is given of Georgescu-Roegen's results [X], partly overlapping those formulated by Arrow but containing interesting further particulars. This investigation will appear in full elsewhere.

It was said above that the articles of Part Two are on the whole more expository in nature. This applies in particular to the opening chapter [XI], where Hildreth and Reiter discuss the use of linear models in the production policy of a firm facing given market prices.[3]

Wood and Geisler [XII] communicate their experience with programming problems as they arise in the practice of a large organization. They develop a model with a nearly triangular coefficient matrix to deal with dynamic situations in which the scheduling problem of successive activities has prominence over the problem of choice between alternative activity combinations. Wood also illustrates the flexibility of linear models by using them to approximate situations characterized by nonlinear growth curves [XIII].

Koopmans and Reiter [XIV] present an application of the theory of Chapter III to a static model of transportation; in this analysis the special way in which "intermediate" commodities occur in the technology leads to the use of linear graphs as a tool of analysis.

Simon's contribution [XV], followed by comments from Coale and Brozen, deals with the various effects of additions to a technology through inventions or innovations. It is shown by graphical illustration how the addition of a new activity may affect the techniques actually used, or only the techniques that would be used under different

---

[3] It may be pointed out that in this article the prices, denoted by p_i, are different in interpretation from the "internal" prices denoted by p_k in Chapter III or by p_{ij} in Chapter XIV but correspond to the "external" prices denoted by π_k in Chapter III, Section 5.11.

availability conditions of primary resources, or may have no effect at all, depending on the input-output ratios of the new activity.

Morgenstern [XVI] abstracts a discussion of the limitations placed on programming methods by the inaccuracy of the statistical data used. This study has since been published in full elsewhere [Morgenstern, 1950].

The mathematical tools presented in Part Three are relatively new to economics. Methods involving convex sets have been used in economics by von Neumann [1937, 1945] in his model already referred to, and by von Neumann and Morgenstern [1944] in the theory of games. In both cases the need for such methods arose from the presence of linear functions of variables which are by their nature nonnegative. This circumstance results in a close mathematical connection between the theory of production and the theory of games, although these theories deal with quite different problems and the variables in question represent quite different entities, that is, levels of activities in production theory and probabilities entering into a "mixed strategy" in the theory of games.

The belief may here be expressed that the theory of point sets in general, and of convex sets in particular, will be an increasingly important tool in economics.[4] In many economic problems a preference ranking of alternatives representable by points in a space is confronted with an opportunity set. Often both the opportunity set and the sets of points preferred-or-indifferent to any given point can be assumed convex. In such cases the use of convexity properties readily permits the study of optimizing choice from all available alternatives. On the other hand, the methods of calculus, more familiar to economists, permit at best a comparison of the chosen alternative with alternatives in its neighborhood, and that only if the required number of derivatives exist.

In these comments the emphasis should fall on the convexity of the point sets studied in Part Three rather than on their polyhedral character arising from the use of a finite basis of points or halflines. We refer here to our previous observation that the use of polyhedral sets, which tends to exaggerate the departure from earlier discussions of production functions, may be a matter of mathematical convenience and approximation only.

A closed convex point set (in a Cartesian space) can be built up from within as the convex hull (convex closure) of a basis or cut down from without as an intersection of halfspaces. This fundamental equivalence was developed by Herman Weyl [1935, 1950], after earlier work by Minkowski [1896], for the case of convex polyhedral cones, where a finite

---

[4] For similar remarks see Arrow [1950, p. 60] and Samuelson [1947, pp. 75, 111].

number of halflines (issuing from the origin) suffice as a basis and a finite number of halfspaces (pivoted on the origin) suffice to form a cone by intersection. The purpose of Gale's chapter [XVII] is to give a paraphrase of Weyl's result for the readers of this book and to illustrate its application to linear models of production and to the theory of games. The relationship between the set of all halflines contained in a polyhedral cone and the set of all halfspaces containing that cone is expressed by Gale in a "duality theorem" [XVII, Theorem 2]. Among its applications used in the study of allocative efficiency is a "separation theorem" [XVII, Theorem 4]. Gale's discussion also illustrates how each property of a cone taken as an intersection of halfspaces can be restated as a property of a system of homogeneous linear inequalities.

In Chapter XVIII, which was developed after Gale's contribution became available in manuscript, Gerstenhaber gives a self-contained discussion of the properties of convex polyhedral cones, properties that have been found to be relevant to the analysis of the model of production of Chapter III. The concepts of a frame and the relative interior of a cone are developed and are employed to obtain a unique decomposition of a cone into open facets. This analysis rests almost entirely on the definition of a cone as a convex hull of halflines but includes an alternative proof of Weyl's theorem of which the duality theorem [XVII, Theorem 2] is a direct consequence. The style of analysis is abstract, and readers unfamiliar with the concepts involved will derive material help from the prior reading of Chapter XVII.

Gale, Kuhn, and Tucker [XIX] discuss a problem of finding a maximal matrix (maximal with respect to all of its elements) permitting certain inequalities to have a solution. They examine this problem in its relation to a minimization problem, in a sense dual to it, and to a game problem symmetrically constructed from the data common to both problems.

The maximization problem referred to is a generalization of, and hence contains as special cases, the maximization of a linear scalar objective function discussed by Dantzig [II] and the maximization (with respect to all elements) of a commodity flow vector which is a linear function of activity levels,[5] as discussed by Koopmans [III]. The mathematical aspects of the methods and theorems used in these earlier studies are thus explored from a more general point of view. The exclusive use of the language of linear inequalities in this chapter should not conceal the affinity of its mathematical content to other articles in the volume formulated wholly or partly in the terminology of convex

[5] A key to corresponding notations in Chapters III and XIX is given in Chapter XIX at the end of Sections 2 and 6.

cones. For instance, the pivotal Lemma 3 of Chapter XIX can be equivalently stated and proved in terms of cone theory.

In Chapter XX Dantzig demonstrates the mathematical equivalence of the linear programming problem and the problem of finding a solution to a game. Computational methods or principles developed for one purpose are thus made available for the other as well. The rapidly growing literature on the theory of games [6] thus has particular relevance to the study of models of production, which are the subject of this book.

Research on computational problems in the maximization of linear functions on convex polyhedral sets is being undertaken by various groups. Any discussion of computation methods at this stage is likely to be highly provisional. Iterative methods seem most appropriate to the nature of the problem. The main method available at present is Dantzig's simplex method, presented by him in Chapter XXI and applied to a game problem by Dorfman [XXII]. A special form of the method for application to the transportation problem [7] of Chapter XIV is also presented by Dantzig [XXIII].

It has been found so far that, for any computation method which seems useful in relation to some set of data, another set of data can be constructed for which that method is obviously unsatisfactory. A variety of methods will therefore have to be explored. Brown [XXIV] outlines a method which was developed independently of a similar method by von Neumann and which is the subject of a more detailed joint publication by these authors.[8] In Chapter XXV some untried suggestions are offered by Brown and Koopmans that might be of use when a systematic exploration of computation methods is undertaken.

---

[6] For a collection of recent studies in this field containing further references to the literature, see Kuhn and Tucker [1950].

[7] A key to corresponding notations in Chapters XIV and XXIII is given in Chapter XIV, Section 2.6.

[8] Included in Kuhn and Tucker [1950].

PART ONE

THEORY OF PROGRAMMING
AND ALLOCATION

Chapter I

THE PROGRAMMING OF INTERDEPENDENT ACTIVITIES: GENERAL DISCUSSION [1]

By Marshall K. Wood and George B. Dantzig

The mathematical model discussed here and in Chapter II is a generalization of the Leontief interindustry model. It is closely related to the one formulated by von Neumann [1937, 1945]. Its chief points of difference lie in its emphasis on dynamic rather than equilibrium or steady states. Its purpose is close control of an organization—hence it must be quite detailed; it is designed to handle highly dynamic problems—hence it puts greater emphasis on time lags and capital equipment; it takes into consideration the many different ways of doing things—hence it explicitly introduces alternative activities; and it recognizes that any particular choice of a dynamic program depends on the "objectives" of the "economy"—hence the selection and types of activities are made to depend on the maximization of an objective function.

Programming, or program planning, may be defined as the construction of a schedule of actions by means of which an economy, organization, or other complex of activities may move from one defined state to another, or from a defined state toward some specifically defined objective. Such a schedule implies, and should explicitly prescribe, the resources and the goods and services utilized, consumed, or produced in the accomplishment of the programmed actions.

The economy or organization for which a program is to be constructed is here conceived of as comprising a finite number of discrete types of activities each of whose magnitudes is to be specified over a certain time period. For convenience, the magnitudes (or levels) of each of the activities will be specified for each of a finite number of discrete time periods,[2] rather than continuously over the total time period involved.

---

[1] This is a revision of a paper presented before the Cleveland Meeting of the Econometric Society on December 27, 1948, and was originally published, in a more extensive form, in *Econometrica*, Vol. 17, July–October, 1949, pp. 193–199. A second paper, with the subtitle "Mathematical Model," contains a more mathematical formulation of the problem and is included as Chapter II of this volume.

[2] The model described here is treated in Chapter II, Section 4, as "A Special Finite Model."

The resources and the goods and services utilized, consumed, or produced by the activities are hereafter referred to generically as "commodities" [3] and are measured in terms of the quantities of specific types of commodities. The quantity of each commodity type used, consumed, or produced by each activity is assumed to be a function of the magnitude of the activity, usually proportional. Two activities are interdependent when they must share limited amounts of a commodity which they use in common, when one produces a commodity which is used by the other, or when each produces a commodity used by a third activity.

These interdependencies arise because all practical programming problems are circumscribed by commodity limitations of one kind or another. The limited "commodity" may be raw materials, manpower, facilities, or funds. One or more of these is almost always limited in any type of program. To some extent, all of them are usually limited in programming problems, since any program must start from a definitely prescribed initial status, at which point all commodities are limited. Generally, these limitations of initial status are felt over several succeeding time periods because of the existence of limitations on the rates of growth of the activities producing the commodities.[4]

There are two general formulations of the programming problem. In the first formulation, the quantities of each of several activities contributing directly to objectives (or "final demand") are specified for each time period; from this it is desired to determine the magnitudes of the required supporting activities, their total requirement for commodities from outside the system, and whether or not these total requirements are consistent with the initial status and subsequent limitations. Procedures for solution of the problem in this formulation have consisted generally of ordering the work in a series of stages. In the first stage, the input requirements of the specified "final demand" activities are computed. In the second stage, those supporting activities whose output is principally utilized by the "final demand" activities are computed. In the third stage, those supporting activities whose output is principally utilized by both the "final demand" activities and the activities whose resource requirements were computed in the second step are computed; and so on.[5] To the extent that the conditions specified in the above arrangement can be met, this procedure yields consistent results. However, when one activity utilizes a commodity produced

[3] The term "item" as used in Chapter II and elsewhere is synonymous with "commodity" as used here.

[4] These growth rate limitations are discussed in Chapters XII and XIII.

[5] This procedure is essentially the Gauss-Seidel method for solution of simultaneous linear systems.

by another, and the other also utilizes a commodity produced by the first, a circular relationship exists which precludes satisfying the conditions of this arrangement, and a satisfactory solution can be produced only by successive iterations of the procedure. The procedure is also deficient in that it does not permit the consideration of alternative processes or activities.

In the second formulation of the programming problem, we seek to determine that program which will, in some sense, most nearly accomplish objectives without exceeding stated resource limitations. At present, such problems can only be solved by successive iterations of the procedure described under the first formulation. Yet this second type of problem is precisely the one which we are constantly required to solve, often under conditions requiring an answer in days or hours.

To accomplish this, it is proposed to represent all the interrelationships in the organization or economy by a large system of simultaneous equations in which the variables are the quantities of the activities to be performed, the coefficients are the requirements of each activity for each commodity, and each equation expresses that the sum of the requirements of all activities for a single commodity equals the sum of the outputs of that commodity from all activities. To prepare a program it is necessary to insert into these equations a detailed specification of the initial status in terms of the quantities of each commodity on hand, any subsequent limitations (such as may be imposed by the capabilities of industries or other activities for expansion), and a statement of objectives.

To compute programs rapidly with such a mathematical model, it is proposed that all necessary information and instructions be systematically classified and stored on magnetized tapes in the "memory" of a large scale digital electronic computer. It will then be possible, we believe, through the use of mathematical techniques now being developed,[6] to determine the program which will maximize the accomplishment of given objectives within those stated resource limitations. Alternatively, it will be possible to determine the program which will minimize requirements, either for funds or for any limiting commodity or group of commodities, needed to accomplish any fixed objective.

The work being done on the mathematical model has clearly shown the necessity for a more precise formulation of objectives. Planners generally have been accustomed to stating objectives in terms of means rather than ends (i.e., they have been accustomed to stating objectives in terms of specific operations whose relations to the accomplishment of

---

[6] Some of these techniques are discussed in greater detail in Chapter II.

basic ends could only be evaluated subjectively). Objectives must be stated in terms of basic ends, thus permitting the consideration of alternative means, if they are to be useful in programming operations designed to maximize objectives within resource limitations.

In military program planning, it is necessary to introduce quantitatively the various limitations of resources which restrict the capabilities of the military establishment during wartime as well as in peacetime. For the most part these may be traced to limitations in the industrial economy of the nation. It is necessary to know what part of the total national production can be made available for military purposes. This cannot be measured solely in terms of the productive capacity of the aircraft industry or of the munitions industry any more than the strength of an air force can be measured solely in terms of the number of groups.

It is necessary to know in detail the capacities of the steel, aluminum, electric power, transportation, mining, chemical, and a multitude of other industries supporting the aircraft, shipbuilding, and munitions industries, just as it is necessary to know the capacities of the training, transportation, maintenance, and supply activities supporting the combat air groups. Further, it is necessary to determine whether these industries (or supporting activities) are balanced in the proper proportions to meet changing requirements.

Thus, since the determination of the "best" program necessarily starts with a consideration of limitations on resources, it must necessarily start with a consideration of the interrelationships of industries in the industrial economy of the nation.

The first steps toward the required analysis of interindustry relationships have been taken by Professor Leontief and by the Bureau of Labor Statistics. These studies consider relationships in a static or equilibrium state. Theoretical work now under way by several groups will make it possible to handle these relationships dynamically and with due consideration of alternative procedures, or processes, as is done in the mathematical model we are now developing for the internal operations of the Air Force.[7]

---

[7] The formal mathematical model is discussed in Chapter II and is illustrated by concrete examples in Chapter XII.

THE PROGRAMMING OF INTERDEPENDENT ACTIVITIES: MATHEMATICAL MODEL[1]

By George B. Dantzig

1. Linear Technologies or Models

Postulates of a linear technology:

Postulate I: *There exists a class of objects $\{A\}$ called "possible activities."*

Postulate II: *There exists a finite set of m things, called "items" (commodities), denoted by the index $i = 1, 2, \cdots, m$.*

Postulate III: *Associated with each possible activity, A, and item, i, there is a set of characteristic "flow functions" (cumulative) of a variable t, $(-\infty < t < +\infty)$:*

$$(1) \qquad\qquad F_i(t \mid A) \qquad\qquad (i = 1, 2, \cdots, m).$$

Postulate IV: *Given any two possible activities, A_1 and A_2, where A_1 and A_2 may be identical, there exists a possible activity, denoted by $A_1 + A_2$, whose characteristic functions are the sum of the corresponding functions for A_1 and A_2, respectively:*

$$(2) \qquad F_i(t \mid A_1 + A_2) = F_i(t \mid A_1) + F_i(t \mid A_2) \quad (i = 1, 2, \cdots, m).$$

Postulate V: *For any $x \geqq 0$ and any possible activity A, there exists a possible activity, denoted by xA, whose characteristic functions are the product of x and the corresponding functions for A:*

$$(3) \qquad\qquad F_i(t \mid xA) = x F_i(t \mid A) \qquad (i = 1, 2, \cdots, m).$$

We shall now discuss physical situations where these postulates may be applicable. The multitude of activities that any large organization or a nation engages in, in the pursuit of its objectives, are examples of a larger class of possible activities. Thus the various observed activities

---

[1] The present paper represents a revision and extension of an earlier paper which appeared in *Econometrica*, Vol. 17, July–October, 1949, pp. 200–211.

are representative building blocks of different types that might be re-combined in varying amounts to form more complex but *possible* activi-ties. The whole set of possible activities we will refer to as a *technology*. Each activity requires many items to flow into it from "outside" the activity over time. It may also produce or make available many of these items over time that in turn may be used in other activities. The total quantities of these items are often limited in amount, and this fact places a restriction on the set of possible activities that can coexist at any one time in what we shall refer to later as a "program."

Thus each activity, from our point of view, is characterized by the flow over time of a set of items which, if one conceives of an activity as occupying physical space, flows from the outside world into the activity or flows from the activity into the outside world. If two or more ac-tivities are considered as a single composite activity, it is postulated that the net flow of any item over time to or from the composite activity is the *sum* of the corresponding flow functions over time of the individual activities.

Natural as this assumption of additivity may seem, it may appear in fact to be "refuted" by many examples. Thus a day shift operation and a night shift operation may each require one machine but certainly do not require two machines when both are operating simultaneously. A careful analysis of their respective flow requirements for this item over time will show, however, that each requires one machine but *at different times;* thus the combined flow functions would also require one machine for both activities at any given time.

One simple consequence of the *additivity assumption*, Postulate IV, is that it includes the existence of *integral multiples* of a possible activity. Thus, setting $A_1 = A_2 = A$, Postulate IV states that it is technically possible to construct another activity whose flow functions are double the respective flow functions of any given activity. By adding A to $2A$, one obtains $3A$, etc. Accordingly, Postulate IV implies Postulate V for $x = 1, 2, 3, \cdots$. Postulate V goes one step further in that it as-sumes *infinite divisibility of an activity.*

The lack of realism of this assumption of divisibility is not to be dis-puted. For example, mass production activities often use (for reasons of economy) huge presses that cannot be constructed below a certain size. To cite another case, a garage may employ labor to repair ma-chinery. In order to reduce the time in shop, it may try to increase the labor force. The activity carried out by this labor force will cease to be economical when the respective jobs of two workers require that they work on the same part at the same time. Accordingly, Postulate V has been introduced as a *mathematical convenience* for studying prop-

erties of large scale systems and development of computational procedures for solving certain dynamic programming (scheduling) problems
for such systems. Thus one must take care in real situations to discover
significant indivisibilities and to make necessary adjustments in the
results.

Let us turn our attention to certain mathematical properties of the
set of postulates. It will be noted that there is a one-to-one correspondence between the addition and scalar multiplication of activities and
the corresponding operations on the vector function, (4), of an activity
A. Because of this isomorphism, *the vector function of time can be identified with A and given the same symbol,*

$$(4) \qquad \{F_1(t \mid A), F_2(t \mid A), \cdots, F_m(t \mid A)\} \sim A.$$

DEFINITION: *The null activity, denoted by 0, is a symbol for the vector
function of time whose m flow functions vanish,*

$$(5) \qquad (0, 0, \cdots, 0) \sim 0.$$

By Postulate V, it is permissible to multiply (4) through by $x = 0$;
thus the null activity is always included in the set of possible activities,
$\{A\}$. By (5), we may write $0A = 0$, where 0 on the left represents the
scalar $x = 0$ whereas on the right it is the vector function of time (5).

The class $\{A\}$ of possible activities is infinite; in fact, it has the power
of the continuum. Thus it is natural to consider a smaller class of activities that may be conveniently used to generate the larger class. For
example, for $x \geqq 0$, the set of activities xA can be generated from A.
Therefore a basic set of "unit" activities could be chosen such that any
other activity would be a positive multiple of some activity in the unit
set of activities. Furthermore, by excluding from this basis any unit
activity that can be expressed as a positive linear combination of k
other activities in the basis, a still "smaller" basic set of activities could
be used to represent $\{A\}$.

A linear technology can thus be categorized according to whether it
can be represented by a linear combination of a *finite set*, a *denumerable
set*, or a *continuum* of basic activities. We shall consider three separate
sets of postulates to cover the *finite technology*, a special *continuous
technology*, and an analogous *denumerable technology*. We shall also use
the term *model* to connote a mathematical representation of a technology.

Postulates of a finite linear technology:

POSTULATES I–V: *Same as for a linear technology.*

POSTULATE VI': *There exists a finite basis, B_1, B_2, $\cdots$, B_n, in $\{A\}$ such that any A can be expressed as a positive linear combination of possible activities in the basis:*

(6) $$A = y_1 B_1 + y_2 B_2 + \cdots + y_n B_n, \qquad y_j \geqq 0.$$

2. LINEAR TECHNOLOGIES WITH TIME SHIFTS

It is, of course, possible to have technologies where a time shift of a possible activity is also a possible activity. For example, the teaching of an algebra course in a university may occur periodically each September and February. It is convenient in such cases to assume that the cumulative flow functions characterizing these activities can be made to coincide by a suitable translation in time. If the possible time shifts of a given activity are finite or denumerable in number, we shall refer to it as a *finite or denumerable model with time shifts*. If any shift τ is permissible, we shall refer to it as a *special continuous model* with time shifts. In models of this kind there may be no finite basis (i.e., the time shifts of a possible activity are not representable as a positive linear combination of a finite set of basic activities). Usually in practice, however, there exists a finite number of activity types such that by taking combinations of different time shifts of these types all other activities can be represented. In this case any activity A can be represented in terms of some "derived basis" B_1^*, B_2^*, $\cdots$, B_n^* where B_j^* (which need not be the same for all A) is derivable from a fixed B_j by various combinations of time translations of B_j. In the denumerable case

(7) $$B_j^* = y_0 B_j(0) + y_1 B_j(\tau_1) + \cdots + y_k B_j(\tau_k) + \cdots , \qquad y_j \geqq 0,$$

where $B_j = B_j(0)$ represents a typical type of activity and $B_j(\tau_k)$ represents a time shift of τ_k of this activity ($k = 1, 2, \cdots$). In the continuous case where any time shift τ is permissible, the sum defining B_j^* above is replaced by an integral. Thus, for example, the steel industry may have a continuously varying production rate $y(\tau)$ over time. In the time interval τ to $\tau + d\tau$, the total quantity of production is approximately $y(\tau)\,d\tau$ and the cumulative flow functions associated with this production are given approximately in vector form by $B_j(\tau)y(\tau)\,d\tau$, where $B_j(\tau)$ represents the activity of producing a unit quantity of production of steel at time τ. The composite flow functions over time of the industry which brings about the production pattern $y(\tau)$ can be represented as an integral

(8) $$B_j^* = \int_{-\infty}^{+\infty} B_j(\tau)y(\tau)\,d\tau, \qquad y(\tau) \geqq 0.$$

The meaning of this vector relation (8) becomes clearer when expressed in terms of the corresponding flow functions $B_j(\tau)$. First, it will be noted that the correspondence between $B_j(\tau)$ and $B_j = B_j(0)$ is defined by

$$F_i(t \mid B_j(\tau)) = F_i(t - \tau \mid B_j) \quad (i = 1, 2, \cdots, m),$$

so that the flow functions of B_j^* can be expressed directly in terms of these for B_j,

$$F_i(t \mid B_j^*) = \int_{-\infty}^{+\infty} F_i(t - \tau \mid B_j) y(\tau) \, d\tau \quad (i = 1, 2, \cdots, m).$$

So far in the continuous case we have considered the situation in which a density (noncumulative) distribution of weights $y(\tau)$ exists representing, say, the *rate* of production at time τ. This does not allow, as in the denumerable case, for a *finite* weight (quantity of production) at a point τ. In order to generalize, consider instead the *cumulative* distribution function of weights $Y(\tau)$, where $Y(\tau)$ *is monotonically nondecreasing*. Any point τ_k where there is a finite jump y_k in the function $Y(\tau_k)$, represents a finite amount of production y_k at time τ_k of the activity $B(\tau_k)$. The Lebesgue-Stieltjes integral may now be used to cover a combination of both situations. This more general way of expressing B_j^* is used in (12) below.

One more point worth noting is that the passage from a finite sum as in (7) to an integral as in (8) tacitly assumes (since the integral is defined as a limit of finite sums) that there exists an activity whose flow functions are equal to the limit of a sequence of corresponding flow functions of a set of activities (see Postulate VIII'').

The above discussion may be formalized as follows:

Postulates of a special linear continuous technology:

POSTULATES I–V: *Same as for a linear technology.*

POSTULATE VI'': *For any τ there exists a possible activity, denoted by $A(\tau)$, that is a shift in time by τ of a given possible activity A:*

(9) $$F_i(t \mid A(\tau)) = F_i(t - \tau \mid A) \quad (i = 1, 2, \cdots, m).$$

POSTULATE VII'': *There exists a finite basis of n possible activities, B_1, B_2, $\cdots$, B_n, in $\{A\}$, such that any possible activity A can be represented by*

(10) $$A = B_1^* + B_2^* + \cdots + B_n^*,$$

where each B_j^* is given in terms of B_j by

(11) $$B_j^* = \int_{-\infty}^{+\infty} B_j(\tau) \, dY_j(\tau) \quad (j = 1, 2, \cdots, n),$$

in which $Y_j(\tau)$ is a monotonic nondecreasing function of τ.

POSTULATE VIII": *If the corresponding flow functions of a sequence of possible activities converge uniformly in t, there exists a possible activity A to whose flow functions the sequence converges.*

The postulates of the finite or denumerable model with time shifts differ from those of the continuous model in that the range of τ for each B_j is restricted to a specified set, S_j, of permissible time shifts of B_j. There are several models that would then satisfy the above postulates. Thus models constructed for Air Force programming purposes often have equally spaced time shifts, but not necessarily the same time shift for each of the set of basic activities. In some cases the model was finite, in others infinite. Von Neumann's model [1937, 1945] represents an earlier example which is denumerable with equally spaced translations. The general dynamic model lately discussed by Leontief, on the other hand, satisfies the postulates of the continuous model.

3. LINEAR PROGRAMS

We shall now turn our attention to the central problem, namely that of considering whether a set of nonvanishing activities can be set up that is self-supporting.

DEFINITION: *A subset of $\{A\}$ of nonvanishing possible activities, A_1, A_2, $\cdots$, A_k, constitutes a possible "program" if*

$$(12) \qquad \sum_{i=1}^{k} A_i = 0.$$

The above equation contains the germ of an interesting philosophical thought, since such a set of activities could apparently arise out of nothing and yet could coexist. The usual situation that arises in practice is one in which it is desired to find a sum of possible activities (or, what is the same thing, an A) which will receive flows from outside the system and will send out flows in *specified amounts.*

DEFINITION: *A required vector function of flows into and away from a set of possible activities will be denoted by* $-E$. The negative of this required set of flows, E, will be referred to as the "exogenous activity."

DEFINITION: *A subset of $\{A\}$ of nonvanishing activities, A_1, A_2, $\cdots$, A_k, constitutes a possible program relative to E if*

$$(13) \qquad A_1 + A_2 + \cdots + A_k + E = 0,$$

i.e., if $-E$ *is contained in* $\{A\}$.

Thus, for a finite model, a possible program relative to E exists if there exist values $x_1, x_2, \cdots, x_n$ such that

(14) $$x_1B_1 + x_2B_2 + \cdots + x_nB_n + E = 0, \qquad x_j \geqq 0.$$

The number of units $x_j \geqq 0$ of the basic unit activity B_j entering into a solution $(x_1, x_2, \cdots, x_n)$ of (14) is called the *level* of the activity. The set $(x_1, x_2, \cdots, x_n)$, provided it exists, is called a *feasible program*.

Expression (14) represents an infinite number of linear equations in a finite number of unknowns, $(x_1, x_2, \cdots, x_n)$. Thus (14) implies one equation for each item-time combination. At most n of these equations can be linearly independent.

Therefore there exists a set of at most n item-time combinations which, if the equations are satisfied for any x_i (nonnegative or otherwise), will be satisfied for all item-time combinations. Not all exogenous activities E relative to $B_1, B_2, \cdots, B_n$ have this property; indeed, E is completely specified once its values are given over a certain finite set ($\leqq n$) of item-time combinations. By such considerations the problem of finding non-negative solutions to an infinite set of linear equations in a finite number of unknowns can be reduced to one of finding nonnegative solutions for a finite subset of these equations.

For the continuous model a possible program is obtained if we can determine monotonic nondecreasing functions, $X_1(\tau), X_2(\tau), \cdots, X_n(\tau)$, such that

(15) $$B_1^* + B_2^* + \cdots + B_n^* + E = 0,$$

where

(16) $$B_j^* = \int_{-\infty}^{+\infty} B_j(\tau) \, dX_j(\tau).$$

4. Criteria for Selection of Programs

It is not always possible to find program levels x_j, or the analogous cumulative levels over time $X_j(\tau)$, in which case there are *no* feasible programs. Should, however, *one* feasible program exist, then in the general case many feasible programs exist (i.e., the levels in terms of basic activities are not unique).

Inequality relations on the quantities of various items or activities are common ways, of course, to express preferences between alternative choices of feasible programs. For example, equations (14) and (15) state an *equality* relation between the flows created by the activities in the program and the complementary flows toward the exogenous activity.

For certain elements of the vector function of time that express the flow of raw materials to support the economy from outside the economy, the inequality $\leq$ might be better, whereas, for other items that are desirable outputs of the economy, the inequality $\geq$ would be superior.

The addition of linear inequality conditions to finite models can, provided the number of such inequality relations is finite, and this need not be the case, be replaced by a system of equalities in nonnegative variables. This means that the general character of the mathematical problem is not altered by the introduction of such restrictions. To illustrate, consider the following relations by way of example: $x \leq a, y \geq b$ $x \geq y$, where $x \geq 0, y \geq 0$ are levels of two activities and a and b are constants. Introducing additional nonnegative variables, $x_1 \geq 0, x_2 \geq 0,$ $z \geq 0$, we may rewrite the system as $x + x_1 = a, y - y_1 = b, x - y - z = 0$.

We shall now introduce the concept of a maximizing principle the purpose of which will be to help define a unique program (except in certain "degenerate" cases).

POSTULATE VII' (finite linear technology): *There exists a linear objective function,*

$$(17) \qquad \sum_{j=1}^{n} \gamma_j x_j = z.$$

POSTULATE IX'' (special linear continuous technology): *There exists a linear objective function,*

$$(18) \qquad \gamma_1^* + \gamma_2^* + \cdots + \gamma_n^* = z,$$

where

$$(19) \qquad \gamma_j^* = \int_{-\infty}^{+\infty} \gamma_j(\tau)\, dX_j(\tau) \qquad (j = 1, 2, \cdots, n).$$

DEFINITION: *We call any program satisfying* (13) *and maximizing z an optimum feasible program.*

For example, in a large business there may be a number of ways to produce a given product. If γ_j represents the negative of the cost per unit of the jth activity, then (17) measures the amount of profit. (See in particular the transportation and nutrition examples at the end of this chapter.)

In the Leontief steady state dynamic model [1948b; also Cornfield *et al.*, 1947], the bill of goods for the final customer is usually specified as constant rates per unit of time for various items.   Thus the exogenous activity E satisfies

$$(20) \qquad\qquad \frac{dE}{dt} = C,$$

where C, a constant vector function of time, is the bill of goods.

The Leontief steady state model is essentially a finite type of model that can be derived from the special continuous model by assuming a constant but unknown rate, x_j, of completed production of an activity, B_j [see (11)],

$$(21) \qquad\qquad \frac{dX(\tau)}{d\tau} = x_j = \text{constant.}$$

By (11), the composite industrial activity B_j^*, derived from B_j, is given by

$$(22) \qquad\qquad B_j^* = x_j \left[\int_{-\infty}^{+\infty} B_j(\tau)\, d\tau \right].$$

Letting $F(t)$ be a typical cumulative flow function for some item associated with B_j, and $F^*(t)$ the corresponding function for B_j^*, then, by (7),

$$(23) \qquad\qquad F^*(t) = x_j \left[\int_{-\infty}^{+\infty} F(t - \tau)\, d\tau \right].$$

Since, in general, however, it is *not* expected that the cumulative flow $F(t) \to 0$ as $t \to \infty$, the integral in (23) will usually not converge.   On the other hand, assuming for simplicity that the *rate of flow* exists over a finite interval and is zero elsewhere, then

$$(24) \qquad \frac{dF^*(t)}{dt} = x_j \left[\int_{-\infty}^{+\infty} \frac{\partial F(t - \tau)}{\partial t}\, d\tau \right] = x_j [\lim_{t \to \infty} F(t)],$$

where $\lim_{t \to \infty} F(t)$ is thus the input (or output) coefficient of the item per unit level, $x_j = 1$, of the composite activity B_j^* in the Leontief model.   Let U_j represent the vector of constant input-output coefficients for B_j^* evaluated at unit level of production, $x_j = 1$.   Then, by substitution in (15), a possible program is obtained if we can determine $x_j \geqq 0$ such that

$$(25) \qquad\qquad x_1 U_1 + x_2 U_2 + \cdots + x_n U_n + C = 0,$$

where C is given by (20).

The bill of goods of the final customer, C, represents the objective to be achieved in the steady state model.   Leontief, however, set up the model so that $n = m$. The solution to (20), therefore, is unique when the determinant of the coefficients, $| U_1, U_2, \cdots, U_n |$, is non-vanishing. If $n > m$, then (25) is not necessarily a uniquely determined system. If one of the items considered is labor, it may be desirable to minimize the use of this item, in which case this equation is omitted from (25), and its left-hand member becomes the linear form z to be minimized (or its negative, maximized).

As a second example, suppose that it is desirable to test in a finite model whether a given feasible program, $x_1^0, x_2^0, \cdots, x_n^0$, constitutes an "efficient point" in the sense of Koopmans [III, Section 5.2]. By re-arranging the subscripts of activities, it is possible to let $x_1^0, x_2^0, \cdots, x_k^0$ specify the amount of consumption by, say, households of certain "desired items," where the consumption of an item by a household is considered an activity. It is assumed $k < n$. If there exists no solution $x_1 \geqq x_1^0, x_2 \geqq x_2^0, \cdots, x_k \geqq x_k^0$ (except all equalities) of (14), then $x_1^0, x_2^0, \cdots, x_n^0$ is defined as an "efficient point" [see also (15)]. It will be noted that this definition expresses an efficient point in terms of activities rather than items. Setting $x_1 = x_1^0 + y_1, \cdots, x_k = x_k^0 + y_k; x_{k+1} = y_{k+1}, \cdots, x_n = y_n$ in (14), a solution $y_j \geqq 0$ is sought to the system

$$(26) \qquad y_1 B_1 + y_2 B_2 + \cdots + y_n B_n + \bar{E} = 0,$$

which maximizes

$$(27) \qquad y_1 + y_2 + \cdots + y_k = z,$$

where $\bar{E}$ is given by

$$(28) \qquad \bar{E} = E + (x_1^0 B_1 + \cdots + x_k^0 B_k).$$

Because of the feasible set of values $x_1^0, x_2^0, \cdots, x_n^0$, there exists at least one solution to (26) with $y_1 = y_2 = y_k = 0$ so that max $z \geqq 0$. If max $z = 0$, then $x_1^0, x_2^0, \cdots, x_n^0$ is an efficient point. If max $z > 0$, then the new solution in terms of x_j constitutes such a point. For the property of efficient points on which this text is based, see Chapter III, Section 5.

5. A SPECIAL FINITE MODEL

Our purpose now is to develop the equations of the dynamic system, using a special finite model. This is the original form of the early models developed for Air Force use. Essentially it is the same as one described by J. von Neumann [1937, 1945]. However, we shall seek programs based on this model, which maximizes a linear objective function, whereas von Neumann investigated the existence of programs whose levels were expanding at a constant rate over time. Because this model is useful for many purposes and reveals the essential computational problem, it will be discussed now. We shall use equally spaced points in time, $t = 0, 1, 2, \cdots, T$, for ease of notation, and we shall assume that each basic activity is associated with some unit time period, $t - 1$ to t, and that the cumulative flow functions of such an activity are step functions with incremental changes only at points of time $t - 1$ and t such that the rate of flow elsewhere is zero.[2] We adopt the following notation:

(a) $t = 0, 1, 2, \cdots, T$ denotes consecutive points in time; the interval $(t - 1, t)$ will be called the tth interval.

(b) $B_j^{(t)}$ represents the jth basic, unit level activity associated with the tth interval.

(c) $\alpha_{ij}^{(t)}$ is the increment added to the cumulative flow function of the ith item for activity $B_j^{(t)}$ at time $t - 1$ (input coefficient).

(d) $\bar{\alpha}_{ij}^{(t)}$ is the discrete increment subtracted from the flow function of the ith item for $B_j^{(t)}$ at time t (output coefficient).

(e) $x_j^{(t)}$ denotes the number of units of $B_j^{(t)}$.

By our convention of signs, $+$ and $-$ indicate *in* and *out*. Thus α and $\bar{\alpha}$ will usually be positive.

No use will be made of the cumulative flow function $F(t \mid A)$. Instead, equation (14) will be replaced by the corresponding equation relating to the discrete additions or subtractions to the flow functions at times $t = 0, 1, 2, \cdots, T$. This is valid since the rate of flow at all other times is zero. Thus the equations of the dynamic system become

$$(29) \qquad \sum_{j=0}^{n_t} \alpha_{ij}^{(t)} x_j^{(t)} = \sum_{j=0}^{n_{t-1}} \bar{\alpha}_{ij}^{(t-1)} x_j^{(t-1)} \qquad \begin{array}{l} (i = 1, 2, \cdots, m; \\ t = 1, 2, \cdots, T), \end{array}$$

where the boundary conditions are obtained by setting $\bar{\alpha}_{ij}^0 = 0$ for $j \geqq 1$, and $x_0^{(t)} = 1$. The objective function to be maximized is

$$(30) \qquad \sum_{t=1}^{T} \sum_{j=1}^{n_t} \gamma_j^{(t)} x_j^{(t)} = z = \max,$$

where $x_j^{(t)} \geqq 0$.

6. The Computational Problem

The fact that the equations of the dynamic system impose additional linear restrictions on the unknown levels of activities, besides the condition that they must always remain nonnegative, leads to a very interesting computational problem that may be formulated in one of two

[2] A slightly more general model is presented in the version of this paper published in *Econometrica*, using uniform flows during the tth time interval as well.

ways: (1) *Maximize a linear function whose variables satisfy a system of linear inequalities.* (2) *Maximize a linear function of nonnegative variables subject to a system of linear equalities.* These two problems are easily shown to be equivalent.

Except for general properties of the solution, very little can be found in the literature that helps to solve numerically systems of equations involving many variables. One important property that is worth noting is the nonexistence of *local maxima. Thus any program which is not optimal can always be improved by making small changes.* A second property worth noting is that *the maximizing solution* [3] *necessarily involves as few activities as possible at positive levels and as many as possible at zero levels* (*except in certain degenerate cases*).

It is proposed to solve linear programming problems which involve maximization of a linear form by means of large scale digital computers because even the simplest programming problems can involve a large number of calculations (see, e.g., the experience with the nutrition and transportation problems mentioned at the end of this chapter). Several computational procedures have been evolved so far, and research is continuing actively in this field.

Matrix notation: The essential form of the system of equations of the dynamic system is more clearly brought out by the use of matrix notation. Let

$$(31) \qquad x^{(t)} = \{x_1^{(t)}, x_2^{(t)}, \cdots, x_{n_t}^{(t)}\}$$

be the column vector of levels of activities in the tth time period; let

$$(32) \qquad \alpha^{(t)} = [\alpha_{ij}^{(t)}], \qquad \bar{\alpha}^{(t)} = [\bar{\alpha}_{ij}^{(t)}]$$

represent the matrices of the input and output coefficients, respectively, in the tth time period; and let the row vector of coefficients of the maximizing form associated with the activity levels that occur in the tth time period only be denoted by

$$(33) \qquad \gamma^{(t)} = (\gamma_1^{(t)}, \gamma_2^{(t)}, \cdots, \gamma_{n_t}^{(t)}).$$

The constant terms in (29) can be written in vector notation also: let

$$(34) \qquad a^{(t)} = (\bar{\alpha}_{10}^{(t-1)} - \alpha_{10}^{(t)}, \bar{\alpha}_{20}^{(t-1)} - \alpha_{20}^{(t)}, \cdots, \bar{\alpha}_{m0}^{(t-1)} - \alpha_{m0}^{(t)})$$

for $t = 1, 2, \cdots, T$. The equations of the dynamic system in matrix notation become

---

[3] In certain degenerate cases there may be more than one solution yielding the same maximum. If so, a unique solution could be obtained by the use of additional maximizing functions.

(35)

$$\alpha^{(1)}x^{(1)} \quad \cdots \quad \cdots \quad \cdots \quad \cdots \quad \cdots = a^{(1)}$$

$$-\bar{\alpha}^{(1)}x^{(1)} \; +\alpha^{(2)}x^{(2)} \quad \cdots \quad \cdots \quad \cdots \quad \cdots = a^{(2)}$$

$$\cdots \quad -\bar{\alpha}^{(2)}x^{(2)} \; +\alpha^{(3)}x^{(3)} \cdots \quad \cdots \quad \cdots = a^{(3)}$$

$$\cdots \quad \cdots \quad \cdots \quad \cdots \; -\bar{\alpha}^{(T-1)}x^{(T-1)} \; +\alpha^{(T)}x^{(T)} = a^{(T)}$$

$$\gamma^{(1)}x^{(1)} \; + \cdots \qquad\qquad +\gamma^{(T)}x^{(T)} = \max,$$

where the $x^{(t)}$ are vectors of nonnegative elements. It should be noted that the general mathematical problem reduces in the linear programming case to consideration of a system of equations of nonnegative variables whose matrix of coefficients is composed mostly of blocks of zeros except for submatrices along and just off the "diagonal." Thus any good computational technique for solving programs would probably take advantage of this fact.[4]

When the matrices $\alpha^{(t)}$ and $\bar{\alpha}^{(t)}$ ($t = 1, 2, \cdots, T$) are square and nonsingular, a direct solution is possible that may lead, however, to negative and nonnegative activity levels (in which case no feasible solution exists).

7. Applications

(a) The interindustry relationship studies of Leontief and the Bureau of Labor Statistics are well known. The relation between the input-output coefficients of the steady state equilibrium model and the special continuous model was developed in (21) and sequel. The more general dynamic model lately considered by Leontief is a special case of a special continuous model.

(b) The Hitchcock-Koopmans transportation problem [Hitchcock, 1941; Koopmans, 1947; and XIV and XXIII below] is an example of a steady state solution that involves the minimization of a linear function. The problem may be stated as follows: A homogeneous product [5] in the amounts of $q_1, q_2, \cdots, q_s$, respectively, is to be shipped from s shipping point origins, and amounts $r_1, r_2, \cdots, r_d$, respectively, are to be received by d destinations; the cost of shipping a unit amount of product from the ith origin to the jth destination is c_{ij}. The problem is to determine

---

[4] See the papers in Part Four of this volume; see also papers by von Neumann [1947, 1948] and Tompkins.

[5] In Koopmans' case the homogeneous product consisted of empty ships to be moved from ports of discharge to next ports of loading, and the "cost" consisted of time spent by these ships in travel.

x_{ij}, the amount shipped from i to j, so as to satisfy

$$\sum_{j=1}^{d} x_{ij} = q_i \qquad (i = 1, 2, \cdots, s),$$

(36)
$$\sum_{i=1}^{s} x_{ij} = r_j \qquad (j = 1, 2, \cdots, d),$$

$$\sum_{i=1}^{s} \sum_{j=1}^{d} c_{ij} x_{ij} = z,$$

and to minimize total transportation costs z.

Because of the special form of the equations, simplified computational procedures are possible. For example, a large scale problem involving about 25 origins and 60 destinations was solved recently in 9 man days by hand computation techniques. As only simple additions and subtractions occurred in the process, even the use of a desk calculator was not required.

(c) The minimum-cost adequate diet problem was formulated by Jerome Cornfield in 1941 and by G. J. Stigler [1945]. It is assumed that (1) the composition in terms of dietary elements (i.e., minerals, calories, vitamins) of a number of foods is known; (2) the prices of the foods are given; and (3) the requirements in terms of dietary elements which will keep a person in good health are known. The problem is then to find a diet which will supply the requirements at minimum cost. Stigler found a solution to the problem by testing various combinations under the assumption that the body could dispose of any surplus of dietary elements. A solution to the problem which demanded that the requirements be met exactly had nearly 50% higher costs. This result illustrates the importance of disposal and storage activities. A problem involving 9 dietary elements and 77 foods took 120 man days to compute by hand. This may be contrasted with the above transportation problem.

(d) A. Cahn [1948] has proposed a warehouse problem which can be solved by linear programming techniques. An entrepreneur undertakes to operate a warehouse of fixed capacity by filling it with goods for which there is a seasonal production and, consequently, a seasonal price. When goods are in season, he can purchase them at a low price and sell them later in the year at a higher price. Each month new goods become available, and the owner must make a decision regarding the disposal or continued storage of his present holdings and the purchase of goods that have just become available to use up his idle capacity.

(e) In Chapter XII an application is given of the discrete type of model to a hypothetical air transport problem.

CHAPTER III

ANALYSIS OF PRODUCTION AS AN EFFICIENT COMBINATION OF ACTIVITIES [1]

By Tjalling C. Koopmans

1. Introduction

1.1. *Technology and choice.* The concept of a production function occupies a central place in the literature on production theory. In some discussions this concept is associated with a particular technological process. The function is then supposed to represent the output of one commodity (say) as a function of the quantities of various factors of production, combined according to a given technological principle or formula. Further elaboration of this concept has led to the distinction between situations where the set of technically possible factor combinations is unrestricted (allowing for continuous substitution between factors) and situations where some factors can only be combined, within the technological principle involved, in fixed ratios to each other (limitational factors).[2] The second type of situation can only be reconciled with the notion of a production function defined in the whole factor space by allowing the production manager to discard parts of the factor quantities specified as being available. The corresponding production

---

[1] This model was first developed in a more special form relating to the transportation industry. In conversation, George B. Dantzig introduced me to the wider applicability of models involving constant production coefficients to the discussion of allocation problems. At this stage I also learned of and benefited from the literature on similar models reviewed in the introduction to this volume. An earlier version of this chapter was presented at the Madison meeting of the Econometric Society, September 10, 1948. The present version has gained from the reading of other papers in the present volume and a manuscript by Paul A. Samuelson [1949]. I am indebted to M. Gerstenhaber and M. L. Slater for valuable suggestions regarding terminology and methods of proof. *Note added in proof:* H. Freudenthal has kindly brought to my attention a fascinating article written by Remak [1929], which contains in intuitive form some of the ideas concerning productive efficiency more fully elaborated in the present chapter and some other chapters of this volume. His treatment of prices, however, seems concerned more with accounting identities than with prices as guides to efficient allocation.

[2] See, among others, N. Georgescu-Roegen [1935], E. Schneider [1933], H. von Stackelberg [1933].

functions have kinks at the points where the ratios of available factor quantities coincide with the technical ratios specific to the process in question.

It has long been realized that the concept of a production function representing a given productive "technique" is unnecessarily restrictive. The "technique" employed in production is itself the result of managerial choice (going beyond the discarding of unwanted factor quantities). Managers choose between, or employ efficient combinations of, several processes to obtain in some sense best results. Speaking still in terms of one product of given quality, an efficient manager chooses that combination of productive activities which maximizes the amount produced for given available quantities of factors which have given qualitative characteristics. In this concept, the quality characteristics of the available factors and of the desired product specify the variables entering in the production function and the nature of the function. The available quantities of the factors specify the values of the variables, and the maximal output specifies the value assumed by the function.

This concept of the production function, generalized to allow for joint production, is adopted in the present study. Since it defines the value of the function as the result of a maximizing or (more generally) an economizing choice, this concept is in the first place *normative*. It represents the best attainable under efficient exercise of choice. The production function so obtained is descriptive of reality only if and when the assumption of efficient choice is a good approximation to reality.

1.2. *Elements of the production problem.* In this article a model of production will be developed in which the following circumstances or considerations are treated formally as distinct elements of the production problem:

(a) the purely technical possibilities of production,

(b) the quantitative limitations on basic resources (primary factors of production) available to the economy,

(c) the general goal or objective to be served by production,

(d) the optimizing choice whereby the technical possibilities are exploited in a coordinated manner toward that objective.

Any production function to be derived from this model will be inclusive rather than aggregative. That is, while no aggregation of commodities will be presupposed, the production function will be thought of as expressing the productive potential of an entire economy, or of any technically well-defined part thereof. We shall use the term "economy" to refer to either the whole or a defined part of what is usually called the economy. Such production function as may be arrived at represents the most favorable achievable relationship between the inputs of individual primary factors of production and the final outputs of individual commodities through that "economy." A number of economists have postulated the existence of such a general transformation function of an economy.[3] When applied to a sufficiently wide concept of the economy, it involves a broader choice of combinations of productive activities than is available to the individual firm. We shall therefore from here on speak of a "transformation function" rather than a "production function."

In some situations the term "function" will not be the one most suited to describe the set of alternative modes of efficient utilization of technological possibilities and available resources toward the stated objective. We shall therefore most often use the term "efficient point set in the commodity space," a concept which will be further defined in Sections 4.2 and 5.2 below and which includes the notion of a transformation function as a special case.

1.3. *Static and dynamic models.* To avoid an accumulation of complications, and in deference to a venerable tradition in economic literature, we shall confine the present study to a static model in which the elements of technology, scarcity, objective, and choice are formalized in terms of variables and relationships thought of as remaining constant during an indefinite period. A dynamic model is formulated elsewhere in this volume by Dantzig [II].

1.4. *The technology: commodities and activities.* The formalization of the technical possibilities that we shall use involves only two basic concepts, the *commodity* and the *activity*. Each *commodity* is assumed to be homogeneous qualitatively and continuously divisible quantitatively. Commodities include *primary factors of production,* such as labor of various kinds, the use of land of various grades, including land giving access to mineral resources; *intermediate products,* such as coal, pig iron, steel; and *final products* the production of which is the objective of the economy under study. We shall denote by

$$(1.1) \qquad\qquad y_n \qquad\qquad (n = 1, \cdots, N),$$

the total *net output* of the nth commodity in the productive system considered. A negative value of y_n signifies a net input of the nth commodity. Each y_n represents a rate of flow per unit of time.

In our static model an *activity* consists of the combination of certain qualitatively defined commodities in fixed quantitative ratios as "in-

[3] See for instance Oskar Lange [1942].

puts" to produce as "outputs" certain other commodities in fixed quantitative ratios to the inputs. The kth activity is defined by a set of
coefficients,

$$(1.2) \qquad\qquad a_{nk} \qquad\qquad (n = 1, \cdots, N),$$

indicating the rate of flow per unit of time of each of the N commodities
involved in the unit amount of that activity. Negative coefficients a_{nk}
indicate that the commodity involved is used up by the activity; positive coefficients, that the commodity is produced. A value $a_{nk} = 0$ indicates that the nth commodity is not involved in the kth activity.

Two basic assumptions are associated with the notion of an activity.
The first of these is *divisibility:* we assume that each activity is capable
of continuous proportional expansion or reduction. If any nonnegative
scalar quantity, x_k, is selected to be the *amount* or *level* of the kth activity,
the corresponding commodity flows are assumed to be given by

$$(1.3) \qquad\qquad x_k a_{nk} \qquad\qquad (n = 1, \cdots, N).$$

This assumption implies the conscious neglect of all indivisibilities in
production. It also implies constant returns to scale for each individual
activity.

The second assumption is *additivity:* we assume that any number of
activities can be carried out simultaneously without modification in the
technical ratios by which they are defined, provided only that the total
resulting net output, y_n, of any commodity, whenever negative, is
within the limitations on primary resources to be discussed in Section
1.6. The joint net output of any commodity from all activities then
equals the sum of the net outputs of that commodity from the individual
activities. This assumption, taken together with the previous one, implies the neglect of economies or diseconomies of scale for the productive
system as a whole (except diseconomies resulting from scarcity of primary
factors).

The two assumptions can be fused in the statement that we postulate
the existence of a finite set of *basic activities*, represented by vectors

$$(1.4) \qquad\qquad a_{(k)} \equiv \begin{bmatrix} a_{1k} \\ a_{2k} \\ \cdot \\ \cdot \\ \cdot \\ a_{Nk} \end{bmatrix},$$

such that any possible *state of production* can be represented by a linear combination of basic activities with nonnegative coefficients, x_k. The resulting net outputs, y_n, can be written as

$$(1.5) \qquad y_n = \sum_{k=1}^{K} a_{nk} x_k, \qquad x_k \geqq 0 \quad (n = 1, \cdots, N; k = 1, \cdots, K).$$

The activity vectors (1.4) can be adjoined to form the *technology matrix*, or briefly the *technology*

$$(1.6) \qquad A \equiv \begin{bmatrix} a_{11} & a_{12} & \cdots & a_{1K} \\ a_{21} & a_{22} & \cdots & a_{2K} \\ \cdot & \cdot & \cdot \cdot \cdot \cdot \cdot \cdot & \cdot \\ a_{N1} & a_{N2} & \cdots & a_{NK} \end{bmatrix}.$$

1.5. *Location and transportation.* In principle, flows of technically the same commodity in two different locations represent two different commodities. Transporting the commodity from P to Q is an activity or set of activities to which the commodity in P is an initial input, that in Q a final output. A particular model defining transportation activities is discussed in Chapter XIV. Whether and to what extent in any particular application transportation and location are explicitly recognized in this manner depends, of course, on the purpose of the analysis and the degree of detail and refinement required. The problem of an optimal degree of aggregation of activities and commodities is outside the scope of this study.

1.6. *The limitations on primary factors.* We shall assume that certain commodities, called primary factors, can be made to flow into the economy from nature (or from the "outside world"), at a rate, possibly limited by a constant, η_n, depending on the commodity, that is,

$$(1.7) \qquad\qquad\qquad \eta_n \leqq y_n.$$

The constant η_n is algebraically smaller than the rate of flow y_n because a net inflow into the economy is represented by a negative number y_n, which cannot exceed the corresponding bound η_n *in absolute value.* Certain commodities, such as water and air, may be available in greater abundance than required for any conceivable objective of the economy. If this can safely be asserted before analysis, the commodity in question is certain to be a free good, which does not give rise to any restrictions on allocative decisions. Its perfunctory role in the model can be expressed by writing $\eta_n = -\infty$, or the commodity can be omitted from the model (i.e., from all activities in which it is physically involved). Whenever its character as a free good in all circumstances is subject to doubt before analysis, the commodity and the effective bound η_n on its availability should be incorporated in the model.

While a commodity could not be a primary factor without being an input to at least one activity, there is no reason why a primary factor could not also appear as output of some other activities.

1.7. *The objective of allocative decisions.* In order to cover a wide variety of cases, we shall assume as little as possible with respect to the aims pursued by the economy. We shall postulate only that there is a specified set of commodities, to be called *desired commodities*, which are required by the economy in the following sense: an addition to the total net output of one or more of the desired commodities which does not entail a reduction in the net output of any other desired commodity is regarded as an improvement. As long as such improvements are possible, the allocation of resources in production is not regarded as efficient.

It is clear that this postulate provides only a partial ordering of points in the space of which the coordinates are flows of desired commodities. No preference is expressed between alternatives A and B if A involves more of one desired commodity, B more of another. We can therefore not expect our model to produce a unique solution to the allocation problem. The postulate will prove sufficient for our more modest aim: to study the set of all points in the desired commodity space resulting from efficient modes of production.

It should be readily admitted that our assumption regarding the valuation of desired commodities ignores the possibility of saturation. To make allowance for saturation would require much more detailed specification of consumers' preferences than it is our present purpose to make.[4] The efficient point set obtained without regard to saturation will be relevant in all those portions of the space of desired commodity flows in which saturation is actually not reached for any desired commodity.

As discussed further below, the desired commodities may include primary factors. All desired commodities which are not primary factors will be called *final commodities*. We can therefore specify $\eta_n = 0$ in (1.7) for each final commodity.[5]

---

[4] An assumption whereby saturation in one commodity arises at a level of flow independent of the flows of other commodities could still be accommodated in our model at small cost in mathematical complication but would add very little to the degree of realism attained.

[5] Such a restriction disregards the fact that certain effects or conditions of production are negatively valued, such as smoke pollution. We could easily allow for this circumstance and still maintain the formal applicability of the objective as stated above by introducing these effects as negative outputs (i.e., inputs) of "desired"

Depending on the context, we shall follow two alternative procedures if the objective places a valuation on a commodity which is also available in nature. To consider an example: the services of land not used in production may be desired for recreational purposes. The first alternative is to treat land as a primary desired commodity. In this way, our efficiency criterion will prescribe maximization of the (negative) net output, or, what is equivalent, minimization of the (positive) net input, of services of land in production. We shall follow this procedure in Section 4, where we do not wish the analysis to be complicated by explicit availability bounds η_n such as occur in (1.7).

Alternatively, we may attach no desirability to the services of land as such but introduce a "reservation" activity whereby the primary commodity "services of land" as such can be converted into an "equal" amount of a new final commodity, "recreational land services." The minimization of the net input of land services in production is now induced by the requirement that land services allotted to production and reservation activities together are limited by the total available according to relation (1.7). By this semantic device we transfer the desirability property that any primary factor might originally possess to a final commodity introduced for that purpose. If, either to begin with, or through the application of this device, no primary factors are at the same time desired goods, then all desired commodities are final commodities, and we shall use the latter term in that case. This alternative is followed in Section 5, where the effect of availability limitations on primary commodities is studied explicitly.

1.8. *The treatment of labor.* In some models considered by Leontief [e.g., 1941] and von Neumann [1937, 1945], labor has been treated as the output of an activity, of which the consumption of various commodities constitutes the set of inputs. The model thus becomes a closed one. We intend to study an open model which does not specify the structure of preferences between the various desired commodities or between consumption and leisure.

In our model, therefore, manpower is a primary factor like land, and the same two alternatives discussed with regard to land are open to us. One possibility is to identify labor with manpower, and treat it, like smoke pollution, as a negatively desired commodity which is also a primary factor. Alternatively, we can treat manpower as a primary factor, not desired in itself, and flowing into the economy at a rate bounded by

commodities, of which the algebraic increase (i.e., the absolute reduction) is deemed desirable. Since setting up such a category of commodities would complicate the notations rather than the reasoning in what follows, we have refrained from doing it.

the given negative number η_n, if n refers to manpower. Besides being used in all productive activities, manpower is then introduced as an input of the activity "recreation," of which the sole output [6] is the positively desired commodity "leisure."

In a more refined model, we may treat a given amount of unskilled manpower as a gift of nature, and manpower of various skills as the outputs of a variety of educational and training activities. The consumption aspects of these activities can be recognized by stipulating that, besides skilled manpower, these activities also produce "educational services" which are desired for their own sake.

1.9. *Intermediate commodities.* If the sets of primary factors and of desired commodities do not between them cover all commodities, the remaining commodities will be called intermediate commodities. Each of these is simultaneously an input of at least one activity and an output of at least one other activity. This necessary property of all intermediate commodities may, but need not, also be a property of individual primary or final commodities.

It may be thought that these statements ignore the existence of waste products. In fact, waste products can be disregarded if they are not used even in part for further production or consumption and provided that their disposal does not require the use of other commodities. Otherwise, waste products can be regarded as intermediate commodities by introducing a disposal activity, in which they appear as inputs and with which no useful [7] outputs are connected. This treatment is desirable in particular if it is not known in advance whether, or in what part of the space of desired commodity flows, the commodity involved will actually come out of the analysis as a waste product.[8] In this respect the position of possible waste products in the analysis is similar to that of possible free goods.

For intermediate products we can specify in (1.7)

(1.8)　　　$\eta_n = 0$　　　if n refers to an intermediate commodity,

because negative net flows are not compatible with the static assumption of constant flows during an indefinite period. However, the incorpora-

---

[6] The effect of recreation on the productivity of manpower when applied in production can be taken into account, if desired, by combining recreation and productive labor into one activity and regarding different percentages of time devoted to recreation as giving rise to different activities.

[7] The meaning of the term "useful" will become clear below, when prices are introduced, if we define "useful" as "positively priced."

[8] In the early days of the oil industry, kerosene was the main desired product and gasoline was disposed of by burning.

tion of disposal activities in the model makes possible a sharpening of the restriction (1.7).   Instead of $0 \leqq y_n$, which follows from (1.8), we may write

(1.9) $y_n = 0$ if n refers to an intermediate commodity.

This can be understood to mean that, whenever an "intermediate" y_n would otherwise turn out best to be positive, we undertake to reduce it to zero by the appropriate amount of a disposal activity. This does not really restrict allocative decisions beyond what is already implied in (1.7), except (and rightly so) in the case where the disposal activities necessary to insure (1.9) consume other useful commodities.

1.10. *Summary of the commodity classification.* The following table summarizes the commodity classification that has been introduced.

Commodity	Desired in Itself	Not Desired in Itself
Not available in nature	Final	Intermediate
Available in nature	Primary desired	Primary not desired

The category "primary not desired" is assumed empty in the discussion of Section 4.   The category "primary desired" is assumed empty in Section 5 (or is rendered empty by suitable construction; see Section 1.7).

1.11. *Managerial choice.* We shall define managerial choice as the selection of nonnegative amounts (or levels) $x_1, \cdots, x_k$ for all possible activities.   This choice is here studied in the abstract.   For the time being, we do not inquire whether it is exercised by one entrepreneur or manager, by a number of independently acting entrepreneurs, by a public planning body, or by a combination of these.   A study of the formal properties of optimizing choice is believed to be a useful preliminary to the study of the effectiveness of alternative social and institutional arrangements in realizing or approaching optimal choice.   We shall touch upon the latter question, though still in an abstract fashion, in Section 5.12.

Managerial choice is exercised subject to the restrictions (1.7) and (1.9) and is assumed to be guided by the objective formulated in Section 1.7.   We have already indicated that in general more than one state of production can result from the pursuit of that objective. The main purpose of our discussion is to study the set of all productive states that realize the broad objective formulated.

1.12. *The role of capital in the model.* The model to be studied implies a state of saturation with regard to reproducible capital. Among the limitations (1.7) on primary resources we have not imposed any limitations on the amount of accumulated products of past flows of primary resources used to increase the productivity of present flows. The reason lies in the plan of analysis. Any such limitation, to make sense in a static model, would have to be imposed on the value of capital rather than on the amounts of specific types of capital equipment. Such a limitation can therefore not be introduced until after the analysis has supplied us with a value concept. In the present chapter, then, the criterion of efficiency in production does not regard a high initial requirement of reproducible capital in a particular method of production as in any way a disadvantage of that method. Of course, the consumption of capital equipment through wear and tear may be expressed by the input coefficients of productive activities.

1.13. *Summary of results.* The model developed in this chapter builds on the work on linear production models referred to in the introduction to this volume. As was said already, we are here concerned with an open model in which the nature of demand is specified only to the extent that an efficiency objective in the space of desired commodities is adopted. Limitations on primary factors are introduced explicitly, but circularity in the use of commodities in production is allowed for. It is an allocation model independent of the concept of a market. However, a price concept applicable to all commodities is *derived* from the requirement of efficient allocation (Sections 4.3–4.7). The ratios between these prices, whenever determinate, are marginal rates of substitution in efficient production, wherever such substitution is possible (Sections 4.8–4.10). In terms of these prices, whether uniquely determinate or not, the two conditions of nonpositive profits on all activities, and of zero profits on all activities engaged in, are found to be necessary and sufficient for efficient use of resources (Section 4.7). These prices may be called efficiency prices in that, if an opportunity to trade with an outside world at these prices is presented, no gain in efficiency can result from the use of that opportunity (Section 5.11). These prices can also be used as a device to decentralize allocative decisions within the productive system studied (Section 5.12). Sections marked by an asterisk (*) are the more technical ones and can be passed over by those interested in results rather than in methods of proof.

2. MATHEMATICAL TOOLS

2.1. *The two equivalent definitions of convex polyhedral cones.* We shall make use of the theory of convex polyhedral cones, hereafter to be referred to briefly as "cones." Such a cone can be defined either as the convex hull of a finite number of halflines out of the origin (*sum definition*) or as the intersection of a finite number of halfspaces whose bounding hyperplanes pass through the origin (*intersection definition*). We shall use the properties, summarized by Gale [XVII], which depend on the equivalence of these two definitions. We shall also use a number of properties, developed by Gerstenhaber [XVIII] in connection with the present investigation, most of which follow directly from the sum definition.

2.2. *Matrix representation of cones.* The *halflines* $(a_{(k)})$ entering into the sum definition of a cone (A) can be uniquely defined by a set of nonvanishing *vectors* $a_{(k)}$, which, again, can be adjoined as the columns of a *matrix* A. In the discussions by Gale and by Gerstenhaber, the explicit representation by vectors and matrices disappears as soon as a minimum of basic properties of cones have been established, because after that no support from matrix properties is needed. In the present chapter, matrix representations have been maintained, perhaps at the cost of mathematical lucidity, but perhaps also in the interest of easier understandability by those accustomed to dealing with systems of linear equations in terms of properties of matrices. Explicit use of matrices will also keep before the reader the relationship between column vectors and discrete activities that represent well-defined pieces of technological knowledge and experience.

Differences in notation and to some extent even in terminology flow from this choice. The cone consisting of all vectors y satisfying (1.8) or, in matrix notation,

$$(2.1) \qquad\qquad y = Ax, \qquad x_k \geqq 0 \qquad\qquad (k = 1, \cdots, K),$$

is denoted by (A) and is said to be *spanned* by the column vectors $a_{(k)}$ of A, or simply by the matrix A, rather than by the halflines $(a_{(k)})$ defined by these vectors. Similarly, a *frame* of A, or of (A), is here a submatrix of A comprising a set of vectors $a_{(k)}$ defining the halflines $(a_{(k)})$ that constitute a frame as defined by Gerstenhaber [XVIII, Definition 28]. But the underlying concept of frame is the same: a set of elements, whether vectors or halflines, in the sum definition of a cone, the omission of any one of which makes the cone "shrink." The matrix representation involves some arbitrariness in the notation for *lineal* cones (i.e., cones containing a nonvanishing vector a along with its negative $-a$), because the frame of such a cone is not unique, even if considered as a set of halflines. In particular, we denote the entire space by

$$(2.2) \qquad (\pm I) \equiv (-I \quad I),$$

where I is the unit matrix, although other frames could serve the same purpose. Similarly, we occasionally denote the *dimensionality space* of a cone (A) [i.e., the "smallest" linear space containing (A)], by

$$(2.3) \qquad (\pm A) \equiv (-A \quad A).$$

Finally, the reader should be cautioned that the $+$ sign is used in two different meanings. When connecting vectors, denoted by $a, \cdots, p, q, \cdots, x, y, \cdots$, or matrices, denoted by $A, B, \cdots, [A \quad B], \cdots, [\pm A], \cdots$, the $+$ sign denotes ordinary vector or matrix addition. When connecting cones, it denotes the *summation of cones*, expressed by

$$(2.4) \qquad (A) + (B) \equiv ([A \quad B]),$$

also denoted $(A \quad B)$, which should again be distinguished from the union of (A) and (B) denoted by $(A) \cup (B)$. The intersection of (A) and (B) is denoted by $(A) \cap (B)$, while $(A) \supset (B)$ or $(B) \subset (A)$ denotes that (B) is contained in (A).

2.3. *Polar and negative polar cones.* In order that prices of scarce commodities shall be positive, it is convenient here to work with the *negative polar* $(A)^-$ of a cone (A), which is the negative,

$$(2.5) \qquad (A)^- \equiv (-A)^+,$$

of the *polar* cone as defined by Gale. It may therefore be useful here to write down the two definitions, together with the definition of the orthogonal complement $(A)^\perp$.

$$(2.6) \quad \begin{cases} \text{Polar} \quad (A)^+: \quad p \, \epsilon \, (A)^+ \text{ whenever } p'a \geqq 0 \text{ for all } a \, \epsilon \, (A), \\ \text{Orthogonal} \\ \quad \text{complement} \, (A)^\perp: \quad q \, \epsilon \, (A)^\perp \text{ whenever } q'a = 0 \text{ for all } a \, \epsilon \, (A), \\ \text{Negative} \\ \quad \text{polar} \quad (A)^-: \quad r \, \epsilon \, (A)^- \text{ whenever } r'a \leqq 0 \text{ for all } a \, \epsilon \, (A), \end{cases}$$

where ϵ denotes "is an element of," and $p'a$ is the inner product of p and a. We have $(A)^+ = (A)^-$ and therefore $= (A)^\perp$ if and only if (A) is a linear space. The properties of $(A)^+$ stated by Gale can easily be translated by (2.5) into similar properties of $(A)^-$. We use $A^+, A^\perp, A^-$ to denote frames of the corresponding cones.

2.4. *Dimensionality, lineality, interior, and relative interior.* Besides the dimensionality space (2.3), we shall use the concept of the *lineality space*,

(2.7) $(A) \cap (-A)$,

of a cone (A), which is the "largest" linear space contained in it. The dimensionalities of these two spaces are called the *dimensionality* and the *lineality* of (A), respectively, to be denoted

(2.8)   dim (A),   lin (A).

The dimensionality of (A) equals the rank of A. A cone is called *lineal* if its lineality is one or more. Hence a lineal cone is a cone containing an entire line through the origin. A cone is called *solid* if lin (A) equals the dimensionality N of the space in which it is considered. The cone then fills that entire space.

If dim $(A) = N$, then (A) has *interior points* [i.e., points possessing a neighborhood contained in (A)], and, if lin $(A) < N$, noninterior or *boundary points*. If dim $(A) < N$, (A) consists entirely of boundary points by this topological definition, but we can define the *relative interior* of (A) as the set of all points interior to (A) in relation to its dimensionality space, thus identifying the relative interior of an N-dimensional cone with its interior. The relative interior of any cone (A) is denoted by $)A($. If A is a frame of (A), then $)A($ is the set of all points y that can be represented by the vectors [see XVIII, Theorem 1]

(2.9) $y = Ax, \qquad x_k > 0 \qquad (k = 1, \cdots, K)$.

The remaining points of (A) make up the *relative boundary* of (A).

2.5. *Inequalities between vectors.* As stated in Section 2.1, a cone can be represented by a set of linear homogeneous inequalities on its vectors. We shall understand inequalities between vectors a, b, $\cdots$ as applying to all their components, as follows:

(2.10) $\begin{cases} a > b \text{ means } \quad a_n > b_n \text{ for all } n. \\ a \geq b \text{ means } \begin{cases} a_n \geqq b_n \text{ for all } n, \text{ and} \\ a_n > b_n \text{ for some } n. \end{cases} \\ a \geqq b \text{ means } \quad a_n \geqq b_n \text{ for all } n. \end{cases}$ $\begin{matrix} \text{If } b = 0, \\ a \text{ is called} \end{matrix}$ $\begin{cases} \text{positive.} \\ \text{semipositive.} \\ \text{nonnegative.} \end{cases}$

The first and third of these relations can synonymously be denoted $a - b \in)I($, $a - b \in (I)$, respectively. Vectors, a, b, $\cdots$, are regarded as column vectors, their transposes, a', b', $\cdots$, as row vectors. The terms "vector" and "point" are used interchangeably, except that "vector" is used wherever matrix operations are involved.

We use the symbol $\equiv$ to express equality by definition.

2.6. *Coordinate cones.* We shall frequently deal with cones spanned by a frame consisting of a set of vectors selected from the matrix

$$(2.11) \qquad\qquad [-I \quad I],$$

comprising all unit vectors along the positive and negative coordinate axes. Such cones will be referred to as *coordinate cones.* It is easily seen that the polar of a coordinate cone is a coordinate cone and can be determined by applying to each coordinate separately the rules for determining the polar of a cone in one-dimensional space, which we state here for the negative polar:

$$(2.12) \quad (0)^- = (\pm 1), \quad (1)^- = (-1), \quad (-1)^- = (1), \quad (\pm 1)^- = (0).$$

Hence, if (C) is a coordinate cone, C a submatrix of (2.11), then $(C)^-$ is spanned by those vectors of (2.11) which are not included in C.

It follows that a coordinate cone can be equivalently defined by a set of inequalities,

$$(2.13) \qquad\qquad \lambda_n a_n \geqq 0,$$

where for each n the constant λ_n is given one or more of the values 0, 1, -1. It will be primarily a matter of convenience whether in any particular case coordinate cones are represented by a set of inequalities (2.13) or by a frame matrix selected from (2.11). Finally, if C_1 and C_2 are submatrices of (2.11), then

$$(2.14) \qquad\qquad (C_1) \cap (C_2) = (C_3),$$

where C_3 consists of all vectors of (2.11) which are common to C_1 and C_2.

2.7. *Displaced cones.* Occasionally we shall use point sets obtained from a cone by adding a constant vector v to all its points. Such a set will be called a *displaced cone* and denoted $(A \mid v)$, where the vector v will be called its *vertex*, and the cone (A) from which it is derived will be called the *generating cone*. A displaced cone is not a cone, except when the vertex vanishes.

3. Fundamental Properties of the Technology

3.1. *Constant amounts of activities.* We reiterate our assumption that the levels x_k, $k = 1, \cdots, K$, of all activities remain constant for an indefinite period. This implies that the net flows y_n, $n = 1, \cdots, N$, of all commodities, as given by (1.5), are also constant over time.

3.2. *The set of possible points.* A point y with coordinates $y_1, \cdots ,$ y_N in the commodity space is called *possible* if there exists a set of non-negative amounts $x_1, \cdots , x_K$ of the respective activities of which the joint effect is the net outputs $y_1, \cdots , y_N$ of the respective commodities. This is expressed mathematically by

DEFINITION 3.2: *A point y in the commodity space is called possible in a technology A if there exists a point x in the activity space satisfying*

$$(3.1) \qquad\qquad y = Ax, \qquad x \geqq 0.$$

This definition limits the vector x to the convex polyhedral cone (I) in the x-space, which is the sum (convex hull) of the positive coordinate halflines $(i_{(k)})$, $k = 1, \cdots , K$, and will be called the (closed) positive orthant. The linear mapping of the x-space onto the y-space (or a part thereof) defined by (3.1) transforms each halfline $(i_{(k)})$ into the halfline $(a_{(k)})$ based on the corresponding column of the technology matrix A and preserves convexity and hence also the sum operation on cones. It follows that (3.1) is equivalent to

$$(3.2) \qquad\qquad y \; \epsilon \; (A),$$

which expresses that the possible point set is the convex polyhedral cone (A) spanned by the technology matrix A.

Possibility is a technological concept. A possible point may be un-attainable because of the restrictions, (1.7) or (1.9), on primary, inter-mediate, or final commodities. We shall therefore use the term *attainable point set* for that subset of the possible point set whose points can be realized within those restrictions (1.7) and (1.9) that are imposed in any particular case. Attainability is thus a concept involving both tech-nological and economic elements since it is defined with reference to availability limitations of commodities in nature.[9]

3.3. *Fundamental postulates concerning the technology.* Before in-vestigating the application of the notion of productive efficiency intro-duced in Section 1.8 to the set of possible points, it will be useful to formulate mathematical conditions on the technology matrix A, to ex-press certain properties of production which are in some sense funda-mental. It is not claimed that in all uses of models of production these properties should be present. Rather, it is believed that in a broad class of cases it will be useful to employ models having these properties. The order in which these properties are introduced is suggested by reasons of mathematical exposition.

---

[9] An element of valuation has also crept into the notion of attainability since (1.9) also precludes positive outputs of intermediate products, which may well be possible within the availability limitations. I have not found a suitable term which would also suggest the presence of this element in the concept.

It will be convenient to stipulate in advance that

$$(3.3) \qquad\qquad \dim (a_{(k)}) = 1 \qquad\qquad (k = 1, \cdots , K),$$

a trivial condition which excludes the possibility of an "empty" activity that does not involve any commodity.

3.4. *Irreversibility of production.* If labor is regarded as a primary input limited in total amount, rather than as the output of a "consumption" activity, the empirical fact that labor is an input for all productive activities entails that the labor row of A contains only negative coefficients. If more than one kind of labor is distinguished, of which one is a primary input, the others intermediate products, the elements of A in the primary labor row are negative or zero. However, in any column (activity) with a zero element in that row, primary labor enters in some sense indirectly as the input to training activities (other columns) of which the output is an input to the activity in question. Since this indirectness may involve the telescoping of several training activities, it is desirable to specify mathematically what property of A is involved in what may be called the primary-input character of labor in all activities. While in the following postulate labor is not explicitly mentioned at all, the remarks just made about labor seem to provide one sufficient justification for its adoption.

POSTULATE A: *It is impossible to find a set of positive amounts of some or all activities, of which the joint effect is a zero net output for all commodities.*

Mathematically, the postulate says that there exists no vector x satisfying

$$(3.4) \qquad\qquad y = Ax = 0, \qquad x \geq 0.$$

The term "irreversibility" for this property is justified as follows. For any given vector,

$$(3.5) \qquad\qquad x' = [x_1 \cdots x_k \cdots x_K],$$

satisfying (3.4) there exists a pair of integers, n_0, k_0, such that

$$(3.6) \qquad\qquad a_{n_0 k_0} x_{k_0} \neq 0,$$

because (3.3) precludes the vanishing of an entire column of A. Define

$$(3.7) \qquad \begin{cases} x'_{(1)} \equiv [0_1 \cdots 0_{k_0-1} \quad x_{k_0} \quad 0_{k_0+1} \cdots 0_K] \geq 0, \\ x'_{(2)} \equiv [x_1 \cdots x_{k_0-1} \quad 0_{k_0} \quad x_{k_0+1} \cdots x_K] \geqq 0, \end{cases}$$

in which the inequalities are consequences of (3.4) and (3.6). If we define further

$$(3.8) \qquad\qquad y_{(1)} \equiv Ax_{(1)}, \qquad y_{(2)} \equiv Ax_{(2)},$$

we have, from (3.4) and (3.7),

$$(3.9) \qquad 0 = Ax = A(x_{(1)} + x_{(2)}) = y_{(1)} + y_{(2)},$$

and, from (3.6), (3.7), (3.8),

$$(3.10) \qquad\qquad y_{(1)} \neq 0, \qquad y_{(2)} \neq 0,$$

the second inequality following from the first by (3.9). Thus, if (3.4) has a solution x, it is possible to find two activity vectors, $x_{(1)}$ and $x_{(2)}$, such that the net output resulting from one of them exactly offsets the net output brought about by the other. To exclude this possibility is equivalent to saying that no mode of production is reversible.

The foregoing argument shows that, if a solution x of (3.4) exists, the possible cone (A) is lineal. Conversely, it follows from the definition of lineality that, if (A) is lineal, there exist vectors

$$(3.11) \qquad\qquad x_{(1)} \geq 0, \qquad x_{(2)} \geq 0$$

such that the quantities (3.8) derived from them satisfy (3.9) and (3.10), and hence

$$(3.12) \qquad\qquad x = x_{(1)} + x_{(2)}$$

is a solution of (3.4). We have thus established the following theorem.

THEOREM 3.4: *The irreversibility postulate, A, is equivalent to the condition that the cone (A) of possible points is pointed (nonlineal).*

Figure 1 illustrates five simple cases, involving three activities and two commodities only. In Cases I and V production is irreversible. In Cases II, III, and IV production is reversible. The diagrams are drawn in the two-dimensional commodity space. The activities are represented by the column vectors $a_{(k)}$, $k = 1, 2, 3$, of A. The circular arcs serve to indicate the possible point set, which is an angle of either 360° [Case III, lin $(A) = 2$], or 180° [Cases II and IV, lin $(A) = 1$], or less than 180° [Cases I and V, lin $(A) = 0$].

3.5. *Impossibility of the Land of Cockaigne.* The next postulate, although mathematically independent of the first, is related to it in its economic interpretation. To common sense it appears "even more true."

POSTULATE B: *It is impossible to find a set of positive amounts of some or all activities, of which the joint product consists of a positive net output for at least one commodity, without causing a negative net output for at least one other commodity.*

This postulate admits Cases I and II but rules out Cases III, IV, and V of Figure 1 because the possible point set contains points of the positive

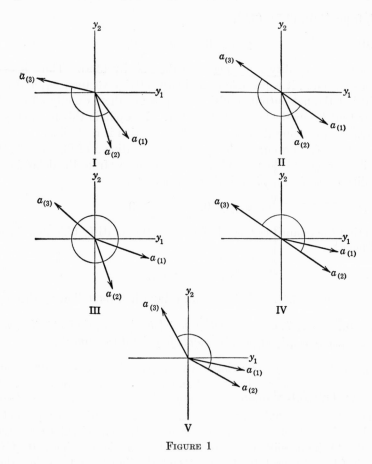

FIGURE 1

quadrant in these cases. A comparison with the cases admitted by Postulate A shows the logical independence of the two postulates.

Mathematically, Postulate B says that there exists no vector x satisfying

$$(3.13) \qquad\qquad y = Ax \geq 0, \qquad x \geq 0.$$

The equivalent condition in terms of convex cones is

(3.14) $(A) \cap (I) = 0$.

It follows immediately that (A) is not solid and is therefore contained
in a halfspace.   It has been proved by Gale [XVII, Theorem 5] that
(3.14) further implies that (A) has a positive outward normal h on the
vertex.   Since the same method of proof will be used below in more complicated cases, we recall the reasoning here.   By taking the negative
polar cones of both sides in (3.14) we obtain, using property (c) of
Chapter XVII, Section 2,

(3.15) $(A)^- + (-I) = (\pm I)$.

By a theorem proved by Gerstenhaber [XVIII, Theorem 13], it follows
from (3.15) that $(A)^-$ contains an interior vector of $-(-I) = (I)$, the

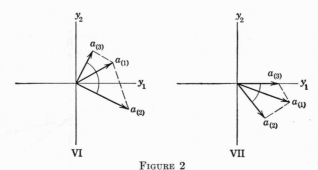

FIGURE 2

closed positive orthant.   In view of the definition (2.6) of the negative
polar, this is equivalent to saying that (A) possesses a positive normal
on the vertex, that is, a vector h satisfying

(3.16) $h'A \leqq 0, \quad h > 0$.

If Postulate A is also satisfied, (A) is pointed and [by XVII, Theorem
3] $(A)^-$ has the dimensionality N of the space.   Hence there exists a
vector h interior to both (I) and $(A)^-$.   It follows from a theorem by
Gerstenhaber [XVIII, Theorem 17, see second part of the proof] that
(A) possesses a normal h on the vertex satisfying

(3.17) $h'A < 0, \quad h > 0$.

Conversely, if (3.16) or (3.17) holds, we have

(3.18) $h'y \leqq 0$ for all $y \, \epsilon \, (A)$ and some $h > 0$,

and Postulate B is satisfied.   Furthermore, if (3.17) holds, (A) is pointed, and by Theorem 3.4 Postulate A is satisfied. These results can be summarized as follows.

THEOREM 3.5.1: *A necessary and sufficient condition that Postulate* B *(impossibility of Cockaigne) be satisfied is that the possible cone* (A) *possesses a positive normal h on the vertex. A necessary condition for this is that* (A) *is nonsolid.*

THEOREM 3.5.2: *A necessary and sufficient condition that Postulates* A *and* B *are both satisfied is that the possible cone* (A) *is pointed and possesses a positive normal h on the vertex.*

For purposes of comparison with criteria for the possibility of production, to be discussed in Section 3.6, we note that, as a corollary of Theorem 3.5.1, Postulate B implies that the cone

$$(3.19) \qquad (-I \quad A)$$

is nonsolid, because it possesses a normal h. Likewise, as a corollary of Theorem 3.5.2, Postulates A and B together imply that the cone (3.19) is pointed. Conversely, Postulates A and B are satisfied if (3.19) is pointed, because then there exists a vector h such that

$$(3.20) \qquad h'[-I \quad A] < 0,$$

which is merely another way of writing (3.17). We thus have the following criterion equivalent to that of Theorem 3.5.2:

THEOREM 3.5.3: *A necessary and sufficient condition that Postulates* A *and* B *are both satisfied is that the cone* (3.19) *is pointed.*

3.6. *The possibility of production without intermediate commodities.* For the formulation of Postulates A and B, it was not necessary to specify which commodities are desired products and which are primary factors. Rather, Postulate B expresses the necessity for the availability of primary factors, without identifying them with particular rows of A. In order to express in a postulate that positive production of one or more desired commodities is possible, it is necessary to specify in advance the commodities of which net inflows are made available by nature. For simplicity we shall first assume that every commodity is either primary or desired, but not both. This rules out intermediate commodities (Section 1.9). It also permits us to refer to the desired commodities as final commodities (Section 1.7). We thus presuppose a partitioning,

$$(3.21) \quad y \equiv \begin{bmatrix} y_{\text{fin}} \\ y_{\text{pri}} \end{bmatrix}, \qquad A \equiv \begin{bmatrix} A_{\text{fin}} \\ A_{\text{pri}} \end{bmatrix}, \qquad y_{\text{fin}} = A_{\text{fin}}x, \qquad y_{\text{pri}} = A_{\text{pri}}x,$$

of the rows of y and A, reflecting the classification of commodities, given in advance, into final and primary commodities, with

$$(3.22) \quad \begin{cases} (3.22 \text{ fin}) & y_{\text{fin}} \geq 0, \\ (3.22 \text{ pri}) & y_{\text{pri}} \geq \eta_{\text{pri}}, \quad \eta_{\text{pri}} < 0, \end{cases}$$

as the restrictions defining the attainable subset of the possible point set (A).

In order to express the possibility of production we may wish to impose on the vector y_{fin} the strong requirement that positive production of all final commodities is possible,

$$(3.23) \quad y_{\text{fin}} > 0.$$

Alternatively, we may leave that question to be answered by analysis and insist only on the weaker requirement that it is possible to produce at least one commodity,

$$(3.24) \quad y_{\text{fin}} \geq 0.$$

We thus have the following postulates: [10]

POSTULATE C_1 (strong): *It is possible to find a set of positive amounts of some or all activities of which the joint primary factor requirements are within the bounds set by nature and of which the joint product consists of positive net outputs for all desired commodities.*

POSTULATE C_2 (weak): *It is possible to find a set of positive amounts of some or all activities of which the joint primary factor requirements are within the bounds set by nature and of which the joint product consists of nonnegative net outputs for all desired commodities, including a positive net output for at least one such commodity.*

To illustrate, let y_1 in Figure 1 correspond to a final commodity, y_2 to a primary factor of which a flow of one unit is available. Then all five cases in Figure 1 satisfy both the weak and the strong postulate because the feasible point set includes in each case points with positive values of y_1 above the line $y_2 = -1$.

A more instructive illustration is obtained if we interpret Figure 1 differently as follows. Let there be two final commodities with net outputs y_1 and y_2, and one primary factor with net output y_3, limited by

$$(3.25) \quad y_3 \geq \eta_3 = -1.$$

---

[10] I am indebted to Herbert A. Simon for a discussion of these postulates. A special case of the strong postulate has been formulated by Hawkins and Simon [1949].

Let this primary factor be required for each of the three activities, and normalize each column of the coefficient matrix A by

$$(3.26) \qquad\qquad a_{3k} = -1 \qquad\qquad (k = 1, 2, 3).$$

The matrix can then be denoted

$$(3.27) \qquad\qquad A = \begin{bmatrix} a_{(1)} & a_{(2)} & a_{(3)} \\ -1 & -1 & -1 \end{bmatrix},$$

where the $a_{(k)}$ are vectors with two elements. Let Figure 1 now represent, in five possible cases, the configurations of the vectors $a_{(k)}$ in the space of the vector $y_{\text{fin}} = \begin{bmatrix} y_1 \\ y_2 \end{bmatrix}$ of final commodities. Then Cases I and II are ruled out by either Postulate C_1 or C_2, because no achievable point is found in or on the boundary of the positive quadrant. Cases III, IV, and V are admitted by either postulate. Figure 2 shows another case (VI) admitted by both postulates, and a borderline case (VII) admitted by (the weak) Postulate C_2 but excluded by (the strong) Postulate C_1.

It should be added that if, in the present interpretation of Figures 1 and 2, we consider the attainable point set in the desired commodity space as limited by (3.22 pri) [i.e., in this case by (3.25)], but without restricting the signs of y_1, y_2, by (3.22 fin), that space is no longer represented by an entire angle, but instead by a convex polygon spanned on the origin and the end-points of the three vectors $a_{(1)}$, $a_{(2)}$, $a_{(3)}$, as suggested in Figure 2 by dotted lines. The available primary factor input is fully used in any point on a dotted line, and partially used in any point in which the origin enters with a positive weight. However, a negative net output of a nonprimary commodity is possible only temporarily, if there is some stock to draw upon, and is impossible in a static model. If we include the requirement (3.22 fin), or $y_1 \geqq 0$, $y_2 \geqq 0$, in the definition of the attainable point set, that set contains only the origin in those cases in Figure 1 ruled out by the strong postulate and consists only of a line segment in Case VII of Figure 2.

Let us now translate the postulates in mathematical terms. Both postulates require that the possible cone (A) contains a point y such that $y_{\text{fin}} \geq 0$. In terms of convex cones this can be expressed in the condition

$$(3.28) \qquad\qquad (B_{\text{fin}}) \equiv (A_{\text{fin}}) \cap (I_{\text{fin}}) \neq 0.$$

Both postulates require further that the coordinates y_{pri} of this point y satisfy the availability restrictions in (3.22 pri). It is easily seen that the latter requirement does not place any restriction on (A). For, if y is a point such that $y_{\text{fin}} \in (B_{\text{fin}})$ as defined in (3.28), but which does not satisfy (3.22 pri), we can always find a positive scalar λ small enough such that λy satisfies (3.22 pri).

Since (the weak) Postulate C_2 contains no other requirements than those stated, (3.28) is equivalent to it. The strong postulate requires in addition that (A_{fin}) contain an interior point of (I_{fin}). Using Theorem 13 of Gerstenhaber [XVIII], and in particular the statement following its proof, we obtain:

THEOREM 3.6.1: *Postulate* C_1 (*the strong postulate*) *of the possibility of production is equivalent to the requirement that the cone*

$$(3.29) \qquad\qquad (-I_{\text{fin}} \quad A_{\text{fin}})$$

be solid.

We shall state without proof a criterion for the weak postulate only in the somewhat simpler case in which the irreversibility Postulate A is satisfied.[11]   In this case, using the definition of a lineal cone given in Section 2.4, we can obtain from (3.28):

THEOREM 3.6.2: *If Postulate* A (*the irreversibility postulate*) *is satisfied, Postulate* C_2 *of the possibility of production is equivalent to the requirement that the cone* (3.29) *be lineal.*

3.7. *The possibility of production with intermediate commodities.* The situation is somewhat more complicated in the presence of commodities which are neither desired nor given by nature.   In this case, the vector y is partitioned according to

$$(3.30) \qquad\qquad y \equiv \begin{bmatrix} y_{\text{fin}} \\ y_{\text{int}} \\ y_{\text{pri}} \end{bmatrix},$$

and the restriction (1.9) or

$$(3.31) \qquad\qquad y_{\text{int}} = 0$$

on the net output vector of intermediate commodities must be added to (3.22). This leads to the following possibility postulates:

POSTULATE D_1 (strong): *It is possible to satisfy Postulate* C_1 *in a manner involving zero net outputs of all intermediate commodities.*

POSTULATE D_2 (weak): *It is possible to satisfy Postulate* C_2 *in a manner involving zero net outputs of all intermediate commodities.*

---

[11] To be precise, we are using only the pointedness of (A_{fin}), not that of (A).

*3.8. *Criteria for the possibility of production with intermediate commodities.* We note that, again, the limitations (3.22 pri) on primary factor availabilities do not restrict the technology matrix A under either postulate. Exploring now in particular the mathematical contents of Postulate D_1, we require only that there exist a solution y_{fin}, y_{int}, x, of

$$(3.32) \qquad y_{\text{fin}} = A_{\text{fin}}x > 0, \qquad x \geqq 0,$$

and

$$(3.33) \qquad y_{\text{int}} = A_{\text{int}}x = 0.$$

In the notation of convex cones we require that there exist a vector y_{fin} such that

$$(3.34) \qquad \begin{pmatrix} A_{\text{fin}} \\ A_{\text{int}} \end{pmatrix} \supset \begin{pmatrix} y_{\text{fin}} \\ 0 \end{pmatrix}, \qquad y_{\text{fin}} > 0.$$

Since it follows from the sum definition of cones that $(A) \supset (B)$ implies $(A \ \ C) \supset (B \ \ C)$, (3.34) implies

$$(3.35) \qquad \begin{pmatrix} -I_{\text{fin}} & A_{\text{fin}} \\ 0 & A_{\text{int}} \end{pmatrix} \supset \begin{pmatrix} -I_{\text{fin}} & y_{\text{fin}} \\ 0 & 0 \end{pmatrix}, \qquad y_{\text{fin}} > 0.$$

If in Theorem 14 of Chapter XVIII we let A stand for $(-I_{\text{fin}})$ and B for $(-y_{\text{fin}})$, we see that the cone at the right in (3.35) consists of the entire subspace of the "fin" coordinates. Hence, for Postulate D_1 to be satisfied, it is necessary that

$$(3.36) \qquad \begin{pmatrix} -I_{\text{fin}} & A_{\text{fin}} \\ 0 & A_{\text{int}} \end{pmatrix} \supset \begin{pmatrix} \pm I_{\text{fin}} \\ 0 \end{pmatrix}.$$

We shall show that this condition is also sufficient.

If (3.36) is true, any vector y_{fin}^0 can be represented by

$$(3.37) \qquad \begin{bmatrix} y_{\text{fin}}^0 \\ 0 \end{bmatrix} = \begin{bmatrix} -I_{\text{fin}} & A_{\text{fin}} \\ 0 & A_{\text{int}} \end{bmatrix} \begin{bmatrix} z \\ x \end{bmatrix}, \qquad z \geqq 0, \qquad x \geqq 0,$$

which is equivalent to

$$(3.38) \qquad y_{\text{fin}}^0 = -z + A_{\text{fin}}x, \qquad z \geqq 0, \qquad x \geqq 0,$$

with x satisfying (3.33). Taking $y_{\text{fin}}^0 > 0$, we conclude that

$$(3.39) \qquad y_{\text{fin}} \equiv y_{\text{fin}}^0 + z = A_{\text{fin}}x > 0$$

also satisfies (3.32). This establishes:

---

* See the last sentence of Section 1.13 (p. 42).

THEOREM 3.8.1: *A necessary and sufficient condition for (the strong) Postulate* D_1 *of the possibility of production with intermediate commodities to be satisfied is that the cone*

$$(3.40) \qquad \begin{pmatrix} -I_{\text{fin}} & A_{\text{fin}} \\ 0 & A_{\text{int}} \end{pmatrix}$$

shall contain the linear space of N_{fin} *dimensions,*

$$(3.41) \qquad \begin{pmatrix} \pm I_{\text{fin}} \\ 0_{\text{int}} \end{pmatrix}.$$

By a similar reasoning we can derive a criterion for the weak postulate, which we state without proof:

THEOREM 3.8.2: *If the irreversibility postulate,* A, *is satisfied, a necessary and sufficient condition for (the weak) Postulate* D_2 *of the possibility of production with intermediate commodities to be satisfied is that the cone* (3.40) *be lineal.*

3.9. *Computational aspects of the criteria for postulates A, B, C and D.* It is worth noting that the criteria given for Postulates A, C_1, D_1, and those given for Postulates B (Theorem 3.5.3), C_2, D_2 in the case in which Postulate A is satisfied, can all be stated as conditions on the lineality of a cone defined by means of the technology matrix A, in one case (D_1) supplemented by a simple condition on the lineality space of such a cone.   The main computational problem involved in the application of these criteria is therefore the determination of the lineality of a cone defined as the convex hull of given vectors.   It is quite possible that, in a variety of circumstances, computational methods are found economical for this purpose which do not require the inversion of matrices.   It is for this reason that we have given explicit criteria for the case where intermediate goods are present.   Alternatively, as shown in (the next) Section 3.10, intermediate goods can be eliminated from the technology before the production possibility criteria are applied, by methods based on polarity of cones, and therefore essentially involving matrix inversion.   In any case, polarity of cones and matrix inversions are essential concepts for the theory of prices of commodities, developed in Sections 4 and 5.

* 3.10. *Reduction of the technology matrix.*   The requirement that net output of intermediate commodities shall vanish is equivalent to intersecting the technologically achievable cone (A) with the linear space

$y_{\text{int}} = 0$. Considered as a cone, this linear space can be denoted by

$$(3.42) \qquad \begin{pmatrix} \pm I_{\text{fin}} & 0 \\ 0 & 0 \\ 0 & \pm I_{\text{pri}} \end{pmatrix}.$$

The intersection is again [by XVII, property (a), Section 2] a (polyhedral) cone, which we denote, after omitting the vanishing "int"-coordinates, by

$$(3.43) \qquad (\bar{A}) \equiv \begin{pmatrix} \bar{A}_{\text{fin}} \\ \bar{A}_{\text{pri}} \end{pmatrix}.$$

We shall say that $\bar{A}$ is obtained by a *reduction* of A which gives effect, once and for all, to the restriction $y_{\text{int}} = 0$. To indicate how $\bar{A}$ is obtained from A, we make use of certain properties [XVII, Section 2] of the mapping of the space of cones (A) onto the space of their negative polars $(A)^-$. We have, interchanging the order of "int"- and "pri"-coordinates,

$$(3.44) \qquad \begin{pmatrix} \bar{A} \\ 0_{\text{int}} \end{pmatrix} \equiv \begin{pmatrix} \bar{A}_{\text{fin}} \\ \bar{A}_{\text{pri}} \\ 0_{\text{int}} \end{pmatrix} \equiv \begin{pmatrix} A_{\text{fin}} \\ A_{\text{pri}} \\ A_{\text{int}} \end{pmatrix} \cap \begin{pmatrix} \pm I_{\text{fin}} & 0 \\ 0 & \pm I_{\text{pri}} \\ 0 & 0 \end{pmatrix}.$$

Let A^- denote a frame of $(A)^-$, and A_{fin}^-, A_{pri}^-, A_{int}^- its submatrices according to the three types of coordinates. Then, indicating under the equality signs the property used, we derive from (3.44)

$$(3.45) \qquad \begin{aligned} \begin{pmatrix} \bar{A} \\ 0_{\text{int}} \end{pmatrix} &\underset{(c)}{=} \begin{pmatrix} A_{\text{fin}}^- & 0 \\ A_{\text{pri}}^- & 0 \\ A_{\text{int}}^- & \pm I_{\text{int}} \end{pmatrix}^- = \begin{pmatrix} A_{\text{fin}}^- & 0 \\ A_{\text{pri}}^- & 0 \\ 0 & \pm I_{\text{int}} \end{pmatrix}^- \underset{(b)}{=} \\[2em] &= \begin{pmatrix} A_{\text{fin}}^- \\ A_{\text{pri}}^- \\ 0 \end{pmatrix}^- \cap \begin{pmatrix} \pm I_{\text{fin}} & 0 \\ 0 & \pm I_{\text{pri}} \\ 0 & 0 \end{pmatrix} = \\[2em] &= \begin{pmatrix} \begin{bmatrix} A_{\text{fin}}^- \\ A_{\text{pri}}^- \end{bmatrix}^- & 0 \\ 0 & \pm I_{\text{int}} \end{pmatrix} \cap \begin{pmatrix} \pm I_{\text{fin}} & 0 \\ 0 & \pm I_{\text{pri}} \\ 0 & 0 \end{pmatrix} = \begin{pmatrix} \begin{bmatrix} A_{\text{fin}}^- \\ A_{\text{pri}}^- \end{bmatrix}^- \\ 0_{\text{int}} \end{pmatrix}. \end{aligned}$$

The equalities in (3.45) without a reference follow trivially from the definitions of cone, polar, sum, and intersection. From (3.45) we conclude:

THEOREM 3.10: *The set of those points y in the commodity space, possible in a technology A involving intermediate commodities, which satisfy the restrictions $y_{int} = 0$, is identical with the set of all possible points in a technology $\bar{A}$ derived from A by*

(3.46)
$$\bar{A} = \begin{bmatrix} A_{fin}^- \\ A_{pri}^- \end{bmatrix}^-.$$

Of course, application of the criteria for Postulates C_1 or C_2 to $(\bar{A})$ is equivalent to application of the criteria for D_1 or D_2, respectively, to (A). The reader who desires a further exercise in operations with the polar transformation of cones may wish to establish the equivalence explicitly.

4. THE EFFICIENT POINT SET IN THE SPACE OF FINAL AND PRIMARY COMMODITIES

4.1. *Primary factors regarded as desired commodities.* We shall now study the application of the allocative objective of production introduced in Section 1.7. It will be useful first, in the present section, to consider the case in which no availability restrictions are placed on the net flows of primary factors. Instead, as already suggested in Section 1.9 with regard to land, we shall include primary factors among the desired commodities, with the interpretation that the objective of the economy is served by the algebraic increase of their net output (i.e., by the decrease of their input). With regard to manpower or land this interpretation is justifiable by the existence of an alternative use of these factors for leisure or recreation. With regard to other primary factors, a justification may be found in a desire for conservation of exhaustible resources, although such a consideration can be adequately expressed only in a dynamic model. However, the question of justification of the objective is not important at this stage because the present case is considered mainly for its mathematical simplicity, as a step toward cases which are both more complicated and more realistic.

With respect to intermediate commodities, we shall assume in the present section that the technology matrix A either does not contain them at the outset, or is already the result $\bar{A}$ of a reduction, as defined in Section 3.9, of an original matrix A so as to eliminate intermediate products. In the second interpretation, we shall omit the bar from the symbol A and speak of the cone (A) as the possible point set in the reduced technology, although it excludes points possible in the original technology but unattainable under the restriction (3.31) on intermediate commodities.

We shall, however, not necessarily assume that A incorporates the restrictions $y_n \geqq 0$ for all n designating nonprimary commodities, mentioned in Section 1.7, although such an assumption can be added whenever desired. Thus qualified, the concept of possibility, as introduced formally by Definition 3.2, differs from that of attainability (see Definition 5.2) in that the availability restrictions on primary commodities, and those on final commodities not implied in the technology A, are disregarded in it.

As a result of these specifications, our commodity space consists of final and primary commodities only, and all of these are regarded as desired commodities.

4.2. *Definition of an efficient point.* A possible point (4.1) in the commodity space is called efficient whenever an increase in one of its coordinates (the net output of one good) can be achieved only at the cost of a decrease in some other coordinate (the net output of another good). This is expressed mathematically in

DEFINITION 4.2: *A point y in the commodity space is called efficient if it is possible [i.e., if $y \in (A)$], and if there exists no possible point $\bar{y} \in (A)$ such that*

$$(4.1) \qquad \bar{y} - y \geq 0.$$

4.3. *A necessary and sufficient condition for efficiency.* We must expect to find more than one point y satisfying this definition. For instance, because of the linear homogeneity of all conditions entering into this definition, the efficiency of y entails the efficiency of λy if λ is a positive scalar. Generally, the efficient point set consists of a set of halflines rather than a single halfline. Application of the criterion of efficiency thus serves only to eliminate a set of clearly wasteful modes of production, leaving us with a set of efficient points from which further choice by other criteria is to be made. These further criteria fall outside the scope of this chapter. We are studying only the properties of the efficient point set and the conditions under which it can be regarded as defining a transformation function.

In this section we shall give a discussion of the case of two commodities, based on diagrammatic illustration, which will help us formulate a theorem concerning the nature of the efficient point set. In the next section we shall prove that theorem for the case of N commodities.

Let the cone AOB in Figure 3 be the possible cone (A). The condition (4.1) can then be interpreted as follows: A point y of (A) will be efficient whenever a displaced cone DyE with vertex y and spanned by halflines yD, yE parallel to the positive coordinate axes has only the point y in

common with the cone † AOB.   It is seen that this requirement excludes
(a) any interior point y' of AOB, and (b) any point y'' on the halfline
OA in the boundary of AOB (except the point 0), but permits (c) all
points y of the halfline OB in the boundary of AOB (including the point
0).   The bounding halfline OB of AOB distinguishes itself from the
bounding halfline OA in that each point y of OB possesses a normal yN
to AOB with positive direction coefficients.   It is clear that each point
possessing such a normal is efficient.   The converse statement, that

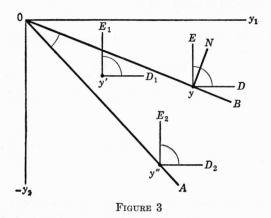

FIGURE 3

each efficient point possesses such a normal, is likewise clear in two
dimensions, but needs more careful argument in the N-commodity case.
It will then be our task to prove the following theorem.

THEOREM 4.3: *A necessary and sufficient condition that a possible point
$y \in (A)$ be efficient according to Definition 4.2 is that y possesses a positive
normal (p) to (A), as defined by (4.7) below.   This implies as a necessary
condition that y is a boundary point of (A).*

*4.4 *Proof of Theorem* 4.3; *the local possible cone.*   It is inconvenient
to work with displaced cones, such as DyE in Figure 3, with a vertex not
in the origin.   This can be avoided by using the concept of the local
possible cone defined as follows.

DEFINITION 4.4.1: *The local possible cone* (D) *in the point* y *of the possible cone* (A) *is the set of all vectors* d *of the form*

$$(4.2) \qquad d = \lambda(\bar{y} - y), \qquad \bar{y} \in (A), \qquad \lambda \text{ a positive scalar.}$$

† No confusion need arise between the use of the letters A, B, $\cdots$ to indicate halflines in Figure 3 and their use to indicate matrices.

It follows easily from the convexity of (A) that the set so defined is indeed a convex cone, and that $y + d \,\epsilon\, (A)$ whenever $\lambda \leqq 1$. The cone (D) therefore contains all directions of variation from the point y of (A), in which it is possible to go (for some positive distance) without going outside the possible cone (A). In other words, (D) is obtained from the displaced cone "projecting" (A) out of the vertex y, by a translation which makes the new vertex coincide with the origin. In Figure 3 the local possible cone in y' is solid, that in y is the halfspace "below" the line $0B$ (extended also beyond 0).

LEMMA 4.4.2: *The local possible cone in y can be represented by*

$$(4.3) \qquad\qquad (D) = (-y \quad A).$$

To prove this lemma, we note that any vector d satisfying (4.2) can be written as

$$(4.4) \qquad d = \lambda(\bar{y} - y) = \lambda(-y + A\bar{x}) = \lambda[-y \quad A] \begin{bmatrix} 1 \\ \bar{x} \end{bmatrix},$$
$$\lambda > 0, \qquad \bar{x} \geqq 0$$

and is therefore a vector of $(-y \quad A)$. To argue the converse, we consider separately those vectors of $(-y \quad A)$ which are not contained in (A) and those which are. Any vector of the first class can, by a suitable positive choice of λ, be expressed as d in (4.4), and therefore satisfies Definition 4.4.1. Any vector of the second class [i.e., any vector d of (A)], can be used to define a vector $\bar{y} = d + y$ which is also in (A), whence d satisfies Definition 4.4.1 with $\lambda = 1$.

It follows from Lemma 4.4.2 that the local possible cone is a convex polyhedral cone. It follows further, by Theorem 14 of Chapter XVIII, but it can even more readily be argued directly from Definition 4.4.1, that the local possible cone (D) in an interior point y of (A) is solid. Since (D) is defined only for points y of (A), it contains the line $(\pm y)$, and therefore its lineality is at least one whenever $y \neq 0$.

To prove Theorem 4.3, we now express Definition 4.2 of efficiency of y by the requirement

$$(4.5) \qquad\qquad (-y \quad A) \cap (I) = 0;$$

[i.e., we cannot from y proceed in a positive direction within (A)]. A condition of this form has already been analyzed in the paragraphs following (3.14) above, the only difference being that $(-y \quad A)$ is known to be lineal. The reasoning previously given therefore now leads to the result that, for y to be efficient, it is necessary and sufficient that there exist a vector p satisfying

$$(4.6) \qquad\qquad p'[-y \quad A] \leqq 0, \qquad p > 0,$$

or, equivalently because of (3.1), a vector p satisfying

$$(4.7) \qquad\qquad p'A \leqq 0, \qquad p'y = 0, \qquad p > 0$$

(a condition applicable also when $y = 0$). This cannot be the case if y is an internal point of (A), because then $(-y \quad A)$ is solid and hence possesses no nonvanishing normal.

Since by Lemma 4.4.2 any halfline (p) normal to $(-y \quad A)$ on 0 generates a displaced halfline normal to (A) on the vertex y, we shall refer to (p), briefly though somewhat inaccurately, as a normal to (A) in y, and to p as a vector normal to (A) in y.

4.5. *Efficient facets.* It has been proved by Gerstenhaber [XVIII, Theorem 35] that the boundary of a convex polyhedral cone (A) is the union of a finite number of its open proper facets,[12] no two of which have a vector in common. We use the term "proper facets" here to designate (closed or open) facets of which the dimensionality is at most $N - 1$.

Closed facets are defined by Gerstenhaber recursively, a closed $(n - 1)$-facet being a cone (F_{n-1}), contained in the boundary of a closed n-facet (F_n), such that no convex cone (F) containing both (F_{n-1}) and a vector not in (F_{n-1}) is contained in the boundary of (F_n). Thus (F_{n-1}) is a maximal convex cone in the boundary of (F_n). By identifying (F_n) with (A) if $n = \dim (A)$, facets of all lower orders n are defined, and the order n is found to equal the dimensionality of (F_n).

A closed facet (F_n) is [XVIII, Theorem 23] spanned by a submatrix F_n of a frame A of (A). An open facet $)F_n($ is here defined as the relative interior of a closed facet (F_n), or equivalently [XVIII, Theorem 1] as the set of vectors obtained by *strictly positive* linear combination of the vectors of F_n. The dimensionality of $)F_n($ is defined as that of (F_n). We shall often use the term "facet" without adjective if the notation specifies whether the facet in question is open or closed, and also in statements applying to both kinds of facets. The dimensionality n of a facet $)F_n($ of a pointed cone (A) equals the number of linearly independent frame vectors of A included in the submatrix F_n. The cone

---

[12] If (A) is pointed this includes the origin as a separate facet, which must here be considered as open. If (A) is lineal, its lineality space is an open facet containing the origin.

AOB of Figure 3 thus has two open 1-facets, $0A$ and $0B$ (each not including 0), and one open 0-facet, 0.

In this two-dimensional example it is obvious that the normals to AOB in all points y of $0B$ are parallel. To formulate the extension of this statement to the case of N commodities we shall associate with each boundary point y of (A) by (4.3) the cone $(D)^-$ consisting of all vectors p normal to (A) in y. This will be referred to, again somewhat inaccurately, as the cone of normals to (A) in y. The extension of the foregoing statement, to be proved as Lemma 4.6 in (the next) Section 4.6, is that all points y of a facet $)F($ have the same cone of normals $(D_F)^-$. From this lemma, the following consequences of Theorem 4.3 are also proved in Section 4.6:

THEOREM 4.5.1: *If one point y of an open facet $)F($ of (A) is efficient according to Definition 4.2, then all points of the closed facet (F) are efficient.*

On the basis of Theorem 4.5.1, a further definition leads to a reformulation of Theorem 4.3.

DEFINITION 4.5.2: *A facet (open or closed) of (A) is called efficient if all its points are efficient.*

THEOREM 4.5.3: *A necessary and sufficient condition that an open or closed facet, $)F($ or (F), of (A) be efficient according to Definition 4.2 is that there exist a vector p satisfying*

$$(4.8) \qquad p'A \leqq 0, \qquad p'F = 0, \qquad p > 0.$$

* 4.6. *Proofs of Theorems* 4.5.1 *and* 4.5.3. We shall first draw some conclusions from the assumption that y is a point of a facet $)F($ as defined by

$$(4.9) \qquad y = Fx_F, \qquad x_F > 0.$$

If in Theorem 14 of Chapter XVIII we let A stand for (F), B for (y), we find that

$$(4.10) \quad (-y \quad F) = (-F \quad F) = \text{dimensionality space of } (F),$$

regardless of the particular value of y satisfying (4.9). Let us denote by (D_F) the local possible cone in a point y of $)F($. Then, from Lemma 4.4.2, since F is a submatrix of A, and using (4.10),

$$(4.11) \quad (D_F) = (-y \quad A) = (-y \quad F \quad A) = (-F \quad F \quad A) = (-F \quad A),$$

again independently of the particular point y of $)F($. It follows that the cone of normals $(D_F)^-$ on (A) in y depends only on the facet $)F($.

Now let $\bar{y}$ be a point of the (closed) facet (F) but not necessarily a point of $)F($. Then

(4.12)
$$-\bar{y} \ \epsilon \ (-F),$$

and the local possible cone $(\bar{D})$ in $\bar{y}$ satisfies

(4.13)
$$(\bar{D}) = (-\bar{y} \ A) \subset (-F \ A) = (D_F).$$

We then have [XVII, Section 1B, property (1^*)] for the cone $(\bar{D})$ of normals on (A) in $\bar{y}$

(4.14)
$$(\bar{D})^- \supset (D_F)^-.$$

These results establish the following lemma.

LEMMA 4.6: *All points y of an open facet $)F($ of (A) have the same cone of normals $(D_F)^-$ to (A). This cone is contained in the cone of normals $(\bar{D})^-$ of any point $\bar{y}$ of the closed facet (F).*

On the basis of this lemma, we may now speak of a normal to (A) on $)F($, or on (F), instead of the previous term: normal to (A) in a point y of $)F($. If p is such a normal, we shall also say that $)F($, or (F), possesses a normal p to (A). Since by Theorem 4.3 the efficiency of a point y is equivalent to the existence of a positive normal to (A) in y, Theorem 4.5.1 follows directly from Lemma 4.6. Theorem 4.5.3 states the required existence of a positive normal explicitly as a condition on the facet $)F($.

4.7. *Economic interpretation of the efficiency conditions.* An interesting interpretation can be given to a vector p normal to (A) on an efficient point y. We shall call it a vector of prices p_n of the commodities $n = 1, \cdots, N$ in the point y. There is in this term no necessary implication of a market in which exchange of commodities between different parties takes place. The terms "shadow prices" or "accounting prices" have been used in various contexts to express this reservation. For the moment, we shall use the general term "prices," subject to different interpretations in different uses of the model.

To see the meaning of this interpretation we rewrite (4.8), having regard to (4.9), as separate conditions on each column vector $a_{(k)}$ of A, as follows:

(4.15)
$$\begin{cases} p'a_{(k)} = 0 & \text{if } x_k > 0, \\ p'a_{(k)} \leq 0 & \text{if } x_k = 0. \end{cases}$$

The expression $p'a_{(k)}$ is interpreted as the net (accounting) profit on the unit of the kth activity, computed on the basis of the price vector p.

Then (4.15) says that no activity in the technology yields a positive profit, while each activity carried out at a positive level to achieve the point y yields a zero profit. We thus find the following equivalent formulation of Theorem 4.5.3 in economic terminology:

THEOREM 4.7: *A necessary and sufficient condition that the activity vector* x *shall lead to an efficient point* $y = Ax$ *in the commodity space is that there exists a vector* p *of positive prices such that no activity in the technology permits a positive profit and such that the profit on all activities carried out at a positive level be zero.*

4.8. *Uniqueness of the price vector* p. Since every efficient facet is contained in the boundary of (A), the dimensionality of an efficient facet (F) is at most $N - 1$. If dim $(F) = N - 1$, then the matrix F has rank $N - 1$, and the second and third conditions in (4.8) determine p up to a positive scalar factor. If dim $(F) < N - 1$, we have

$$(4.16) \quad \begin{aligned} \dim (D_F)^- &= N - \mathrm{lin}\, (D_F) \\ &= N - \mathrm{lin}\, (-F \quad F \quad A) = N - \dim (F) > 1, \end{aligned}$$

because of Theorem 3 of Chapter XVII, and because [XVIII, Theorem 23 (5)] the lineality space of (A) is contained in any facet (F) of (A). Thus we have: [13]

THEOREM 4.8: *A necessary and sufficient condition for the uniqueness (but for a positive scalar factor) of a price vector* p *associated with a point* y *of an efficient open facet* $)F($ *is that* (F) *have the dimensionality* $N - 1$.

From the computational point of view, it may be noted that, once an efficient $(N - 1)$-facet $)F($ has been found, the determination of the corresponding price vector requires the solution of a system of linear equations represented by the second condition (4.8). The first and third conditions are then simultaneously satisfied by proper choice of the sign of p.

4.9. *Marginal rates of substitution defined by a unique price vector.* If for an efficient facet (F) we have dim $(F) = N - 1$, the components p_n of the unique price vector p associated with F can be regarded as defining marginal rates of substitution between all commodities on (F). If y and

---

[13] It might be thought that the condition of positiveness of p might cut out just one halfline (p) from a two-or-more-dimensional cone of normals $(-y \quad A)^-$ such as arises if dim $(F) < N - 1$. However, the intersection of the *closed* cone $(-y \quad A)^-$ with the *open* set $)I($ expressing the positiveness of p is either empty or contains an infinite number of halflines.

$\bar{y}$ are two points of (F), and hence both efficient, we have, from the second condition (4.8), $p'\bar{y} = 0 = p'y$, hence also

$$(4.17) \qquad\qquad p'(\bar{y} - y) = 0.$$

Within the limits of the facet (F), therefore, choice between different modes of production y, $\bar{y}$, $\cdots$ opens the same alternatives as would trading at the constant prices p. To take an example, if

$$(4.18) \qquad \bar{y}_1 > y_1, \qquad \bar{y}_2 < y_2, \qquad \bar{y}_n = y_n, \quad (n = 3, \cdots, N),$$

then (4.17) implies

$$(4.19) \qquad\qquad p_1(\bar{y}_1 - y_1) = p_2(y_2 - \bar{y}_2).$$

An amount $(y_2 - \bar{y}_2)$ of commodity "2" is "traded" for an amount $(\bar{y}_1 - y_1)$ of commodity "1" at the price

$$(4.20) \qquad\qquad p_{12} = p_1/p_2$$

of the unit of "1" expressed in terms of units of "2."

It is important to emphasize the two conditions that must be satisfied for these relative prices p_{nm} to be applicable. In the first place, the relative prices refer only to a change from one efficient point y to another efficient point $\bar{y}$. That is, commodities are substituted for each other in these ratios *only after efficiency has been reached and provided that efficiency is maintained* in the change in activity levels. Secondly, the set of substitution ratios belonging to an efficient $(N - 1)$-dimensional facet applies only to changes between points *on that same facet*, including its relative boundary. Upon entering an adjoining $(N - 1)$-facet, a different set of substitution ratios becomes applicable to changes within that facet. No set of constant substitution ratios applies to comparisons between points of different $(N - 1)$-facets.

4.10. *Nonincreasing marginal rate of substitution.* It is easily seen that if, in increasing the net output of a commodity "1" in efficient exchange for a decrease in the net output of a commodity "2," the point y passes from one efficient $(N - 1)$-facet to another, the marginal rate of substitution (4.20) cannot jump upward at the passage. Let u, v, w be three efficient points such that

$$(4.21) \qquad \begin{cases} u_1 < v_1 < w_1, \\ u_2 > v_2 > w_2, \\ u_n = v_n = w_n \qquad (n = 3, \cdots, N), \end{cases}$$

where we will think of u and w as on different closed efficient $(N - 1)$-

facets, and of v as on the relative boundary of each. Now suppose we had

(4.22)
$$\frac{v_2 - w_2}{w_1 - v_1} < \frac{u_2 - v_2}{v_1 - u_1}$$

as illustrated by Figure 4. Then, because of the convexity of the possible point set (A), we could find a possible point

(4.23)
$$\bar{v} = \lambda u + (1 - \lambda)w, \qquad 0 \leq \lambda \leq 1,$$

such that

(4.24)
$$\bar{v}_1 > v_1, \qquad \bar{v}_2 > v_2, \qquad \bar{v}_n = v_n \quad (n = 3, \cdots, N),$$

by choosing

(4.25)
$$\frac{v_2 - w_2}{u_2 - w_2} < \lambda < \frac{w_1 - v_1}{w_1 - u_1},$$

the possibility of which follows easily from (4.22). This would contradict the assumed efficiency of v. Therefore (4.22) cannot be true.

This result can be applied, of course, to rates of substitution between final commodities, between primary commodities, and between a final and a primary commodity. It can also be extended to proportional changes in the outputs or availabilities of two groups of commodities, as follows. Consider the partitionings

(4.26)
$$y_{\text{fin}} = \begin{bmatrix} y_{\text{I}} \\ y_{\text{II}} \end{bmatrix}, \qquad y_{\text{pri}} = \begin{bmatrix} y_{\text{III}} \\ y_{\text{IV}} \end{bmatrix},$$

and enlarge the technology matrix to

(4.27)
$$\ddot{A} = \begin{bmatrix} 1 & 0 & 0 & 0 & 0 \\ 0 & 0 & A_{\text{I}} & 0 & 0 \\ a_{\text{II}} & 0 & A_{\text{II}} & -I_{\text{II}} & 0 \\ 0 & a_{\text{III}} & A_{\text{III}} & 0 & -I_{\text{III}} \\ 0 & 0 & A_{\text{IV}} & 0 & 0 \\ 0 & -1 & 0 & 0 & 0 \end{bmatrix}, \quad a_{\text{II}} < 0, \quad a_{\text{III}} > 0.$$

The first column introduces an activity that "bundles" the final commodities "II" in given proportions into a new composite final commodity with net output y_0, say. The second activity bundles the primary commodities "III" into a composite with net output y_{N+1}, say. The third column contains the original technology matrix A with two rows of zeros added. The last two columns introduce disposal activities on all commodities subject to bundling.

Treating the commodities "II" and "III" as intermediate, restricted by

$$y_{II} = 0, \qquad y_{III} = 0,$$

the application of our result to y_{N+1} and y_0 establishes that the marginal productivity of a set of primary commodities, under proportional increase in availabilities, in terms of the proportional increase in the outputs of a set of final commodities, is nonincreasing, outputs or availabilities of all other final and primary commodities being held constant. Of course, if "II" comprises all final, "III" all primary, commodities, the marginal productivity dy_{N+1}/dy_0 is a constant.

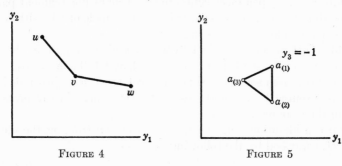

FIGURE 4   FIGURE 5

4.11. *An equivalent characterization of the efficient point set.* So far we have not proved the existence of an efficient $(N - 1)$-facet, and it is not difficult to construct a technology matrix of rank N, which satisfies Postulates A, B, C of Section 3, such that none of its $(N - 1)$-facets has a positive normal. The three 2-facets of the nonsingular technology matrix

$$(4.28) \qquad A = \begin{bmatrix} 1 & 1 & 0.6 \\ 1 & 0.5 & 0.8 \\ -1 & -1 & -1 \end{bmatrix}$$

have as normals the column vectors of

$$(4.29) \qquad P = [p_{(1)} \; p_{(2)} \; p_{(3)}] = \begin{bmatrix} -3 & -1 & 1 \\ -4 & 2 & 0 \\ -5 & 1 & 1 \end{bmatrix},$$

none of which is positive. The example is illustrated in Figure 5, which exhibits the intersection of (A) with the plane $y_3 = -1$. Thus (A) is the cone projecting the triangle $a_{(1)}a_{(2)}a_{(3)}$ out of the origin $y_1 = y_2 = y_3 = 0$, which may be thought of as above the paper in which the figure is drawn.

The following illustration may help to visualize the nature of the efficient point set. Attach a source of light at each coordinate axis at the locations [14] $y_n = +\infty$, $n = 1, \cdots, N$, respectively, and let (A) be represented by an opaque body. By Postulate B of Section 3, all sources are located outside (A). Any facet which receives light from all sources consists of efficient points only. Any open facet which is in the shade of (A) with respect to at least one source does not contain any efficient points, although lower-dimensional facets in its relative boundary may contain efficient points. In particular, the origin $y = 0$ is an efficient point on the relative boundary of all facets, because of Postulate B. An open facet containing a straight line segment parallel to a coordinate axis is to be regarded as in the shade of (A) with respect to the corresponding source of light.

If this construction is applied to the example of Figure 5, the facet $)a_{(2)}$ $a_{(3)}($ is in the shade from sources 1, 2, and 3, the facet $)a_{(1)}$ $a_{(3)}($ is in the shade from source 1, while the facet $)a_{(1)}$ $a_{(2)}($ just falls in the shade from source 2. Similarly, of the 1-facets, only $)a_{(1)}($ receives light from all three sources.

These considerations suggest a method of constructing the efficient point set, expressed by the following theorem.

THEOREM 4.11: *Let A be a technology matrix satisfying Postulate B. Let*

$$(4.30) \qquad\qquad \tilde{A} \equiv [-I \quad A]$$

be the technology matrix obtained from A by adjoining costless disposal activities for all commodities. Then the efficient point set in the technology A is the union of all closed facets of $(\tilde{A})$ which do not contain any of the column vectors of $-I$.

* 4.12. *Proof of Theorem 4.11.*[15] We shall first establish three useful lemmas.

LEMMA 4.12.1: *If (F) and (G) are facets of a convex polyhedral cone (A) such that*

$$(4.31) \qquad\qquad (G) \supset (F), \qquad \dim (G) > \dim (F),$$

---

[14] The illustration remains good, but is less easily grasped, if a finite positive location is selected for each source.

[15] A simple and elegant proof of Theorem 4.11, based on Theorem 26 of Chapter XVIII, was suggested by M. Slater. He has also pointed out that Theorem 4.11 remains vacuously true if Postulate B is not satisfied. The method of proof here followed, and in particular Lemmas 4.12.1 and 4.12.2, have usefulness for the discussion of topological properties of the efficient point set in Sections 4.13–4.14.

then the cone of normals $(-G \quad A)^-$ *to* (A) *on* (G) *is contained in the relative boundary of the cone of normals* $(-F \quad A)^-$ *to* (A) *on* (F).

PROOF: From (4.31) it follows [XVII, Section 1B, property (1*)] that

$$(4.32) \qquad\qquad (-F \quad A)^- \supset (-G \quad A)^-.$$

Therefore [XVIII, Theorem 14] we shall have established the contention if we can show that

$$(4.33) \quad \lin \left(-(-F \quad A)^- + (-G \quad A)^- \right) < \dim \left(-F \quad A \right)^-.$$

This is equivalent [XVII, Theorem 3] to

$$(4.34) \quad \dim \left((F \quad -A) \cap (-G \quad A) \right) > \lin \left(-F \quad A \right) = \dim (F),$$

the equality being based on Theorem 31 of Chapter XVIII.

Now, on the one hand, we have, by (4.31),

$$(4.35) \quad (F \quad -A) \cap (-G \quad A) \supset (F \quad -A) \cap (-F \quad A) = (\pm F).$$

The middle member represents the lineality space of $(-F \, A)$ which, because (F) is a facet of (A), is [XVIII, Theorem 31] equal to the dimensionality space $(\pm F)$ of (F). On the other hand, we have, because $(-G) \subset (-A)$,

$$(4.36) \qquad\qquad (F \quad -A) \cap (-G \quad A) \supset (-G),$$

whereas by the inequality in (4.31) $(-G)$ cannot be contained in $(\pm F)$; hence (4.35) and (4.36) imply (4.34). This completes the proof of Lemma 4.12.1.

LEMMA 4.12.2: *If* (F) *is a facet of a convex polyhedral cone* (A), *and* $p \neq 0$ *a vector in the relative interior of the cone of normals* $(-F \quad A)^-$ *to* (A) *on* (F), *then*

$$(4.37) \qquad\qquad (F) = (p)^{\perp} \cap (A).$$

It will be noted that this lemma specifies a class of hyperplanes $(p)^{\perp}$ that can be used for S in Theorem 33(2) of Chapter XVIII. To prove (4.37), we use the definition (2.6) of the orthogonal complement $(p) \perp$ to conclude from the premise

$$(4.38) \qquad\qquad 0 \neq p \; \epsilon \;)[-F \quad A]^-($$

that $(F) \subset (p^{\perp})$. Since $(F) \subset (A)$, we conclude that (F) is contained in the right-hand member of (4.37). Conversely, if there were a vector a in $(p)^{\perp} \cap (A)$ but not in (F), there would be [XVIII, Theorem 33(1)] a facet (G) of (A) properly containing both (F) and a to which p is normal, contrary to (4.38) and Lemma 4.12.1.

LEMMA 4.12.3: *A facet of $(\tilde{A})$ as defined in* (4.30) *contains a column vector of* $(-I)$ *if and only if it does not possess a positive normal.*

PROOF: Any normal p to $(\tilde{A})$ on any of its facets must satisfy

$$(4.39) \qquad p \, \epsilon \, (\tilde{A})^- = (-I \quad A)^- = (I) \cap (A)^-.$$

Therefore, if a facet $(\tilde{F})$ of $(\tilde{A})$ does not possess a positive normal p, then the cone of normals

$$(4.40) \qquad\qquad\qquad (-\tilde{F} \quad A)^-$$

on $(\tilde{F})$ to $(\tilde{A})$ must be contained in the boundary of the positive orthant (I). It follows easily from the convexity of (4.40) that

$$(4.41) \qquad (-\tilde{F} \quad \tilde{A})^- \subset (_nI) \text{ for some } n, \qquad 1 \leqq n \leqq N,$$

where $_nI$ denotes a matrix obtained from the unit matrix I by deleting the nth column (which we denote by $i_{(n)}$). Taking negative polars in (4.41), we obtain

$$(4.42) \qquad (-\tilde{F} \quad \tilde{A}) \supset (-I \quad i_{(n)}) \supset (\pm i_n) \text{ for some } n.$$

It follows that $-i_{(n)}$ is in the lineality space of $(-\tilde{F} \quad \tilde{A})$. Since, by (4.30), $-i_{(n)} \, \epsilon \, (\tilde{A})$, it follows [XVIII, Theorem 32] that

$$(4.43) \qquad -i_{(n)} \, \epsilon \, (\tilde{A}) \cap \text{lin space of } (-\tilde{F} \quad \tilde{A}) = (\tilde{F}).$$

Conversely, if a facet $(\tilde{F})$ possesses a positive normal p to $(\tilde{A})$,

$$(4.44) \qquad\qquad p'\tilde{A} \leqq 0, \qquad p'\tilde{F} = 0, \qquad p > 0,$$

it cannot contain a vector $-i_{(n)}$. This completes the proof of Lemma 4.12.3.

We proceed to the proof of Theorem 4.11. Let (F) be an efficient facet of (A). Then (F) possesses a positive normal to (A),

$$(4.45) \qquad\qquad p \, \epsilon \, (-F \quad A)^- \cap \,)I(,$$

which, since $)I($ is an N-dimensional open set, can be selected in the relative interior of $(-F \quad A)^-$. Then Lemma 4.12.2 establishes the first equality in

$$(4.46) \quad (F) = (p)^\perp \cap (A) = (p)^\perp \cap (-I \quad A) \equiv (p)^\perp \cap (\tilde{A}).$$

The second equality in (4.46) is a consequence of (4.45), which can be written as

$$(4.47) \qquad\qquad p'A \leqq 0, \qquad p'F = 0, \qquad p > 0,$$

to show that

$$(4.48) \qquad p'\tilde{a} \equiv p'[-I \quad A] \begin{bmatrix} z \\ x \end{bmatrix} = -p'z + p'Ax < 0$$

whenever $z \leq 0$, $x \leqq 0$, and hence $p'\tilde{a} = 0$, $\tilde{a} \epsilon (\tilde{A})$ implies $\tilde{a} \epsilon (A)$. It follows [XVIII, Theorem 33 (1)] that (F) is a facet of $(\tilde{A})$ which, by (4.47), possesses a positive normal to $(\tilde{A})$. It follows from Lemma 4.12.3 that (F) is a facet of $(\tilde{A})$ not containing a column vector of $-I$.

Conversely, let $(\tilde{F})$ be such a facet of $(\tilde{A})$ and hence, by Lemma 4.12.3, possessing a normal p satisfying (4.44), which we select again in the relative interior of $(-\tilde{F} \quad \tilde{A})^-$. Then, by the same reasoning applied in reverse,

$$(4.49) \qquad (\tilde{F}) = (p)^{\perp} \cap (\tilde{A}) = (p)^{\perp} \cap (A) \equiv (F),$$

where [XVIII, Theorem 33 (1)] (F) is a facet of (A) which by its definition has p as a positive normal, and hence is efficient.

Since by Theorem 4.5.1 the efficient point set by Definition 4.2 is made up entirely of efficient facets, this concludes the proof of Theorem 4.11.

4.13. *Topological classification of efficient point sets.* We shall use Theorem 4.11 to give a brief heuristic discussion and classification of topologically different cases with regard to the efficient point set, illustrated by graphical examples in a three-dimensional commodity space ($N = 3$). We shall visualize halflines and cones in that space by their intersection with the plane

$$(4.50) \qquad\qquad h'y = -1,$$

where h is a vector which satisfies

$$(4.51) \qquad\qquad h'\tilde{A} = h'[-I \quad A] < 0$$

and is therefore positive. The existence of such a vector, whenever Postulates A and B of Section 3 are satisfied, is guaranteed by Theorem 3.5.2. By proper choice of the units of measurement for the commodities, we can make all components of h equal to 1. Thereby the intersection of (4.50) with $(-I)$ becomes an equilateral triangle (for $N > 3$ a regular simplex), as shown in Figure 6a, to be denoted by $\{-I\}$. The intersection of (4.50) with the various octants is shown in Figure 6b, where the origin can be thought of as located above the paper.

Because of (4.51), every frame vector of (A) intersects the plane (4.50) in a finite point, and (A) intersects (4.50) in a polygon $\{A\}$ obtained as the convex hull of those points. Finally, $(\tilde{A})$ intersects (4.50) in a polygon $\{\tilde{A}\}$ which is the convex hull of $\{A\}$ and $\{-I\}$. We use the relations between $\{A\}$, $\{-I\}$, $\{\tilde{A}\}$, illustrated in diagrams, to discuss corresponding relations between (A), $(-I)$, $(\tilde{A})$.

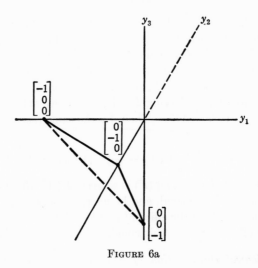

FIGURE 6a

The simplest case, illustrated in Figure 6c, is that where $(-I)$ consists entirely of internal vectors of (A). In that case (A) and $(\tilde{A})$ are identical, and no facet of (A), or its dimensionality space, contains a column vector of $-I$. The cone (A) is necessarily N-dimensional, and

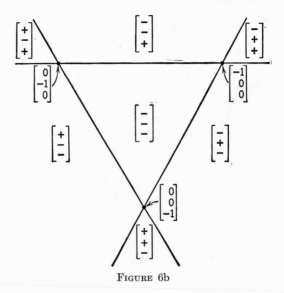

FIGURE 6b

the efficient point set is its entire $(N-1)$-dimensional boundary, topologically equivalent to an entire $(N-1)$-dimensional linear space.

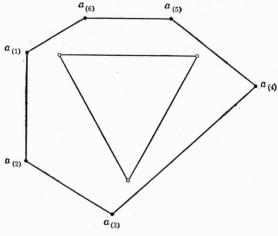

FIGURE 6c

The second case is that in which (A) and $(-I)$ again have an internal vector in common but $(-I)$ contains vectors outside (A). This case is illustrated in Figure 6d. The dotted lines show how (A) is extended

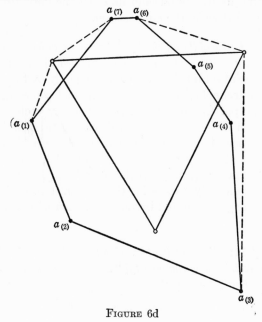

FIGURE 6d

to $(\tilde{A})$.   The application of Theorem 4.11 shows that the efficient point set consists of the adjoining closed facets $(a_{(1)} \quad a_{(2)})$ and $(a_{(2)} \quad a_{(3)})$, and the separate closed facet $(a_{(6)} \quad a_{(7)})$.   These two 2-dimensional parts of the efficient point set are joined only by their common relative boundary point in the origin, so that deletion of the origin would destroy the connectedness of the efficient point set.   For $N = 3$, at most three so separated sections can arise in this way, some or all of which may degenerate to a 1-facet.

A third conceivable case, that in which (A) is contained in $(-I)$, is excluded by either of the Postulates C_1, C_2 of Section 3.   Therefore the boundary of $(\tilde{A})$ contains at least one column vector a of A, which is not in $(-I)$, unless $(\tilde{A})$ is solid.   By Theorem 4.11, the halfline (a) must therefore be part of the efficient point set.   In the light of Theorem 3.5.1, this establishes

THEOREM 4.13: *If the technology matrix A satisfies Postulates* B *and* C_1 *or* C_2, *of Section 3, the efficient point set according to Definition 4.2 contains at least one halfline* (a) *based on a column vector a of A.*

The fourth case is that in which $(-I)$ and (A) have no internal vector in common.   Topologically, this case is not different from that subcase of the second case, in which the part of (A) outside $(-I)$ is contractible to a point within itself.   Because of its economic importance, this case will be explored further in the next section.

4.14.   *Contractibility of the efficient point set when at least one nonprimary desired commodity exists.*   Our examples suggest that the splitting up of the efficient point set into subsets connected only by the origin cannot occur unless the technology matrix A permits *each* commodity to appear as a negative output (net inflow) for some activity vector $x \geqq 0$.   The latter assumption will rarely be satisfied in realistic situations, because in most applications it is known in advance that certain desired commodities are not given by nature.   In Section 4.1, we have left open the possibility of incorporating in A the restriction $y_n \geqq 0$, n designating a nonprimary commodity, expressing that circumstance.   The following statement is strongly suggested by our discussion and is believed to be valid.

ASSERTION 4.14: *Whenever the technology matrix A satisfying Postulate* B *of Section 3 restricts one commodity, "1" say, to nonnegative net outputs but permits positive outputs of it,*

(4.52) $y = Ax$, $x \geqq 0$ implies $y_1 \geqq 0$ and permits $y_1 > 0$, *the efficient point set with the origin $y = 0$ deleted is contractible within itself to a point.*

In Section 4.15 we give suggestions toward a proof of this assertion.

* **4.15. Outline for a proof of Assertion 4.14.** It seems a fruitful approach to such a proof to utilize the one-to-one mapping of the open facets $)\tilde{F}($ of $(\tilde{A})$ on the open facets $)\tilde{F}^{(-)}($, say, of its negative polar $(\tilde{A})^-$. The closed facet $(\tilde{F}^{(-)})$ corresponding to $)\tilde{F}^{(-)}($ may be defined, for instance, as the cone of normals to $(\tilde{A})$ on $(\tilde{F})$ and is then found to equal the intersection

$$(4.53) \quad (\tilde{F}^{(-)}) \equiv (-\tilde{F} \quad \tilde{A})^- = (-\tilde{F} \quad \tilde{F} \quad \tilde{A})^-$$
$$= (\pm\tilde{F})^- \cap (\tilde{A})^- = (\tilde{F})^\perp \cap (\tilde{A})^-$$

of the orthogonal complement $(\tilde{F})^\perp$ of the dimensionality space $(\pm\tilde{F})$ of $(\tilde{F})$ with the negative polar $(\tilde{A})^-$ of $(\tilde{A})$. Then, from Lemma 4.12.2 and the definition of $(\tilde{A})^-$, it is seen that $(\tilde{F})$ is the cone of normals to $(\tilde{A})^-$ on any point of $)\tilde{F}^{(-)}($. From this it follows [XVIII, Theorem 33 (1)] that

$$(4.54) \qquad (f)^\perp \cap (\tilde{A})^- \qquad \text{with } 0 \neq f \in)\tilde{F}($$$

is a facet of $(\tilde{A})^-$, which by Lemma 4.12.2 does not depend on the choice of f, hence equals $(\tilde{F}^{(-)})$ as given by (4.53). Hence $(\tilde{F}^{(-)})$ is indeed a facet of $(\tilde{A})^-$. Furthermore we have

$$(4.55) \qquad \dim)F(+ \dim)F^{(-)}(= N.$$

In particular, the vertex of (A) is mapped into the interior $)A^-($ of $(A)^-$.

If we define two facets $)F_r($ and $)F_s($ whose dimensionalities differ by one as incident whenever one is in the relative boundary of the other, it follows from Lemma 4.12.1 that the mapping preserves incidence, while reversing the order of the dimensionalities. It is to be expected that topological properties of the union of a set of open facets depend on the incidence relations among these facets only. Then the union U of a set S of facets $)F($ has the same contractibility properties as the union $U^{(-)}$ of the set $S^{(-)}$ of corresponding facets $)F^{(-)}($.

The efficient point set is now to be defined as the union U of the set S of all open facets of $(\tilde{A})$ not containing a vector of $-I$, exclusive of the origin. By the definition (4.23) of $(\tilde{A})$ we have

$$(4.56) \qquad (\tilde{A})^- = (-I \quad A)^- = (I) \cap (A)^-,$$

showing that $(\tilde{A})^-$ is contained in the closed positive orthant (I). By

Lemma 4.12.3 any facet $)\tilde{F}^-($ contained in the boundary of (I) must be the mapping of a facet $)\tilde{F}($ of $(\tilde{A})$ containing a vector of $-I$, and conversely. Hence the set S is mapped into the set $S^{(-)}$ of all proper open facets of $(\tilde{A})^-$ not contained in the boundary of (I). Our task is then to prove that the union $U^{(-)}$ of $S^{(-)}$ is contractible within itself to a point. It is easily seen that $U^{(-)}$ contains no boundary points of (I).

The assumption (4.52) implies that

$$(4.57) \qquad\qquad -i_{(1)} \,\epsilon\, (A)^-, \qquad i_{(1)} \,\notin\, (A)^-,$$

if $i_{(1)}$ denotes the first column vector of I. This makes it possible to map $U^{(-)}$ one-to-one and bicontinuously on a subset V of the first co-ordinate hyperplane

$$(4.58) \qquad\qquad (i_{(1)})^\perp = (\pm_1 I),$$

(where $_1I$ denotes the unit matrix with the first column deleted) as follows: With each point p of $U^{(-)}$ we associate its orthogonal projection

$$(4.59) \qquad\qquad _{(1)}p \equiv p - p_1 i_{(1)} \,\epsilon\, (\pm_1 I)$$

on the plane (4.58). Since $_{(1)}p$ is in (I) whenever p is, and since by (4.57) $_{(1)}p$ is in $(A)^-$ whenever p is, $p \,\epsilon\, U^{(-)} \subset (\tilde{A})^-$ implies by (4.56) that $_{(1)}p \,\epsilon\, (\tilde{A})^-$; hence by (4.56) and (4.59) we have, say,

$$(4.60) \qquad\qquad _{(1)}p \,\epsilon\, (\tilde{A})^- \cap (_1 I) \equiv (Q).$$

Conversely, it can be shown from (4.59) that, if $_{(1)}p$ is a point of (Q) which is not in its relative boundary, then the point

$$(4.61) \qquad\qquad p = {}_{(1)}p + p_1 i_{(1)},$$

where p_1 is defined as the highest value of $\bar{p}_1$ for which

$$(4.62) \qquad\qquad \bar{p} = {}_{(1)}p + \bar{p}_1 i_{(1)} \,\epsilon\, (\tilde{A})^-,$$

is finite and in $U^{(-)}$. In this way a one-to-one bicontinuous mapping can be established between $U^{(-)}$ and a point set V equal to the cone (Q) or obtainable from (Q) by deleting a part or the whole of its relative boundary. The contractibility properties of (Q) are not affected by such a deletion.

It should be pointed out that $U^{(-)}$, and hence V, is indeed nonempty. This follows from Theorem 4.13 and the fact that (4.52) implies Postulate C_2 of Section 3.6. If we assume that Postulate A is also satisfied, then $(A)^-$ is N-dimensional. It is seen to follow from (4.59) that both $U^{(-)}$ and (Q) are then $(N-1)$-dimensional.

5. The Efficient Point Set in the Final Commodity Space under Given Availability Restrictions on Primary Commodities

5.1. *The set of attainable points.* In the preceding section, we have studied the notion of allocative efficiency in the possible point set, that is, accepting the restrictions expressing the possibilities of technology, and also the inavailability in nature of nonprimary commodities, but ignoring the nonhomogeneous restrictions expressing the limited availability of primary commodities. Thus, in Section 4, the space of desired commodities includes both final and primary commodities, the latter in the sense that their conservation is deemed desirable.

We shall now regard only the final commodities as desired. Intermediate commodities we place, as before, under the restrictions (1.9) or

$$(5.1) \qquad\qquad y_{\text{int}} = 0.$$

Concerning the primary commodities, we shall assume that they are available in rates of flow limited by the inequalities (1.7), which we restate here in the form

$$(5.2) \qquad\qquad y_{\text{pri}} \geqq \eta_{\text{pri}}, \qquad \eta_{\text{pri}} < 0.$$

These limits cannot, it is assumed, be exceeded by any means, but within these limits an increase in the input (an algebraic decrease in the negative net output) of any primary commodity is not regarded as in any way undesirable or costly. The attainable point set is now defined as in

DEFINITION 5.1: *A point y in the commodity space is called attainable if there exists a point x in the activity space such that*

$$(5.3) \qquad y \equiv \begin{bmatrix} y_{\text{fin}} \\ y_{\text{int}} \\ y_{\text{pri}} \end{bmatrix} = Ax, \qquad x \geqq 0, \qquad y_{\text{fin}} \geqq 0,$$

and such that y_{int} and y_{pri} satisfy (5.1) and (5.2), respectively.

Any attainable point is a possible point by Definition 3.2, but the converse is not necessarily true.

5.2. *Redefinition of the efficient point concept.* Since it is now only in the net flows of final commodities that increases are desired for their own sake, the definition of efficiency must be revised to read:

DEFINITION 5.2: *A point y in the commodity space is called efficient if it is attainable and if there exists no attainable point ȳ such that*

$$(5.4) \qquad\qquad \bar{y}_{\text{fin}} - y_{\text{fin}} \geq 0.$$

In words, Definition 5.2 says that an attainable point y is called efficient whenever an increase in one of its final commodity coordinates (in the net output of one final good), within the availability limitations on primary commodities and the zero-net-output restriction on intermediate commodities, can be achieved only at the cost of a decrease in some other final coordinate (the net output of another final good).

As explained in Section 3.10, the restriction (5.1) on flows of intermediate goods can be satisfied once and for all by an appropriate reduction of the technology matrix. We shall again assume that this reduction of A has already been carried out and omit the bar from the reduced technology matrix $\bar{A}$, except in Sections 5.10–5.12, where the implications of our results for the intermediate commodity space are explored. In all other parts of Section 5, therefore, y and A contain no coordinates representing intermediate products, and the restriction (5.1) in Definition 5.1 of an attainable point can be ignored.

5.3. *The role of the availability restrictions on primary commodities.* It may be expected, and will be confirmed in Section 5.14, that, if y is an efficient point according to Definition 4.2 satisfying (5.2) and (5.3) in such a way that the equality sign in (5.2) holds for all components of y_{pri}, then y is also an efficient point according to Definition (5.2). The reader may therefore ask himself whether the present assumptions can lead to any results that cannot be read from the theorems of Section 4. It will be seen below that the present assumptions do give rise to a new possibility, namely, the case where a point y is efficient according to Definition 5 although for some components of y_{pri} the inequality sign in (5.2) holds. The commodities in question will be called *free primary commodities* in y.

Other consequences of the imposition of availability restrictions arise from the fact, to be proved in Lemma 5.8.1 below, that the efficient point set according to Definition 5.2 is bounded. It is therefore possible (Section 5.6) to obtain efficient points by the maximization of a linear function. This is important for purposes of computation of efficient points, and also for the construction of rules for the attainment of efficiency under given institutional circumstances such as those specified in Section 5.12.

5.4. *Reformulation of the necessary and sufficient condition for efficiency.* We shall use a simple example to suggest a theorem analogous to Theorem

4.3, to be proved in (the next) Section 5.5.   Consider the technology

$$
(5.5) \qquad A = \begin{array}{cccccc} (1) & (2) & (3) & (4) & (5) & (6) \\ \left[\begin{array}{cccccc} 0 & 0.8 & 1.0 & (0.9) & 0.62 & 0.0 \\ -1 & -1.0 & -1.0 & (-1.0) & -0.8 & -0.6 \\ 0 & -0.5 & -0.8 & (-1.0) & -1.0 & -1.0 \end{array}\right], \end{array}
$$

in which y_1 is the only final commodity flow, while y_2 and y_3 are the two primary commodity flows restricted by

$$
(5.6) \qquad\qquad y_2 \geqq -1, \qquad y_3 \geqq -1,
$$

respectively.   The activity vectors $a_{(1)}$, $a_{(2)}$, $\cdots$, $a_{(6)}$ have been so normalized that the unit amount of each activity fully uses the available flow of that primary commodity whose availability limit controls the maximum level of that activity if carried out alone.   Thus the unit amount of each activity 1, 2, 3, or 4 uses up the available flow of commodity 2, and the unit amount of each activity 4, 5, or 6 uses up the available flow of commodity 3.   Activity 4 is not a frame activity but represents that combination of activities 3 and 5 (with weights $\frac{5}{9}$ each) which fully utilizes the available flows of both primary commodities.

Figure 7 (in which the sign convention has been reversed for y_2 and y_3) exhibits the attainable point set, a polyhedron with vertices O, $a_{(1)}$, $a_{(2)}$, $a_{(3)}$, $a_{(4)}$, $a_{(5)}$, $a_{(6)}$, η.   The disposal activities 1 and 6 have been added mainly to improve the readability of the figure.   It is immediately clear from this figure that the point $a_{(3)}$ is the only efficient point in the present case.   For no other attainable set of activities does y_1 reach the value 1.   If we introduce a disposal activity 7 for the third commodity alone (with coefficients 0, 0, -1), a weighted combination of the activity vectors $a_{(3)}$ and $a_{(7)}$ will represent the vector $a_{(8)}$, and all points of the line segment $\overline{a_{(3)}a_{(8)}}$ are efficient.   If we introduce an activity 9 which allows the first commodity to be produced from the third alone (with coefficients 0.5, 0, -1, say), then only the vector $a_{(10)}$ (with coordinates 1.1, -1, -1) indicates an efficient point.

In order to formulate a theorem suggested by Figure 7 it will be useful to associate with each attainable point y a partitioning of the primary commodities into two sets, according to whether or not the availability limit on each commodity flow is reached in y.   Similarly we partition the final commodities according to whether their net output is positive or zero in y.   After such permutation of coordinates as may be neces-

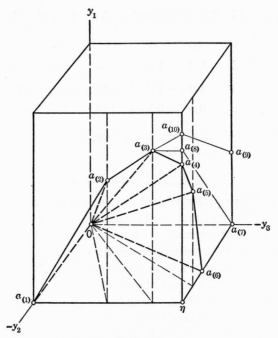

FIGURE 7

sary, these partitionings may be denoted by

$$(5.7) \begin{cases} (5.7 \text{ fin}) \quad y_{\text{fin}} \equiv \begin{bmatrix} y_{\text{fin}+} \\ y_{\text{fin } 0} \end{bmatrix}, \quad y_{\text{fin}+} > 0, \quad y_{\text{fin } 0} = 0, \\[2em] (5.7 \text{ pri}) \quad y_{\text{pri}} \equiv \begin{bmatrix} y_{\text{pri}=} \\ y_{\text{pri}>} \end{bmatrix}, \quad y_{\text{pri}=} = \eta_{\text{pri}=}, \quad y_{\text{pri}>} > \eta_{\text{pri}>}. \end{cases}$$

We shall also apply this partitioning to a normal p to (A) in y, and to various matrices, it being understood that the partitioning has a meaning only in association with an attainable point y.

THEOREM 5.4.1: *A necessary and sufficient condition that an attainable point y be efficient according to Definition 5.2 is that there exists a vector p, normal to the possible cone (A) in y, which has positive components for all final commodities, nonnegative components for all primary commodities whose availability limit is reached in y, and zero components for all primary commodities whose availability limit is not reached in y,*

$$(5.8) \qquad p_{\text{fin}} > 0, \qquad p_{\text{pri}=} \geqq 0, \qquad p_{\text{pri}>} = 0.$$

This implies as a necessary condition that y is a boundary point of (A).

Thus, in the case in Figure 7, where only the activities numbered 1 to 6 are possible, the efficient point $a_{(3)}$ possesses, among others, a vector normal to (A), with components $(1, 1, 0)$. The same vector defines the unique normal to (A) in all efficient points on $\overline{a_{(3)}a_{(8)}}$ if activity $a_{(7)}$ is added. If activity $a_{(9)}$ is added, the efficient point $a_{(10)}$ possesses the unique normal to (A) defined by $(1, 0.6, 0.5)$. In each of the three cases mentioned, no other points possess a normal to (A) with the required properties. The reader may wish to visualize the proof given in Section 5.5 by applying it to these examples.

For brevity of expression, we shall introduce a term for the vector p.

DEFINITION 5.4.2: *A vector p normal to (A) in an efficient point y will be called a price vector associated with y in the technology A if it satisfies the conditions* (5.8).

Before giving a proof of Theorem 5.4.1 in Section 5.5, we note another necessary condition for efficiency, which follows from the restriction (5.3) of the attainable point set to nonnegative values of y_{fin}.

THEOREM 5.4.3: *In an efficient point y according to Definition* 5.2, *either we have $y_{\text{fin}} = 0$ or the availability limit is reached by at least one of the primary commodity flows.*

The proof follows from the fact that, if $y_{\text{fin}} \neq 0$, (5.3) prescribes that $y_{\text{fin}} \geq 0$. Then y can only be efficient if at least one of the availability restrictions on y_{pri} precludes the presence in the attainable point set of a point

$$(5.9) \qquad \bar{y} = \nu y, \qquad \nu \text{ scalar}, \qquad \nu > 1.$$

It follows that $p_{\text{pri}=}$ in (5.8) contains at least one coordinate.

* 5.5. *Proof of Theorem* 5.4.1; *the local attainable cone.* We now associate with each attainable point y a *local attainable cone*, comprising all directions of variation from y in which attainability is preserved in a neighborhood of y, as follows.

DEFINITION 5.5.1: *The local attainable cone (E) in the attainable point y is the set of all points (vectors) e of the form*

$$(5.10) \quad e = \lambda(\bar{y} - y), \qquad \bar{y} \text{ attainable}, \qquad \lambda \text{ a positive scalar.}$$

Because of the convexity of the attainable point set, the set so defined is indeed a convex cone, and $y + e$ is attainable whenever $\lambda \leq 1$. In order to prove an analogue of Lemma 4.4.2, we associate with each attainable point y the following coordinate cone based on the partitioning (5.7),

$$(5.11) \quad (C) = \begin{pmatrix} C_{\text{fin}} & 0 \\ 0 & C_{\text{pri}} \end{pmatrix}, \quad (C_{\text{fin}}) = \begin{pmatrix} \pm I_{\text{fin}+} & 0 \\ 0 & I_{\text{fin } 0} \end{pmatrix},$$

$$(C_{\text{pri}}) = \begin{pmatrix} I_{\text{pri}=} & 0 \\ 0 & \pm I_{\text{pri}>} \end{pmatrix}.$$

For later use, we note the following expressions for the negative polars of C, C_{fin}, C_{pri},

$$(5.12) \quad (C)^- = \begin{pmatrix} C_{\text{fin}}^- & 0 \\ 0 & C_{\text{pri}}^- \end{pmatrix}, \quad (C_{\text{fin}})^- = \begin{pmatrix} 0 \\ -I_{\text{fin } 0} \end{pmatrix},$$

$$(C_{\text{pri}})^- = \begin{pmatrix} -I_{\text{pri}=} \\ 0 \end{pmatrix},$$

which are found by applying the rule stated in Section 2.6.

LEMMA 5.5.2: *The local attainable cone in y can be represented by*

$$(5.13) \qquad (E) = (-y \quad A) \cap (C).$$

To prove this lemma, we observe from a comparison of Definitions 4.4.1 and 5.5.1 that the local attainable cone in y is obtained from the local possible cone $(-y \quad A)$ by deleting those vectors d such that $\bar{y} = y + \mu d$ violates the restrictions (5.2), (5.3) for *all* positive values of the scalar $\mu = \lambda^{-1}$. In view of (5.7), a vector d escapes being deleted under this criterion if and only if

$$(5.14) \qquad d_{\text{fin } 0} \geqq 0, \qquad d_{\text{pri}=} \geqq 0.$$

The value of $d_{\text{pri}>}$ is immaterial because the last relation in (5.8) can always be satisfied by $\bar{y}$ if we take a sufficiently small value of μ. The restriction (5.14) is expressed by the intersection in (5.13).

It follows from Lemma 5.5.2 [XVII, Section 2, property (a)] that the local attainable cone is polyhedral.

Coming now to the proof of Theorem 5.4.1, we note that Definition 5.2 of an efficient point y is equivalent to the condition that in y we shall have $(E_{\text{fin}}) \cap (I_{\text{fin}}) = 0$, or, in full array of coordinates,

$$(5.15) \qquad (E) \cap \begin{pmatrix} I_{\text{fin}} & 0 \\ 0 & \pm I_{\text{pri}} \end{pmatrix} \subset \begin{pmatrix} 0 \\ \pm I_{\text{pri}} \end{pmatrix}.$$

Substituting from (5.13) for (E) we obtain

(5.16)
$$(-y \quad A) \cap (C) \cap \begin{pmatrix} I_{\text{fin}} & 0 \\ 0 & \pm I_{\text{pri}} \end{pmatrix} = (-y \quad A) \cap \begin{pmatrix} I_{\text{fin}} & 0 \\ 0 & C_{\text{pri}} \end{pmatrix} \subset \begin{pmatrix} 0 \\ \pm I_{\text{pri}} \end{pmatrix}.$$

Taking negative polars and using (5.12), we obtain the equivalent condition

(5.17) $\qquad (-y \quad A)^{-} + \begin{pmatrix} -I_{\text{fin}} & 0 \\ 0 & -I_{\text{pri}=} \\ 0 & 0 \end{pmatrix} \supset \begin{pmatrix} \pm I_{\text{fin}} \\ 0 \\ 0 \end{pmatrix}.$

This condition is in turn equivalent to the following statement: For each vector r such that

(5.18) $\qquad\qquad\qquad r_{\text{pri}} = 0,$

there exist vectors p, q, satisfying

(5.19) $\quad p \,\epsilon\, (-y \quad A)^{-}, \qquad q_{\text{fin}} \leqq 0, \qquad q_{\text{pri}=} \leqq 0, \qquad q_{\text{pri}>} = 0,$

such that

(5.20) $\qquad\qquad\qquad p + q = r.$

By taking $r_{\text{fin}} > 0$ we read from this that, if y is efficient, there exists a vector p normal to (A) in y with the properties (5.8) required by Theorem 5.4.1. Conversely, if (A) possesses a normal (p) in y satisfying (5.8), any vector r satisfying (5.18) can be expressed as

(5.21) $\qquad\qquad r = \kappa p + q, \qquad \kappa$ a positive scalar,

by proper choice of κ and a vector q satisfying (5.19). Hence y is efficient. This establishes the necessary and sufficient condition in Theorem 5.4.1. The necessary condition follows, as before, from the fact that an internal point y of (A) possesses no nonvanishing normal to (A).

5.6. *Efficient points and maximization of a linear function of final commodity flows.* Let us assume that a linear function of final commodity flows, with positive coefficients,

(5.22) $\qquad\qquad L \equiv \pi'_{\text{fin}} y_{\text{fin}}, \qquad \pi_{\text{fin}} > 0,$

reaches a maximum, within the attainable point set, in a point y. Then we have

(5.23) $\qquad\qquad \pi'_{\text{fin}}(\bar{y}_{\text{fin}} - y_{\text{fin}}) \leqq 0$

for every attainable point $\bar{y}$. This and the restriction on π_{fin} in (5.22) are obviously incompatible with

$$(5.24) \qquad\qquad \bar{y}_{\text{fin}} - y_{\text{fin}} \geq 0.$$

Hence y is efficient.

Conversely, let y be an efficient point. Then, by Theorem 5.4.1, there exists a vector p normal to (A) in y satisfying (5.8). It follows that for every possible point $\bar{y}$, and hence for every attainable point $\bar{y}$,

$$(5.25) \qquad\qquad p'(\bar{y} - y) \leq 0,$$

or, in view of the third relation (5.8),

$$(5.26) \qquad p'_{\text{fin}}(\bar{y}_{\text{fin}} - y_{\text{fin}}) + p'_{\text{pri}=}(\bar{y}_{\text{pri}=} - y_{\text{pri}=}) \leq 0,$$

where the partitioning (5.7 pri) applied to $\bar{y}$ and y is that associated with y. From the second relation (5.7 pri) and the second relation (5.8) we derive that the attainability of $\bar{y}$, which implies $\bar{y}_{\text{pri}} - \eta_{\text{pri}} \geq 0$, further implies

$$(5.27) \qquad p'_{\text{pri}=}(\bar{y}_{\text{pri}=} - y_{\text{pri}=}) = p'_{\text{pri}=}(\bar{y}_{\text{pri}=} - \eta_{\text{pri}=}) \geq 0.$$

Combining (5.26) and (5.27), we conclude that (5.23) holds in all attainable points $\bar{y}$ if p_{fin} is substituted for π_{fin} in the definition (5.22) of the function L. Hence the function L so obtained is maximized, within the attainable point set, in y.

The first statement in the following Theorem 5.6 summarizes these results. The second statement, to be proved in Section 5.7, adds information about the set of vectors π_{fin} for which L reaches a maximum in a given efficient point y.

THEOREM 5.6: *A necessary and sufficient condition for the efficiency, according to Definition 5.2, of an attainable point y is that there exist a positive vector π_{fin} such that the linear function (5.22) of final commodity flows reaches a maximum, within the attainable point set, in y. If π_{fin} is such a vector, then there exists a price vector p associated with y such that, for the partitioning (5.7) associated with y,*

$$(5.28) \qquad\qquad \pi_{\text{fin}+} = p_{\text{fin}+}, \qquad \pi_{\text{fin}\,0} \leq p_{\text{fin}\,0}.$$

This theorem makes it possible to compute efficient points by any of the methods for maximizing a linear function under linear inequalities as restraints, discussed elsewhere in this volume [XXI, XXIV, XXV]. It also leads up to an existence proof for efficient points.

* 5.7. *Proof of the second statement in Theorem 5.6.* The proofs given in Section 5.6 could be put so simply in terms of linear inequalities that their formulation by means of polar transformation of cones seemed artificial and unnecessary.[16] To show the last statement in Theorem 5.6, it is helpful to express the condition (5.24) that L reach a maximum, within the attainable point set, in y, by the condition

$$(5.29) \qquad\qquad (E) \subset \begin{pmatrix} \pi_{\text{fin}} \\ 0 \\ 0 \end{pmatrix}^{-} ,$$

where (E) is the local attainable cone in y. Using the expression (5.13) for (E), taking negative polars, and using the expression (5.12) for $(C)^{-}$, we see that (5.29) is equivalent to

$$(5.30) \qquad (-y \quad A)^{-} + \begin{pmatrix} 0 & 0 \\ -I_{\text{fin}\,0} & 0 \\ 0 & -I_{\text{pri}=} \\ 0 & 0 \end{pmatrix} \supset \begin{pmatrix} \pi_{\text{fin}+} \\ \pi_{\text{fin}\,0} \\ 0 \\ 0 \end{pmatrix} .$$

This can be the case only if $(-y \quad A)^{-}$ contains a vector p, of which the subvectors $p_{\text{fin}+}$, $p_{\text{fin}\,0}$, $p_{\text{pri}=}$, $p_{\text{pri}>}$ satisfy (5.28) and (5.8).

5.8. *Existence of an efficient point.* The attainable point set is the intersection of the possible cone (A) with the displaced coordinate cone (see Section 2.7)

$$(5.31) \qquad\qquad (I \mid \eta),$$

where

$$(5.32) \qquad\qquad \eta \equiv \begin{bmatrix} 0_{\text{fin}} \\ \eta_{\text{pri}} \end{bmatrix} .$$

As such it is the intersection of closed halfspaces (each having either the origin or the point η in its boundary), and therefore a closed convex set. Hence Theorem 5.6 assures the existence of an efficient point if we can prove, as we shall now do,

LEMMA 5.8.1: *The attainable point set is bounded whenever Postulate B of Section 3.5 is satisfied.*

Theorem 3.5.1 implies that there exists a positive vector h such that

$$(5.33) \qquad\qquad h'y \leqq 0$$

for every possible point y. With the notation (5.32), the attainable

---

[16] The reader interested in the mechanics of proofs may wish to "translate" the foregoing proofs in terms of properties of cones.

point set consists of all possible points y satisfying

(5.34) $$ y \geqq \eta. $$

Hence, for any coordinate y_n, $n = 1, \cdots, N$, of an attainable point y,

(5.35) $$ h_n y_n \leqq - \sum_{\substack{m=1 \\ (m \neq n)}}^{N} h_m y_m \leqq - \sum_{m \neq n} h_m \eta_m. $$

Since $h_n > 0$ for all n, finite upper and lower bounds for each coordinate of an attainable point are thus given by (5.35) and (5.34). This establishes Lemma 5.8.1.

It is easily seen [17] that a linear function L defined on a compact (closed and bounded) convex set S reaches its maximum either in one point, or in all points of a convex set, $S_{\max}$. Therefore we have from Lemma 5.8.1:

THEOREM 5.8.2: *If Postulate B of Section 3.5 is satisfied by the technology matrix A, then there exists for each positive vector π_{fin} at least one efficient point y according to Definition 5.2., in which the linear function (5.22) reaches its (absolute) maximum in the attainable point set.*[18]

It is, of course, quite possible that different positive vectors p_{fin} (different in more than scale) lead to the same efficient point y or set of such points, as can easily be shown by examples. Therefore Theorem 5.8.2. establishes only the existence of one efficient point. Under the assumptions stated so far, this might still be the origin, a trivial case which we wish to exclude. This is done by the following theorem.

[17] To see this, denote by $l\pi \equiv (\pi'y/\pi'\pi)\pi$ the orthogonal projection of a point y on the halfline $(\pm\pi)$. Then the scalar coordinate l measures the position of the projection $l\pi$ on $(\pm\pi)$, and $L = \pi'y = l\pi'\pi$ depends on l only. Hence, if S_π (denoted $S\text{mod}\pi^\perp$ in XVIII) represents the projection of S on $(\pm\pi)$, S_π is a closed line segment on which L reaches a maximum in $l_{\max}\pi$, say. Then $S_{\max}$ consists of all points of S of which $l_{\max}\pi$ is the projection.

This proof employs the notion of a limiting process underlying the definition of a closed set. A simultaneous proof of both Lemmas 5.8.1 and 5.8.2 that uses finite processes only can be based on a theorem by Weyl [1935, 1950, § 4, II] that the intersection of a finite number of displaced halfspaces $(a_{(k)} \mid \alpha_k)$, $k = 1, \cdots, K$, if not empty, is the convex hull of a finite number of points if and only if the cone $(a_{(1)}, \cdots, a_{(K)})$ is solid.

[18] It is implied in Theorem 5 of Gale, Kuhn, and Tucker [XIX] that, while Postulate B is sufficient for the existence of an efficient point by Definition 5.2, the following weaker Postulate $\overline{\text{B}}$ is necessary and sufficient: *There is no $x \geqq 0$ such that $y_{\text{fin}} \equiv A_{\text{fin}}x \geqq 0$, $y_{\text{pri}} \equiv A_{\text{pri}}x \geqq 0$.* Under this postulate, the availability restrictions, $y_{\text{fin}} \geqq 0$, $y_{\text{pri}} \geqq \eta_{\text{pri}} < 0$, exclude a bonanza in final commodities but do not necessarily exclude one in primary commodities only (since $y_{\text{fin}} = 0$ might permit $y_{\text{pri}} \geqq 0$). Because there seems to be little economic meaning in a technology matrix which satisfies $\overline{\text{B}}$ but not B, we have not used Postulate $\overline{\text{B}}$.

THEOREM 5.8.3: *The origin is not an efficient point according to Definition 5.2 whenever Postulate C_2 (the weak postulate of the possibility of production) of Section 3.6 is satisfied.*

For, in that case, (A) contains a vector a with $a_{fin} \geq 0$, and there exists an attainable point $y = \lambda a$, $\lambda > 0$ such that $y_{fin} \geq 0$. Hence 0 is not efficient.

5.9. *The prices of intermediate commodities.* It will be argued in Section 5.14 below that the efficient point set according to Definition 5.2 is "in general" $(N_{fin} - 1)$-dimensional. As long as the availability limits η_{pri} are not regarded as subject to variation, it is not possible, even in the absence of intermediate products, to interpret the components of p_{pri} as determining marginal rates of substitution. In Section 5.11 we shall give another interpretation of the "price vector" p, which applies independently of whatever restrictions the efficiency requirement may place on the components of y. Since this interpretation applies also to intermediate commodities, we shall first study the extension of a vector p normal to (A) in the space of final and primary commodities to that of intermediate commodities. We state the relevant theorem here and devote Section 5.10 to its proof.

THEOREM 5.9: *Theorems 4.3, 5.4.1, and 5.6 remain valid as characterizations of the efficient point set, under the appropriate definition, if the technology matrix A and the price vector p allow for intermediate commodities, while possibility and attainability are defined so as to imply the restriction (5.1) that the net outputs of all intermediate commodities are zero.*

* 5.10. *Proof of Theorem 5.9.* In Sections 5.10–14 we return to the notation $\bar{A}$ of Section 3.10 for a technology matrix in the space of final and primary commodities, obtained from an original technology matrix A in the space of final, primary, and intermediate commodities (partitioned in that order), by a reduction based on the restrictions (5.1) on intermediate commodity flows. Similarly we use the notation $\bar{y}$, $\bar{p}$ for a boundary point of $(\bar{A})$ and a vector normal to $(\bar{A})$ in $\bar{y}$, respectively. The present analysis applies to any boundary point $\bar{y}$ and any normal $\bar{p}$ to $(\bar{A})$ in $\bar{y}$, whether or not a normal satisfying the conditions (4.8) or (5.8) for efficiency, according to the appropriate definition, exists.

The condition that $\bar{p}$ is a normal to $(\bar{A})$ in $\bar{y}$ is, according to Lemma 4.4.2, expressed by

$$(5.36) \qquad \bar{p} \,\epsilon\, (-\bar{y} \ \ \bar{A})^{-}.$$

We shall prove

LEMMA 5.10: *Any vector $\bar{p}$ normal to the reduced possible cone $(\bar{A})$ in a point $\bar{y}$ can be supplemented by a vector p_{int} to form a vector,*

$$(5.37) \qquad \binom{\bar{p}}{p_{\text{int}}} \equiv p \,\epsilon\, (-y \quad A)^{-},$$

normal to the original possible cone (A), from which $(\bar{A})$ is derived by (3.45), in the point

$$(5.38) \qquad y \equiv \begin{bmatrix} \bar{y} \\ 0 \end{bmatrix} \equiv \begin{bmatrix} y_{\text{fin}} \\ y_{\text{pri}} \\ 0_{\text{int}} \end{bmatrix}.$$

Conversely, if p is such a vector normal to (A), its subvector $\bar{p}$ is normal to $(\bar{A})$ in $\bar{y}$.

To prove the first contention, let $\bar{p}$ satisfy (5.36). Then

$$(5.39) \qquad \binom{p_{\text{fin}}}{p_{\text{pri}}} \equiv \bar{p} \,\epsilon\, (-\bar{y})^{-} \cap (\bar{A})^{-} = \binom{-y_{\text{fin}}}{-y_{\text{pri}}}^{-} \cap \binom{A^{-}_{\text{fin}}}{A^{-}_{\text{pri}}}$$

by (3.45). Hence there exists a vector $q \geqq 0$ such that

$$(5.40) \qquad \begin{bmatrix} p_{\text{fin}} \\ p_{\text{pri}} \end{bmatrix} = \begin{bmatrix} A^{-}_{\text{fin}} \\ A^{-}_{\text{pri}} \end{bmatrix} q.$$

We define

$$(5.41) \qquad p_{\text{int}} \equiv A^{-}_{\text{int}} q,$$

and show that

$$(5.42) \qquad p \equiv \begin{bmatrix} p_{\text{fin}} \\ p_{\text{pri}} \\ p_{\text{int}} \end{bmatrix} = \begin{bmatrix} A^{-}_{\text{fin}} \\ A^{-}_{\text{pri}} \\ A^{-}_{\text{int}} \end{bmatrix} q \equiv A^{-}q$$

satisfies (5.37), as follows. The condition (5.37) can be written as

$$(5.43) \quad p \equiv \binom{\bar{p}}{p_{\text{int}}} \epsilon \binom{-\bar{y}}{0}^{-} \cap (A)^{-} = \left(\begin{bmatrix} -y_{\text{fin}} \\ -y_{\text{pri}} \end{bmatrix}^{-} \begin{matrix} 0 \\ 0 \end{matrix} \atop \begin{matrix} 0 \quad \pm I_{\text{int}} \end{matrix} \right) \cap \binom{A^{-}_{\text{fin}}}{\begin{matrix} A^{-}_{\text{pri}} \\ A^{-}_{\text{int}} \end{matrix}}.$$

This condition is satisfied on account of (5.39), because the addition of the "int"-coordinates in (5.43) only requires p_{int} to be derivable from A^{-}_{int} by the same weight vector q by which $\bar{p}$ is derived from $\begin{bmatrix} A^{-}_{\text{fin}} \\ A^{-}_{\text{pri}} \end{bmatrix}$, as specified in (5.41). To prove the second contention, let p satisfy (5.43). Then $\bar{p}$ satisfies (5.36).

It should be emphasized that there is no restriction on the sign of the components of p_{int}. Negative prices adhere to by-products of which "too much" is obtained in the process of producing other positively priced things, while the disposal of the excess consumes positively priced commodities. Negative values can occur only for those components of p_{int} corresponding to commodities for which no costless disposal activities are present in the technology matrix A.

5.11. Interpretation of the price vector when net output variations are restricted. In Sections 5.11–5.13 we shall follow the interpretations of the technology matrix, of attainability, and of the price vector associated with an efficient point, which allow for the presence of intermediate commodities.

It has already been remarked in Section 5.9 that, when the attainability restrictions (5.1) and (5.2) enter into the definition of the efficient point set, the interpretation of the associated price vector as indicating substitution ratios in efficient production is no longer applicable to all commodities, although it still applies to final commodities as before. Moreover, even where that interpretation was applicable to all commodities, under Definition 4.2 of efficiency, it was limited to points in the relative interior of $(N-1)$-dimensional facets.

It is desirable to develop an interpretation of the price vector which is not subject to the foregoing limitations. Let us imagine that, through communication with an economy *outside* that described by the technology matrix A, a possibility is provided to trade any commodity against any other at constant relative prices given by a price vector

$$(5.44) \qquad \pi \equiv \begin{bmatrix} \pi_1 \\ \cdot \\ \cdot \\ \cdot \\ \pi_N \end{bmatrix}.$$

It is natural to interpret such prices as "efficiency prices" at the point y whenever the net output vector y cannot be improved upon (by increasing one component without decreasing any others) through the use of this trading opportunity in combination with changes in amounts of productive activities. We shall show that such improvement is not possible if and only if π is a price vector associated with y in the original technology A.

The possibility to trade with an outside world at prices π can be introduced formally by adding to the technology a set of "exchange activities." Since a value $\pi = 0$ would have no meaning, we can without loss of generality assume that π_1 is positive. Let Π then represent the matrix

$$(5.45) \qquad \Pi \equiv \begin{bmatrix} -\pi_2 & -\pi_3 & \cdots & -\pi_N \\ \pi_1 & 0 & \cdots & 0 \\ 0 & \pi_1 & \cdots & 0 \\ \cdot & \cdot & \cdots & \cdot \\ 0 & 0 & \cdots & \pi_1 \end{bmatrix}, \qquad \pi_1 > 0,$$

and let the new technology matrix, extended by exchange activities, be

$$(5.46) \qquad \mathring{A} \equiv [-\Pi \quad \Pi \quad A].$$

The point y is efficient in the original technology A if and only if the cone

$$(5.47) \qquad (P) \equiv (-y \quad A)^-$$

of normals to (A) in y contains a vector p satisfying the requirements (5.8) of Theorem 5.4.1. Assume this to be the case, and consider the question whether y is efficient in the new technology (5.46). To answer this, the same criterion must be applied to the cone of normals to $(\mathring{A})$ in y, as given by

$$(5.48) \qquad \begin{aligned} (\mathring{P}) &\equiv (-y \quad \mathring{A})^- = (-y \quad -\Pi \quad \Pi \quad A)^- \\ &= (-y \quad A)^- \cap (-\Pi \quad \Pi)^- = (P) \cap (\pm\Pi)^- \end{aligned}$$

[XVII, Section 2, property (b)]. However, since Π by (5.45) has the rank $N - 1$ and satisfies

$$(5.49) \qquad \pi'\Pi = 0,$$

the negative polar of the linear $(N - 1)$-dimensional space $(\pm\Pi)$ is its orthogonal complement,

$$(5.50) \qquad (\pm\Pi)^- = (\pm\Pi)^\perp = (\pm\pi).$$

Hence the cone $(\mathring{P})$ in (5.48) is one of the following four cones

$$(5.51) \qquad (0), \quad (-\pi), \quad (\pi), \quad (\pm\pi).$$

We recall that the criterion of efficiency of y in $(\mathring{A})$ is whether or not $(\mathring{P})$ contains a vector p satisfying (5.8). Since 0 and $-\pi$ do not satisfy (5.8), y is efficient in the enlarged technology (5.46) if and only if π is in (P) [is a normal to (A) in y] and satisfies (5.8). This completes the proof of

THEOREM 5.11: *A necessary and sufficient condition, that an efficient point y shall remain efficient after the addition to the technology, by (5.46), of exchange activities (5.45) at constant relative prices π, is that π be a price vector associated with y in the original technology A.*

5.12. *The attainment of efficiency under a regime of decentralized decisions.* Theorem 5.11 suggests the possibility of using the device of efficiency prices in institutional situations where the responsibility for allocative decisions is distributed over several individuals. So far the conditions for efficiency have been discussed without reference to the institutional arrangements under which decisions about the components of the activity vector x are arrived at. One possible use of our results would be for a centralized decision-making agency to possess all the information that goes into the technology matrix A, and to choose an activity vector x such that by the proper mathematical criteria the output vector $y = Ax$ is an efficient point. An opposite extreme is a situation in which knowledge of each column $a_{(k)}$ of A is available only to the individual who determines the level x_k of that activity. Even in this extreme case of decentralization, efficiency is still achievable if we assume that information about an appropriate price vector p is made available to all managers.

To show this, we shall consider an allocation model in which the various decisions which together determine the activity vector x are parceled out to a number of individuals or administrative organs, each of which makes these decisions according to definite rules of behavior. In defining the rules of behavior, we shall use the concept of the profitability of the kth activity with reference to the price vector p. This is defined as the vector product

$$(5.52) \qquad q_k \equiv p'a_{(k)}$$

and represents the "accounting revenue" secured from carrying out the kth activity in the amount $x_k = 1$.

Let the players in our allocation game be called the helmsman (or central planning board), a custodian for each commodity, and a manager for each activity. Consider the following rules of behavior:

I. *For the helmsman:* Choose a vector p_{fin} of positive prices on all final commodities, and inform the custodian of each such commodity of its price.

II. *For all custodians:* Buy and sell your commodity from and to managers at one price only, which you announce to all managers. Buy all that is offered at that price. Sell all that is demanded up to the limit of availability.

III. *For all custodians of final commodities:* Announce to managers the price set on your commodity by the helmsman.

IV. *For all custodians of intermediate commodities:* Announce a tentative price on your commodity. If demand by managers falls short of supply by managers, lower your price. If demand exceeds supply, raise it.

V. *For all custodians of primary commodities:* Regard the available inflow from nature as a part of the supply of your commodity. Then follow the rule on custodians of intermediate commodities, with the following exception: Do not announce a price lower than zero but accept a demand below supply at a zero price if necessary.

VI. *For all managers:* Do not engage in activities that have negative profitability. Maintain activities of zero profitability at a constant level. Expand activities of positive profitability by increasing orders for the necessary inputs with, and offers of the outputs in question to, the custodians of those commodities.

The dynamic aspects of these rules have on purpose been left vague. It is not specified by how much managers of profitable activities should increase their orders, or by how much custodians of commodities in short or excess supply should change the price. Neither is it indicated how during a temporary disequilibrium a commodity in short supply is apportioned to managers. These questions would be highly relevant if our purpose were to design an allocation model which automatically seeks and finds an efficient point from some initial nonoptimal situation. However, our present purpose is only to demonstrate that an efficient point, once achieved, is maintained if all players follow the rules stated. More precisely:

THEOREM 5.12: *Let $p_{\text{fin}} > 0$ be a vector of positive prices of final commodities announced by the helmsman under rule I. Then a necessary and sufficient condition that the vectors $x \geqq 0$, p_{int}, $p_{\text{pri}} \geqq 0$ will remain constant under the rules II–VI is that the point $y \equiv Ax$ is efficient and that*

$$(5.53) \qquad\qquad p \equiv \begin{bmatrix} p_{\text{fin}} \\ p_{\text{int}} \\ p_{\text{pri}} \end{bmatrix}$$

is a price vector associated with y.

To prove this theorem, we read from rules IV, V, and VI, respectively, the following necessary and sufficient conditions for the constancy over time of p_{int}, p_{pri}, and x, respectively, where, of course, $x \geqq 0$:

$$(5.54) \qquad\qquad y_{\text{int}} \equiv A_{\text{int}}x = 0,$$

$$(5.55) \quad \begin{cases} \text{(a)} \ y_{\text{pri}} = A_{\text{pri}}x \geqq \eta_{\text{pri}}, \\ \text{(b)} \ p_{\text{pri}} \geqq 0, \\ \text{(c)} \ y_n \ = \eta_n \text{ if } p_n > 0 \text{ and } n \text{ refers to a primary commodity,} \end{cases}$$

$$(5.56) \qquad\qquad p'A \leqq 0, \qquad p'a_{(k)} = 0 \quad \text{if} \quad x_k > 0.$$

The conditions (5.54) and (5.55a) express the fact that y is attainable. Condition (5.56) says that p is a normal to (A) in y, and (5.55b) and (5.55c) plus the premise $p_{\text{fin}} > 0$ are equivalent to (5.8). By Theorem 5.4.1, the conditions (5.54), (5.55), and (5.56) are necessary and sufficient conditions that y is efficient and that p is a price vector associated with y. This completes the proof of Theorem 5.8.

The reader will have noticed that the behavior prescribed for individuals by the rules I–VI is similar to that which results from the operation of competitive markets. The rules on the custodians are only personalizations of the properties of competitive markets. The vector p_{fin} which ultimately gives direction to the allocation of resources in production, instead of being set by a helmsman, could equally well be the result of competitive bidding by many consumers, each of whom maximizes his individual utility. The behavior attributed to each manager could also come about as the result of each activity being carried out independently by many entrepreneurs bidding competitively for the input commodities of that activity and selling its output commodities competitively.

However, the "personal" formulation also has relevance to problems of economic organization. The rules suggest methods whereby a planned economy can strive for efficient allocation of resources in production. With respect to an economy in which entrepreneurs individually make production decisions, the rules help in the appraisal of alternative forms of economic organization or of market behavior from the point of view of efficiency. Finally, the analysis may be applied to production decisions within the firm or the public enterprise, which can be regarded as planned economies on a smaller scale.

5.13. *Comparison with discussions in welfare economics.* It may be useful to explore some connections between the present analysis and the discussions by Lange [1938], Lerner [1944], Reder [1947], and others of allocation problems in a welfare economy.[19] The managers postu-

[19] For a more detailed discussion of these connections, see Koopmans [1951].

lated by these authors are in control of plants in which many activities (as here considered) are carried out in supposedly efficient combinations. The problem how to achieve efficient production within the plant is presumed solved in the discussions referred to, but is here analyzed on the basis of a particular model of technology. This model is, in one sense, narrower than the type of technology admitted by the authors mentioned in that we have ruled out indivisibilities and increasing or decreasing returns to scale. In another sense the present model is more general, since it does not depend on the notion of a continuous family of productive activities (a production function in the traditional sense) for the definition of marginal rates of substitution.

Accepting the narrower assumptions regarding technology made in the present study, the concept of "prices at marginal cost" used in the discussions referred to can be identified with our "efficiency prices." The main result of these discussions can be summarized in the statement that allocation of each commodity in the various productive processes, in such a manner as to equate the value of its marginal product in all its actual uses at a level that cannot be exceeded in any potential uses, is a necessary condition for efficient allocation of resources. The present analysis implies further that, in a technology as assumed, observance of this rule also forms a sufficient condition for efficient allocation of resources.

* 5.14. *Comparison of the analyses of Sections 4 and 5; topological properties of the efficient point set under availability restrictions.* So far we have in Section 5 used the methods rather than the results of Section 4. It may be useful in a brief heuristic discussion to lay somewhat closer connections between the two analyses.

Let $\mathfrak{E}$ denote the efficient point set according to Definition 4.2, $\mathfrak{E}(\eta_{\mathrm{pri}})$ the efficient point set by Definition 5.2. While we have found that a sufficient number of sufficiently diverse activities in the technology A makes $\mathfrak{E}$ an $(N - 1)$-dimensional set, we cannot expect the same to hold for $\mathfrak{E}(\eta_{\mathrm{pri}})$. Counting only restrictions that take the form of equalities, each point of $\mathfrak{E}(\eta_{\mathrm{pri}})$, besides having to be on the boundary of (A), is subject to restrictions on y_{int}, y_{pri} and p_{pri} which together are equal in number to the number $N_{\mathrm{pri}} + N_{\mathrm{int}}$ of primary and intermediate commodities. We would therefore expect the set $\mathfrak{E}(\eta_{\mathrm{pri}})$ to be at most $(N_{\mathrm{fin}} - 1)$-dimensional, where $N_{\mathrm{fin}} = N - N_{\mathrm{int}} - N_{\mathrm{pri}}$ is the number of final commodities. This is necessarily true of the more relevant set $\mathfrak{E}_{\mathrm{fin}}(\eta_{\mathrm{pri}})$ of points y_{fin} in the final commodity space consisting of all subvectors y_{fin} of vectors y of $\mathfrak{E}(\eta_{\mathrm{pri}})$.

Defining $\mathfrak{E}_{\mathrm{fin}}$ as consisting of all y_{fin} such that $y \in \mathfrak{E}$, we note that every point y_{fin} of $\mathfrak{E}_{\text{fin}}$ belongs to an $\mathfrak{E}_{\text{fin}}(\eta_{\text{pri}})$ for a particular value of η_{pri}. This is the value $\eta_{\text{pri}} = y_{\text{pri}}$, where y_{pri} is the vector supplementing y_{fin} and $y_{\text{int}} = 0$ to a vector y of $\mathfrak{E}$. Therefore $\mathfrak{E}_{\text{fin}}$ is contained in the union $\mathfrak{E}_{\text{fin}}^{*}$ of the sets $\mathfrak{E}_{\text{fin}}(\eta_{\text{pri}})$ for all negative values of η_{pri}. However, $\mathfrak{E}_{\text{fin}}$ need not contain all points of $\mathfrak{E}_{\text{fin}}^{*}$, for the union $\mathfrak{E}^{*}$ of all $\mathfrak{E}(\eta_{\text{pri}})$ consists of all facets of the reduced technological cone (A) possessing a normal p satisfying

$$(5.57) \qquad p_{\text{fin}} > 0, \qquad p_{\text{pri}} \geq 0,$$

whereas $\mathfrak{E}$ allows only $p_{\text{pri}} > 0$.

The relationships between $\mathfrak{E}^{*}$ and $\mathfrak{E}$ will be useful in studying the topological properties of $\mathfrak{E}(\eta_{\text{pri}})$ for a given value of η_{pri}. We may define an open facet of $\mathfrak{E}(\eta_{\text{pri}})$ as a set of efficient points y which (a) are on the same open facet $)F($ of the (reduced) cone (A), and (b) have the same partitioning (5.7) of y_{pri}. Then every facet $)F($ of (A) which is in $\mathfrak{E}$ contributes as facets of $\mathfrak{E}(\eta_{\text{pri}})$ its intersections with all open proper facets of the displaced cone (5.31). In addition, contributions to $\mathfrak{E}(\eta_{\text{pri}})$ may come from open facets $)F($ of (A) which are not in $\mathfrak{E}$ but possess a normal p satisfying (5.57), and of which the union when closed can be expected to be contractible, within itself, into its common boundary with $\mathfrak{E}$.

We shall not attempt a topological analysis of $\mathfrak{E}(\eta_{\text{pri}})$, but we base on the foregoing considerations the conjecture that, under the restrictions (5.1), (5.2), and (5.3) and for any $\eta_{\text{pri}} < 0$, the contractibility properties of $\mathfrak{E}(\eta_{\text{pri}})$ are the same as those of $\mathfrak{E}$.

CHAPTER IV

THE AGGREGATE LINEAR PRODUCTION FUNCTION AND ITS APPLICATIONS TO VON NEUMANN'S ECONOMIC MODEL[1]

BY NICHOLAS GEORGESCU-ROEGEN

In a series of studies Professor Leontief [1936, 1941] presented an analysis of the structure of the American economy through a new technique known today as the input-output relationships technique. This was the first attempt to apply the general equilibrium theory to the analysis of an economic reality.

A few years later Professor von Neumann [1937, 1945], making use of similar simplifying assumptions, arrived at an extremely interesting theoretical result for the general equilibrium theory, namely, that the equilibrium conditions were actually fulfilled by at least one alternative of the economic system.

The evidence that it is possible to analyze an economic reality from the point of view of general equilibrium theory—provided one is willing to grant certain restrictive assumptions and to undertake the difficult task of computing the numerous input-output coefficients—and that the same type of simplifications enables us to establish more definite theoretical results explains the recent growing interest among economists in linear economic models. This appears to be, in fact, a revival of the Walrasian assumption regarding the constancy of production coefficients under a more general form.

The purpose of this chapter is to discuss the concepts of technological horizon and of the aggregate linear production function—the latter is

[1] The results contained in this chapter may be reproduced in whole or in part for any purpose of the United States Government, under whose contract they were completed.

These results were presented for the first time on March 22, 1949, at a meeting of the staff of Harvard Economic Research Project. The author wishes to acknowledge the helpful criticism and the valuable suggestions of Professor Wassily W. Leontief. It is hardly necessary to add that, for any faults the chapter may contain, the author is solely responsible. The facilities of the Institute of Research and Training in Social Sciences at Vanderbilt University extended to the author in preparing the final version are gratefully acknowledged.

analogous to the classical concept of production function—and to use the concept of the technological horizon in proving the results obtained by von Neumann for his economic model along lines more accessible to economists. The considerations of this chapter cover the more general case where the set of given processes of production is not necessarily finite but may have the power of the continuum.

The last point distinguishes the approach contained in this chapter from the contributions of von Neumann and of Koopmans, who have considered only the case of a finite number of given processes.

1. LINEAR PROCESSES

Let us think of an economy involving n perfectly defined commodities, $G_1, G_2, \cdots, G_n$. Let a_i, b_i represent nonnegative quantities of G_i. An economic transformation is the possibility of obtaining $(b_1, b_2, \cdots, b_n)$ from $(a_1, a_2, \cdots, a_n)$. This can be denoted by

$$(1) \qquad \left(\begin{pmatrix} a_1, a_2, \cdots, a_n \\ b_1, b_2, \cdots, b_n \end{pmatrix} \right), \quad \text{or} \quad ((a_i; b_i)).$$

The a's are *inputs* and the b's, *outputs*. But a transformation may correspond to an actual process of production, transportation, training, consumption, disposal activity, storage, etc.

To eliminate the economic transformation *ex nihilo*, it will be assumed that at least one a_i is positive or, in other words, that

$$(2) \qquad \sum_{i=1}^{n} a_i > 0.$$

In some special cases the existence of the transformation (1) leads implicitly to that of

$$(3) \qquad \left(\begin{pmatrix} \lambda a_1, \lambda a_2, \cdots, \lambda a_n \\ \lambda b_1, \lambda b_2, \cdots, \lambda b_n \end{pmatrix} \right)$$

also, for any positive value of λ. If so, the totality of transformations (3) for $\lambda > 0$ will be referred to as a *linear process*.

A linear process is completely determined by any one of its transformations. The linear process defined by the transformation (1) will be denoted by

$$(4) \qquad P \begin{pmatrix} a_1, a_2, \cdots, a_n \\ b_1, b_2, \cdots, b_n \end{pmatrix} = P(a_i; b_i).$$

The transformation *actually* used in defining P will be called the *base* of the linear process. According to the definition of a linear process,

(5) $$P(a_i; b_i) \equiv P(\lambda a_i; \lambda b_i)$$

for any $\lambda > 0$. Therefore any transformation of P may be taken as base.

The transformations belonging to the same linear process represent different scales of production of that process. Thus $((\lambda a_i; \lambda b_i))$ represents the scale of production measured by λ if $((a_i; b_i))$ is taken as the unit of scale. Symbolically this is written

(6) $$P(\lambda a_i; \lambda b_i) = \lambda P(a_i; b_i).$$

If all the transformations of a process can actually be carried out, the process is called *achievable*.

The formulation of a linear process presented above is basically that of von Neumann, which differs from that used by Koopmans or by Leontief.

Indeed, process (4) conveys two distinct pieces of information:

(a) that the transformation requires some preexisting stocks of commodities $(a_1, a_2, \cdots, a_n)$;

(b) that the transformation brings about a modification of the stocks $(a_1, a_2, \cdots, a_n)$ determined by the differences $(\gamma_1, \gamma_2, \cdots, \gamma_n)$, where

(7) $$\gamma_i = b_i - a_i.$$

The γ's represent *flows*, and they may be positive or negative.

Koopmans' formulation of a linear process takes into consideration only aspect (b). In his notation a_{ik} corresponds to γ_i in this chapter.[2]

As the current production undeniably requires some preexisting stock [information conveyed by (a)], the formulation of von Neumann is preferred to the other for the purpose of this chapter. It must, however, be admitted that even formulation (4) presents some disadvantages in handling certain economic problems. It does not offer more detailed information regarding the *inner circuits* of flows. Relation (7) furnishes only the ultimate result after all compensations between positive and negative flows have taken place.

To help make this point clearer, let us think of a process requiring a certain stock of electric generators, for instance, and producing, among other things, such generators at a speed just sufficient to keep the stock constant. With adequate notation, this means $a_1 = b_1$. There is, therefore, no trace of the production and consumption of generators. The corresponding flows have, so to speak, vanished from the picture. Some-

---

[2] See Chapter III, relation (1.4). Leontief's formulation is a particular case of (1.4) where only one flow is positive.

times such disappearing flows do not raise any difficulty.   This is so if the corresponding commodity, G_i, is produced and consumed within the same plant like, to cite an extreme case, the melted glass in a glass factory.   It is seen, therefore, that the problem of handling disappearing flows is closely connected with that of defining and classifying the commodities.   On the other hand, in actual applications integration of industries or of processes should be expected to bring about the disappearance of some commodities.   This may be the underlying reason why Leontief ignores in his model the amount of output consumed by the industry itself [Leontief, 1941, p. 14].

To return to the comparison between processes as treated by von Neumann and Koopmans, it is easily seen that, from the *formal* point of view, the latter's process can be assimilated to a particular case of (4), namely,

$$
(8) \qquad P\begin{pmatrix} -a_{1,k}, & -a_{2,k}, & \cdots, & -a_{r,k}, & 0, & \cdots, & 0 \\ 0, & 0, & \cdots, & 0, & a_{r+1,k}, & \cdots, & a_{n,k} \end{pmatrix},
$$

where the $a_{j,\,k}$ for $j \leq r$ are nonpositive, but not all null, and for $j > r$ are nonnegative.   This may be written in the simplified way:

$$
(9) \qquad\qquad P(a_{1,k}, a_{2,k}, \cdots, a_{n,k}),
$$

which is basically Koopmans' notation.   Therefore, most formal properties of a model based on process (4) will be, *mutatis mutandis*, valid also for the corresponding models using formulation (9).

2. The Technological Horizon

The definition of a linear process given above (5) makes it possible to represent $P(a_i; b_i)$ in the $2n$-dimensional space $(a_1, a_2, \cdots, a_n, b_1, \cdots, b_n)$ by a straight halfline Δ starting at 0, the origin of the coordinate system, and passing through the point $(a_1, a_2, \cdots, a_n, b_1, \cdots, b_n)$. Any point on Δ represents a given scale of production of the process P. Thus Δ is the only *image* of P, and only one P corresponds to a given Δ.   For the sake of brevity, it will be possible, therefore, to refer unequivocally to the process P as the process Δ.

Two processes, P_1 and P_2, are distinct if, and only if, their images, Δ_1 and Δ_2, are distinct.

LEMMA 1: *If $P_1(a_{1i}; b_{1i})$, $P_2(a_{2i}; b_{2i})$ are two achievable processes and Δ_1, Δ_2 their respective images, any straight halfline Δ belonging to the angle (Δ_1, Δ_2) is the image of an achievable process P.*[3]

---

[3] No ambiguity is involved in the definition of the angle (Δ_1, Δ_2) since this angle is always $\leq \pi/2$, Δ_1, Δ_2 being in the positive orthant.

Let $p(a_i; b_i)$ be any point on Δ. As this belongs to the angle (Δ_1, Δ_2), two points, $p_1(a'_{1i}, b'_{1i})$, $p_2(a'_{2i}, b'_{2i})$, exist on Δ_1 and Δ_2, respectively, such that

$$(10) \qquad a_i = a'_{1i} + a'_{2i}, \qquad b_i = b'_{1i} + b'_{2i} \quad (i = 1, 2, \cdots, n).$$

The transformation $((a_i; b_i))$ may be regarded as the result of the simultaneous transformations $((a'_{1i}, b'_{1i}))$, $((a'_{2i}, b'_{2i}))$, and it is therefore possible actually to carry it out. As any transformation belonging to P can actually be carried out, the latter is *achievable*. Obviously,

$$(11) \qquad \begin{aligned} a'_{1i} &= \lambda_1 a_{1i}, & b'_{1i} &= \lambda_1 b_{1i}, & \lambda_1 &> 0 \\ a'_{2i} &= \lambda_2 a_{2i}, & b'_{2i} &= \lambda_2 b_{2i}, & \lambda_2 &> 0 \end{aligned} \qquad (i = 1, 2, \cdots, n),$$

and, with the help of (6), we may write

$$(12) \qquad P = \lambda_1 P_1 + \lambda_2 P_2.$$

The process P will be said to have been derived from P_1 and P_2 by *integration*.

COROLLARY: *The images of all achievable processes form a convex cone.*[4]

Let us now consider the *technological information*. By this is meant a set of *actually* recorded processes achievable under the prevailing *technological knowledge*. This set, together with those processes derived by integration from the set of those initially recorded, forms a set of achievable processes (Lemma 1) which must be a convex cone, H (Corollary). The cone H will be referred to as the *technological horizon of the given technological information*.[5]

The technological information may consist of a finite or of an infinite set of processes. A process belonging to the technological information will be denoted by

$$(13) \qquad P_i(a_{ik}; b_{ik}),$$

where i represents an element of a given set, not necessarily finite but having at most the power of the continuum.

---

[4] A convex cone is here defined as a set (Δ) of straight halflines Δ such that, if $\Delta_1, \Delta_2 \in (\Delta)$ and, if the angle $(\Delta_1, \Delta_2) < \pi$, any Δ belonging to the angle (Δ_1, Δ_2) belongs to (Δ). This definition does not include the case of a convex cone consisting of only two directly opposed halflines, Δ_1, Δ_2. (Δ_1 and Δ_2 are directly opposed when they have the same origin and together form a whole straight line.)

[5] Relating the technological horizon to the technological information and not to the technological knowledge aims at avoiding a definition which would not be operational. Indeed, if one tried to define the technological horizon of technological knowledge, one would soon discover that it seems rather impossible to find a workable criterion according to which it could be ascertained whether all achievable processes have been included in the horizon.

If this structure of H is assumed, another question must be considered from the beginning, namely, whether H includes its boundary or not, or, in other words, whether it is or is not a closed cone. At first glance this question may seem to have no economic significance. This is not so, however, as will be shown later on.[6] It will be assumed throughout the subsequent parts of this chapter that H is a *closed* cone.

3. COMPARISON OF LINEAR PROCESSES

At this point of the argument it is necessary to introduce an *economic* criterion on which to base the choice between two linear processes. In the search for such a criterion, it is realized immediately that the criterion must involve (a) the value of outputs,

$$(14) \qquad V = \sum_{k=1}^{n} b_k y_k,$$

and (b) the cost of inputs,

$$(15) \qquad C = \sum_{k=1}^{n} a_k y_k,$$

where $Y(y_1, y_2, \cdots, y_n)$ is a given price constellation of the commodities G_i.

At the same time, since the criterion will be used for the choice between *linear processes* (and not between economic *transformations*), *it must be independent of the scale of production*, whereas V, C, and $V - C$ are not.

Replacing V (or C) by V/b_k (or C/b_k) will not solve the difficulty since for some processes b_k may be zero. Even if it were not so, the criterion would then depend on the choice of k. The only simple criterion which has at the same time a definite economic meaning seems to be

$$(16) \qquad \phi = \frac{V}{C} = \frac{\sum b_k y_k}{\sum a_k y_k}.$$

The last expression represents the *return to the dollar*. It is made up of interest rate and rate of profit.[7]

[6] If the technological information consists of a finite number of processes, H is always a closed cone. The question raised assumes decisive importance for technological information containing an infinite number of processes in connection with the existence of economic equilibrium (see below, Section 6). One may see a relation between the closedness of H and the continuous substitution of one factor of production for another in the case where this substitution cannot be carried to the point of completely eliminating one factor of production.

[7] Von Neumann makes use of ϕ, speaking of it as a potential function with no economic meaning attached to it. He expresses the opinion that "a direct interpretation of the function ϕ would be highly desirable" [1945, p. 1].

The return to the dollar fails, however, to lead to a definite value in some special cases. This is so for all processes involving *only* free goods (i.e., only goods for which $y_k = 0$). The value of ϕ will in this case be indeterminate. We may dismiss these alternatives as absurd. It must not be overlooked, however, that economic theory, if it aims at explaining anything at all, cannot adopt such a standpoint. All processes and all goods must be considered in our initial data. The theory has to explain why some processes are not used and why some goods are free, and cannot take these results for granted.

To avoid the indeterminateness of ϕ, von Neumann's assumption that for each commodity in every process

$$(17) \qquad\qquad a_k + b_k > 0 \qquad\qquad (k = 1, 2, \cdots, n)$$

will be retained [1945, relation (9)]. We should not overlook the limitations introduced thereby. In economic terms (17) means that all processes of the technological horizon must include every commodity, either as input or as output.

With the same intention of avoiding the indeterminateness of ϕ, we shall assume that not all goods are free (i.e., at least one y_i is positive),

$$(18) \qquad\qquad \sum_{k=1}^{n} y_k > 0.$$

We shall further denote by $\phi(P, Y)$ the return to the dollar for the linear process P and for the price constellation Y.

DEFINITION: *For two given linear processes, P_1 and P_2, and a price constellation, Y, the process P_1 will be called* more profitable *than P_2 if*

$$(19) \qquad\qquad \phi(P_1, Y) > \phi(P_2, Y).$$

This definition is not basically different from that used in the elementary theory of the firm. Let us consider the two transformations belonging, respectively, to P_1 and P_2 and such that the corresponding input costs are equal, $C_1 = C_2$. P_1 is more profitable than P_2 if the values, V_1 and V_2, of the outputs corresponding to these transformations are such that $V_1 > V_2$. Obviously, if this is so, (19) is fulfilled, and conversely.

DEFINITION: *If*

$$(20) \qquad\qquad \phi(P_1, Y) \geqq \phi(P_2, Y)$$

for every price constellation, P_1 will be called technically superior *to P_2.*

We shall show this by writing symbolically $P_1 \geq P_2$.

Condition (20) is equivalent to

(21) $$(\sum b_{1k}y_k)(\sum a_{2k}y_k) - (\sum b_{2k}y_k)(\sum a_{1k}y_k) \geqq 0$$

for all nonnegative values of y_k. This does not lead to simple analytical restrictions for the a's and b's. Writing

(22) $$\alpha_{ik} = \frac{b_{ik}}{a_{ik}}$$

for what may be called the *productivity ratio* of the commodity G_k in the linear process P_i, a necessary condition for technical superiority, easily derived from (21), is that [8]

(23) $$[\alpha_1] \geqq [\alpha_2].$$

This is not, however, a sufficient condition.[9]

If in P_1 and P_2 all outputs are zero except that of G_1, for instance, (21) becomes equivalent to the classical condition that all average productivity coefficients of P_1 be greater than those of P_2,

(24) $$\frac{b_{11}}{a_{1k}} \geqq \frac{b_{21}}{a_{2k}} \qquad (k = 1, 2, \cdots, n).$$

Other special cases lend themselves to an immediate comparison according to (20). Thus it is obvious that

(25) $$P(a_i; b_i) < P(a_i - \Delta a_i; b_i + \Delta b_i)$$

for

(26) $$[a] \geq [\Delta a] \geqq 0, \qquad [\Delta b] \geqq 0,$$

(but not simultaneously $[\Delta a] = 0$, $[\Delta b] = 0$), provided that $P(a_i - \Delta a_i; b_i + \Delta b_i)$ is also achievable.

[8] At this point some notations used throughout the chapter need to be explained. Thus $[x]$ means the vector $(x_1, x_2, \cdots, x_m)$. The relation $[x] > 0$ stands for $x_1 > 0$, $x_2 > 0$, $\cdots$, $x_m > 0$. The relation $[x] \geq 0$ means that some x_k, *but not all*, may be zero, while $[x] \geqq 0$ will be used when $x_k = 0$ for all k is not an excluded alternative.

[9] The analytical difficulty of expressing (21) in terms of a's and b's and also the insufficiency of (23) are shown by the following fact: the necessary and sufficient conditions that

(i) $$A_{11}y_1^2 + 2A_{12}y_1y_2 + A_{22}y_2^2 \geqq 0 \quad \text{for} \quad y_1, y_2 \geqq 0$$

are

(ii) $$A_{11} \geqq 0, \qquad A_{22} \geqq 0, \qquad A_{12} + \sqrt{A_{11}A_{22}} \geqq 0;$$

or, in alternative form,

(iii) $\begin{cases} (a) & \text{if } A_{12} \geqq 0, \text{ then } A_{11} \geqq 0, \qquad A_{22} \geqq 0; \\ (b) & \text{if } A_{12} < 0, \text{ then } A_{12}^2 \leqq A_{11}A_{22}, \quad A_{11} > 0. \end{cases}$

It is easily seen that, for two commodities, the conditions (23) represent only A_{11}, $A_{22} \geqq 0$, and consequently they could not be sufficient for (i).

4. THE AGGREGATE LINEAR PRODUCTION FUNCTION

If H is a $2n$-dimensional cone, it has interior elements. If P is such an element, then, according to (25), a process technically superior to P and belonging to H can always be found. The use of the same procedure to find a process belonging to H and technically superior to P can fail, therefore, only if P belongs to the boundary of H. (H contains its boundary since we assumed it to be a closed cone.)

Now let $P^0(a_i^0; b_i^0)$ belong to the boundary of H, and let

$$(27) \qquad L(M) = \sum_{k=1}^{n} A_k a_k + \sum_{k=1}^{n} B_k b_k = 0$$

be a supporting plane of H passing through P^0. This means that

$$(28) \qquad\qquad L(P^0) = 0$$

and that

$$(29) \qquad\qquad L(P) \geqq 0$$

for all $P \in H$. The necessary and sufficient condition that all processes $\bar{P}^0(a_i^0 - \Delta a_i^0; b_i^0 + \Delta b_i^0)$ for $[\Delta a^0] \geqq 0$, $[\Delta b^0] \geqq 0$ (but not both $[\Delta a^0] = 0$, $[\Delta b^0] = 0$) be outside of H is that a supporting plane (27) exists for which $L(\bar{P}^0) < 0$ for any such $\bar{P}^0$.[10] Because of (28), this condition becomes

$$(30) \qquad -\sum_{k=1}^{n} A_k \Delta a_k^0 + \sum_{k=1}^{n} B_k \Delta b_k^0 < 0,$$

which yields

$$(31) \qquad\qquad [A] \geqq 0, \qquad [B] \leqq 0.$$

The case of both $[A] = 0$, $[B] = 0$ is excluded by (27). The condition (31) eliminates from H some additional processes which are technically inferior to some others though not necessarily all such processes.

The set of processes of the boundary of H which have not been so far eliminated will be referred to as the *aggregate linear production function* and denoted by F. The processes belonging to F will be called *efficient*.[11]

---

[10] Cf. Gale [XVII, Theorem 5] and Koopmans [III, Sections 3.5 and 4.4] for corresponding statements regarding polyhedral cones. A proof of this statement for nonpolyhedral cones can be based on a statement by Bonnesen and Fenchel [1948, top of p. 5, passage in italics].

[11] This term was first introduced by Koopmans and applied to economic transformations [III, Section 4.2]. Obviously, all transformations of an efficient process are efficient.

It can also be shown that the aggregate linear production can be expressed in terms of a continuous function. Because of the convexity of H, a continuous homogeneous function,

$$(32) \qquad\qquad y = f(a; b),$$

can be found such that $y = 0$ on the boundary of H, $y < 0$ for the interior of H, and $y > 0$ in all other cases.[12]   The aggregate production function will therefore be determined by

$$(33) \qquad\qquad f(a; b) = 0, \qquad f(a - \Delta a; b + \Delta b) > 0$$

$$\text{if} \quad [a] \geqq [\Delta a] \geqq 0, \qquad [\Delta b] \geqq 0.$$

The concept of aggregate production function can be applied to a single industry, to a group of industries, or to a closed economy, the the latter being defined as the totality of all processes of production and consumption—including consumption of consumers' goods as a labor-producing process as well as any other achievable process.

The aggregate production function F leads to two categories of *iso-curves:*

(1) the *output isoquants* (analogous to the classical isoquants of the production function) obtained by all *points* of F for which $[b]$ is a constant;

(2) the *input isoquants* (analogous to the classical opportunity cost curves) corresponding to $[a]$ constant.

The relations (29) and (31) lead to the following conclusions:

(i) *The output isoquants are convex toward the origin of the coordinate system* (a).

(ii) *The input isoquants are concave toward the origin of the coordinate system* (b).

(iii) *Any input yields decreasing returns with respect to any output.*[13]

The first two results show that in a linear model the marginal rate of substitution is increasing for inputs and decreasing for outputs.

It is worth stressing that the properties regarding the marginal rate of substitution and the marginal productivity, (i)—(iii), are direct consequences of the linearity assumption (5) and are, in a way, structural aspects of the linear models.   For nonlinear models these assumptions have to be introduced as distinct technological laws.

It can be shown that, by integrating nonlinear processes, we may obtain output isoquants concave toward the origin, if the assumption of increasing marginal rate of substitution is not explicitly introduced.   As

---

[12] This follows immediately from Urysohn's Theorem [Sierpinski, 1934, p. 71].

[13] The result (iii) was also obtained by Koopmans for his model [III, Section 4.10].

an illustration let us consider two processes of producing B, with limitational factors A_1 and A_2,

$$(34) \quad \begin{cases} \text{(a)} & b = f_1(a_1), \quad a_2 = \lambda a_1; \\ \text{(b)} & b = f_2(a_1), \quad a_2 = \mu a_1. \end{cases}$$

Their integration leads to the isoquants determined by the system

$$(35) \quad a_1' + a_1'' = a_1, \quad \lambda a_1' + \mu a_1'' = a_2, \quad f_1(a_1') + f_2(a_1'') = b,$$

which yields

$$(36) \quad \frac{da_2}{da_1} = \frac{\mu f_1' - \lambda f_2'}{f_1' - f_2'}, \quad \frac{d^2 a_2}{da_1^2} = \frac{(\mu - \lambda)}{(f_1' - f_2')^3} [f_1''(f_2')^2 + f_2''(f_1')^2].$$

It is seen that, if no other process besides (34) exists in the technological information, the isoquants of the integrated process may have any shape. If, however, the principle of decreasing marginal rate of substitution is accepted, and if the output isoquants of the integrated process *are* concave, it follows that achievable processes other than those deduced by integration must necessarily exist and that our technological information is incomplete.

In this light the law of increasing marginal rate of substitution appears as a criterion which, in certain cases, will signal the absence of some processes from the technological information. Whenever concave output isoquants are obtained, this is so. The criterion works only by its negative side, in the sense that if the isoquants are convex it does not necessarily follow that the technological information is complete. This accounts for the absence of any such criterion in the case of linear technological information.

5. Illustration of Economic Equilibrium in a Closed Linear Model

There are different ways of defining the economic equilibrium in a model, closed or open. We shall illustrate the way the problem of economic equilibrium of a linear model can be handled by considering a closed economy where all processes are of von Neumann's type. The model will consist of a certain technological horizon, H, and certain economic principles describing the mechanism of the model. These principles may lead, through a process of elimination, to a certain set of processes and to certain price constellations. If so, these processes and price constellations constitute the equilibrium of the model. It is obvious that, when the equilibrium of the model is defined in this way, the equilibrium may (i) exist and be unique, (ii) exist and be indeterminate, or (iii) not exist at all. To find out which of these alternatives is true constitutes the most important question in dealing with an economic problem.

The two following economic principles will be used here for describing the mechanism of the model:

(a) Given a price constellation, that process will be chosen which will maximize the return to the dollar or, what comes to the same thing, that process which for a given cost of input will maximize the value of the output [the most profitable process to the entrepreneur; see (19) above].

(b) Given a process of production, the competitive forces of the economy will bring about that price constellation which makes the return to dollar a minimum (i.e., which will make profits zero and the rate of interest the smallest possible). In a closed model such as the one described here, the only social cost is waiting, and its cost is the interest. Therefore we may say that the price constellation brought about by the competitive forces will make the social cost minimum [von Neumann, 1945, relations (7 **) and (8 **)].

Von Neumann proves that in a model where H consists of processes defined as in Section 1 and where the principles (a) and (b) are accepted, there is at least one price constellation Y^0 and at least one process P^0 which fulfill the conditions (a) and (b),

$$(37) \qquad \phi(P^0, Y^0) \geqq \phi(P, Y^0), \qquad \phi(P^0, Y^0) \leqq \phi(P^0, Y),$$

for any $P \in H$ and for any Y. The alternative proof given in the next section does not require the number of processes in the technological information to be finite.

6. ALTERNATIVE PROOF OF VON NEUMANN'S RESULTS

For the argument of this section we retain the assumption contained in (17) and also assume that H is a *closed* cone. By intersecting the technological horizon H with the linear space

$$(38) \qquad \sum_{k=1}^{n} a_k + \sum_{k=1}^{n} b_k = 1,$$

we obtain a convex, bounded, and closed point set, Γ. To each point of Γ there corresponds a unique linear process of H and vice versa. It is therefore possible to refer unequivocally to a point of Γ as a process P. On the other hand, any constellation of prices (assumed nonnegative and not all null) can be represented by a unique point of the simplex S defined by

$$(39) \qquad \sum_1^n y_k = 1.$$

The return to the dollar is therefore a function, $\phi(P, Y)$, of a point $P \in \Gamma$ and of a point $Y \in S$.

THEOREM 1: *For a given P, ϕ reaches its greatest lower bound in S.*

It is always possible to renumber the variables (commodities) in such a way that, for a given P,

$$(40) \qquad \frac{b_1}{a_1} = \frac{b_2}{a_2} = \frac{b_3}{a_3} = \cdots = \frac{b_r}{a_r} = \mu,$$

$$\frac{b_k}{a_k} \geqq \mu' > \mu \qquad \text{for} \quad k > r.$$

The greatest lower bound (g.l.b.) of ϕ over S is reached for the price constellation Y_P, for which

$$(41) \qquad y_k = 0 \qquad \text{for} \quad k > r,$$

the other prices for $k \leqq r$ being subject only to the condition $\sum_1^r y_k = 1$. Therefore

$$(42) \qquad \text{g.l.b. over } S \text{ of } \phi = \phi(P) = \phi(P, Y_P) = \mu \leqq \phi(P, Y),$$

where Y is any price constellation.

The value of μ will be referred to as the *rate of growth* of the process P. Since not all a_k can be zero, by (2), the rate of growth is always finite. The integer r will be called the *rank* of P.

THEOREM 2: *The function $\phi(P)$ is continuous over Γ.*

Since the function

$$(43) \qquad z_k = b_k/a_k$$

is continuous at all points for which $a_k \neq 0$, we can, for any positive δ_k, find α_k, β_k such that, for all $|\epsilon_k| < \alpha_k$, $|\eta_k| < \beta_k$,

$$(44) \qquad \left| \frac{b_k}{a_k} - \frac{b_k + \eta_k}{a_k + \epsilon_k} \right| < \delta_k.$$

Some restrictions will have to be imposed, such as $\alpha_k < a_k$, $\beta_k < b_k$, and, if $b_k = 0$, then $\eta_k \geqq 0$.

If $a_k = 0$, $b_k > 0$ for a given μ_k, then we can find α_k, β_k such that for all $0 < \epsilon_k < \alpha_k$, $|\eta_k| < \beta_k < b_k$,

$$(45) \qquad\qquad (b_k + \eta_k)/\epsilon_k > \mu_k.$$

Let us choose $\delta_k < \delta < (\mu' - \mu)$, $\mu_k > \mu'$. From (40) it follows that the minimum of ϕ for any $P(a_k + \epsilon_k; b_k + \eta_k)$ lies between $\mu - \delta$ and $\mu + \delta$ if ϵ_k and η_k are such that (44) and (45) are fulfilled. This proves the theorem.

Since Γ is *closed* and *bounded*, we have the following:

COROLLARY: $\phi(P)$ *reaches its smallest upper bound in* Γ.

NOTATION: Let M be the maximum of $\phi(P)$ over Γ and let $\Gamma^0 \subset \Gamma$ be the set of processes P^0 for which

$$(46) \qquad\qquad \phi(P^0) = M.$$

Also let σ be the *minimum* rank of the processes belonging to Γ^0.

THEOREM 3: *There are* σ *commodities for which*

$$(47) \qquad\qquad \frac{b_1}{a_1} = \frac{b_2}{a_2} = \cdots = \frac{b_\sigma}{a_\sigma} = M$$

for all $P \epsilon \Gamma^0$.

Let $P^1 \epsilon \Gamma^0$ be a process of rank σ satisfying (47) and $P^2 \epsilon \Gamma^0$ such that, for some $k \leqq \sigma$,

$$(48) \qquad\qquad b_k^2/a_k^2 > M.$$

If this were so, the process $x_1 P^1 + x_2 P^2$ $(x_1, x_2 > 0; x_1 + x_2 = 1)$, which evidently belongs to Γ, would either belong to Γ^0 but have a lower rank than the minimum, σ, or have a rate of growth greater than the maximum, M.

COROLLARY: *The set* Γ^0 *is convex.*

THEOREM 4: *If* $P \epsilon \Gamma$, *it is impossible to have*

$$(49) \qquad\qquad b_k/a_k > M$$

for all values of $k \leqq \sigma$.

Let us assume that there is one $P \epsilon \Gamma$ for which

$$(50) \qquad\qquad b_k = Ma_k + v_k, \qquad v_k > 0,$$

for all $k \leqq \sigma$. Let P^0 be a process belonging to Γ^0 and having the rank σ.

It follows that

(51) $$b_k^0 = Ma_k^0 + u_k, \qquad u_k > 0,$$

for all $k > \sigma$. Let T be the maximum of

(52) $$(Ma_k - b_k)/u_k$$

for $k > \sigma$. If

(53) $$x_0/x > T, \qquad x_0, x > 0, \qquad x_0 + x = 1,$$

the process $xP + x_0P^0$ would have a rate of growth greater than the maximum one.

THEOREM 5: *A price constellation Y^0 with $y_k = 0$ for all $k > \sigma$ can be found such that, if $P^0 \,\epsilon\, \Gamma^0$,*

(54) $$\phi(P^0, Y^0) \geqq \phi(P, Y^0)$$

for any $P \,\epsilon\, \Gamma$.

Let us consider the mapping of Γ by which to each element of Γ is made to correspond the element

(55) $$(Ma_1 - b_1, Ma_2 - b_2, \cdots, Ma_\sigma - b_\sigma),$$

and denote by $\mathfrak{M}$ the set of all points (55). The set $\mathfrak{M}$ is closed and convex. According to Theorem 4, $\mathfrak{M}$ has no points in the interior of the negative orthant, Ω^-, and, since the origin of the coordinate system belongs to $\mathfrak{M}$, the origin is a boundary point if $\mathfrak{M}$ is σ-dimensional. Therefore a plane passing through the origin,

(56) $$\Pi(Ma - b) = \sum_1^\sigma (Ma_k - b_k)y_k = 0,$$

can be found such that $\Pi(Ma - b) \geqq 0$ for any $[Ma - b] \,\epsilon\, \mathfrak{M}$ and $\Pi(Ma - b) \leqq 0$ for any $[Ma - b] \,\epsilon\, \Omega^-$ [Bonnesen and Fenchel, 1934]. Since (56) is a supporting plane of the negative orthant, we have $[y] \geq 0$.[14] If $\mathfrak{M}$ is not σ-dimensional, it will be contained in at least one plane with the same properties as (56).

[14] This statement can be proved as follows: The vectors $V_k(0, 0, \cdots, -1, 0, \cdots, 0)$ $(k = 1, \cdots, \sigma)$ belong to Ω^-, but they cannot all belong to (56). Let $V_1, V_2, \cdots, V_s$ $(0 \leqq s < \sigma)$ be those vectors belonging to (56), and $V_{s+1}, V_{s+2}, \cdots, V_\sigma$ be those not belonging to (56). It follows immediately that $y_k = 0$ for $k \leqq s$, and $y_k > 0$ for $s < k \leqq \sigma$. Hence $[y] \geq 0$. This provides an extension of Theorem 3 of Chapter XVII.

Under all circumstances, if Y^0 is the constellation $(y_1, y_2, \cdots, y_\sigma, 0, \cdots, 0)$ where $y_1, y_2, \cdots, y_\sigma$ are the coefficients of the supporting plane (56), and if $P \in \Gamma$ [i.e., $(Ma - b) \in \mathfrak{M}$], it follows that

$$(57) \qquad \sum_1^\sigma (Ma_k - b_k)y_k \geqq 0,$$

or

$$(58) \qquad \phi(P^0, Y^0) = M \geqq \frac{\displaystyle\sum_1^\sigma b_k y_k}{\displaystyle\sum_1^\sigma a_k y_k} = \phi(P, Y^0).$$

It is worth stressing that Y^0 may not be unique and also that y_k may be zero even for some $k \leqq \sigma$.

THEOREM 6: *If* Γ *is a* $(2n - 1)$-*dimensional set (or* H *a* $2n$-*dimensional cone), the set* Γ^0 *belongs to the boundary of* Γ.

Instead, we shall prove that, if $P^0 \in \Gamma^0$ were an interior element of Γ, a process $P^* \in \Gamma$ could be found having a rate of growth greater than M, which is an impossibility.

Indeed, if P^0 were interior to Γ, $2n$ processes $P^i(a^i; b^i)$ belonging to Γ could be found such that

$$(59) \qquad P^0 = \sum_{i=1}^{2n} \alpha_i^0 P^i, \qquad [\alpha^0] > 0, \qquad \sum_1^{2n} \alpha_i^0 = 1,$$

and such that

$$(60) \qquad \sum_{i=1}^{2n} \lambda_i P^i = 0$$

does not admit a solution $[\lambda] \neq 0$.

The system of inequalities

$$(61) \qquad \sum_{i=1}^{2n} \alpha_i(b_k^i - M_k a_k^i) > 0 \qquad (k = 1, 2, \cdots, n),$$

where

$$(62) \qquad M_k = b_k^0/a_k^0,$$

admits a nontrivial solution $[\alpha^*]$. The necessary and sufficient condition for the existence of this solution is that the convex hull defined by the points

$$(63) \qquad m_k(b_k^1 - M_k a_k^1, b_k^2 - M_k a_k^2, \cdots, b_k^{2n} - M_k a_k^{2n})$$

should not contain the origin [Dines, 1936, Theorem 2]. This is easily seen to be so since, according to (60), the system

$$(64) \qquad \sum_{k=1}^{n} x_k(b_k^i - M_k a_k^i) = 0 \qquad (i = 1, 2, \cdots, 2n)$$

does not admit a nontrivial solution.

On the other hand, we can always assume that $[\alpha^*] > 0$. Indeed, if $[\alpha]$ is replaced by $[\alpha^0]$ in (61), the system will be satisfied with the sign $>$ replaced by $=$. Therefore, if $[\alpha^*]$ is a nontrivial solution of (61) and if x^* and x^0 are positive scalars, $x^*[\alpha^*] + x^0[\alpha^0]$ will be another solution of (61). If x^* and x^0 are appropriately chosen, it is always possible to have $x^*[\alpha^*] + x^0[\alpha^0] > 0$.

If $[\alpha^*] > 0$, $\sum_1^{2n} \alpha_i^* = 1$, the process

$$(65) \qquad P^* = \sum_{1}^{2n} \alpha_i^* P^i$$

belongs to Γ. But, according to (61), P^* has a rate of growth greater than M. This proves the theorem.

Simple examples may be constructed in order to prove that, if Γ is not a $(2n - 1)$-dimensional set, P^0 may be an interior point of Γ if the latter is considered in its proper dimensional space.

7. Summary and Concluding Remarks

The results of the preceding section may be summarized as follows:

(a) Given any linear technological horizon, there exists at least one equilibrium process (by Corollary to Theorem 2).

(b) All equilibrium processes have the same rate of growth, which is the greatest possible one (by Theorem 3).

(c) There is a group of commodities, $G_1, G_2, \cdots, G_\sigma$, which have the same productivity ratio, (22), in all equilibrium processes. Therefore the latter are of the form

$$(66) \quad P^0 \begin{pmatrix} a_1, & a_2, & \cdots, a_\sigma, & a_{\sigma+1}, & \cdots, a_n \\ a_1 M, & a_2 M, & \cdots, & a_\sigma M, & a_{\sigma+1} M + u_{\sigma+1}, & \cdots, a_n M + u_n \end{pmatrix},$$

with $u_k \geqq 0$, and form a convex set (Theorem 3 and Corollary).

(d) If the technological horizon is a $2n$-dimensional cone, the technological information must contain at least one equilibrium process. (This follows from Theorem 6 and the fact that Γ^0 is, by Corollary to Theorem 3, a convex set.) Therefore M and σ can be derived by examining only the processes contained in the technological information. If, however, the technological horizon has fewer dimensions than $2n$, all processes should be taken into consideration in order to determine the equilibrium solutions.

(e) There exists at least one equilibrium price constellation (Theorem 5). It must be of the form

$$(67) \qquad Y^0(y_1, y_2, \cdots, y_\sigma, 0, 0, \cdots, 0).$$

(f) All commodities G_k which have a productivity ratio greater than the maximum rate of growth in at least one equilibrium process are necessarily free goods. These correspond to $k > \sigma$. But other commodities may also be free because some y_k ($k \leqq \sigma$) may be zero in the equilibrium price constellation.

(g) The return to the dollar for the equilibrium solutions cannot be greater than that for any other price constellation or lower than that for any other process, because of (42) and (54). This is the saddle point property,

$$(68) \qquad \phi(P^0, Y^0) \leqq \phi(P^0, Y), \qquad \phi(P^0, Y^0) \geqq \phi(P, Y^0).$$

(h) Considering *only* the commodities which are not necessarily free goods, it is seen that the equilibrium process is unique but that the same may not be true for the equilibrium price constellation.[15] The latter conclusion leads to rather uncomfortable economic results. Thus some goods may be free according to one equilibrium price constellation and have a positive price according to another.

In order to illustrate the unsatisfactory type of price equilibrium which may be obtained in many cases, we shall refer to the technological horizon defined by the following two processes:

$$P^1(a_1^1 = 1, \qquad a_2^1 = 1, \qquad b_1^1 = 1, \qquad b_2^1 = 1),$$

$$P^2(a_1^2 = 3, \qquad a_2^2 = 2, \qquad b_1^2 = 2, \qquad b_2^2 = 3).$$

The only equilibrium process is P^1, which leads to a stationary economy. However, the equilibrium prices are subject only to the condition $y_2 \leqq y_1$. This could hardly be regarded as a determinate economic equilibrium [see Champernowne, 1945, pp. 14–15].

(i) Despite the fact that some goods may be *ad libitum* either free or not, the equilibrium rate of interest (the return to the dollar for null profits) is unique and will not be affected by the shifting of some goods from one category to another.

---

[15] The apparent symmetry of prices and quantities ends here.

CHAPTER V

RELAXATION PHENOMENA IN LINEAR
DYNAMIC MODELS [1]

By Nicholas Georgescu-Roegen

In a short article published in the first volume of *Econometrica*, Ph. Le Corbeiller [1933] pointed out the possibility of using relaxation phenomena as a model for business cycles. However, Le Corbeiller's suggestion has found little echo among economists, and the literature shows only sporadic references to his paper. Paul A. Samuelson [1947, p. 339], speaking of this possible approach, admits that practically nothing has been done along this line. The only economic problem which could be regarded as having something to do with relaxation is the famous cobweb problem, but this has been developed independently of any relation to the concept of relaxation.

Le Corbeiller's article was inspired by the work of B. van der Pol [1926]. Relaxation phenomena occupy an important place in modern physics. The difficulty in dealing with such phenomena is that, although most of them are of a *periodic* nature, this periodicity cannot be described by a sine curve. An example of a relaxation phenomenon is found in a hammer which strikes in a periodic way.[2] Obviously, describing such a movement involves additional difficulties in comparison with the case of the movement of a pendulum. The latter has a *symmetric* periodicity, the former, an *asymmetric* one. This is due to the fact that the movement of the hammer can be decomposed into two distinct phases, one before and one after the energy is released through the shock. The two courses of the hammer, toward and away from the

---

[1] The results contained in this chapter may be reproduced in whole or in part for any purpose of the United States Government, under whose contract they were completed.

The results were presented for the first time during two meetings of the staff of the Harvard Economic Research Project in April, 1949. The author wishes to acknowledge the many inspiring discussions with Professor W. W. Leontief regarding the topics developed here. It is hardly necessary to add that, for any faults the chapter may contain, the author is solely responsible. The facilities of the Institute of Research and Training in the Social Sciences at Vanderbilt University extended to the author in preparing the final version are gratefully acknowledged.

[2] For other examples from the field of physics, see Le Corbeiller [1931].

object being hit, take place under two *different regimes* which lead to two *different phases* of its movement.

However, not all movements that have an asymmetric periodicity are relaxation phenomena. A ball moving without friction over the surface of a washboard with asymmetric waves does not involve any relaxation in the sense used by the writers mentioned. In the latter sense, a relaxation phenomenon takes place only when the difference between the "up" and "down" swings is created by a certain *discontinuity in the regime.* Such a discontinuity will introduce a discontinuity in the *speed* of the movement (at least in size or in direction). Therefore the movements related to each phase will be described by a *different function.*[3]

The aim of van der Pol's contribution was to approximate these two different functions by a single analytic function. This was achieved by considering the periodic solutions of the differential equation

$$(1) \qquad \frac{d^2y}{dt^2} + \epsilon(y^2 - 1)\frac{dy}{dt} + y = 0$$

for large values of ϵ. By this procedure the analytical difficulty was solved from the practical point of view. But this veiled the real meaning of relaxation, which is the discontinuity of the regime. Indeed, as has already been pointed out, periodicity in the classical sense is a secondary aspect of the oscillations of relaxation. In economics, where most of the so-called periodic phenomena, such as business cycles, for instance, are treated as periodic phenomena in the classical sense only in order to simplify the problem, the discontinuity aspect retains its full significance. This point of view finds an admirable illustration in a dynamic model presented by Leontief in a paper read during February, 1949, before the staff of the Harvard Economic Research Project. The contribution contained in the present chapter has its origin in the author's attempt to answer one problem raised by Leontief in his paper.

The dynamic model presented by Leontief is an extension of his earlier static model [Leontief, 1941]. It is defined by the system

$$(F_1) \qquad \begin{aligned} x_1 &= a_{21}x_2 + b_{11}\dot{x}_1 + b_{21}\dot{x}_2, \\ x_2 &= a_{12}x_1 + b_{12}\dot{x}_1 + b_{22}\dot{x}_2, \end{aligned}$$

where x_1, x_2 are output flows, $\dot{x}_1$, $\dot{x}_2$ are derivatives with respect to time, and the a's and b's are constants.

---

[3] From the point of view of the Dirichlet definition of a function, this distinction is not possible. However, the laws of the movement, being derived from certain differential equations of an algebraic, or at least analytical, structure, are, in general, analytic functions. As any analytic function has an individuality of its own, it is a perfectly justified attitude to regard two such functions as distinct.

The system (F_1) takes account of the fact that production requires both input flows and stocks (or inventories). In this particular formulation, inputs and stocks are supposed to be proportionate to outputs. The ratios between input flows and output flows are referred to as *input coefficients* (or a's), and the ratios between stocks and outputs are the *capital coefficients* (or b's).

The system (F_1) leads to the classical solution

$$(S_1) \qquad \begin{aligned} x_1 &= c_1 e^{\lambda_1 t} + c_2 e^{\lambda_2 t}, \\ x_2 &= c_1 u_1 e^{\lambda_1 t} + c_2 u_2 e^{\lambda_2 t}, \end{aligned}$$

where c_1 and c_2 are integration constants determined by the initial values of x_1 and x_2. Leontief assumes further that at a *turning point*, defined in terms of $\dot{x}_1$ (the change of the demand for x_1), a discontinuity is introduced in the behavior of the entrepreneurs such as to make $b_{11} = 0$ in (F_1). The next phase of the system will, therefore, be defined by the equations

$$(F_2) \qquad \begin{aligned} x_1 &= a_{21}x_2 + 0 + b_{21}\dot{x}_2, \\ x_2 &= a_{12}x_1 + b_{12}\dot{x}_1 + b_{22}\dot{x}_2, \end{aligned}$$

and will last until the demand for x_1 has reached a certain level determined by the one which existed when the second phase began.

The solution of (F_2) is

$$(S_2) \qquad \begin{aligned} x_1 &= c_1' e^{\mu_1 t} + c_2' e^{\mu_2 t}, \\ x_2 &= c_1' v_1 e^{\mu_1 t} + c_2' v_2 e^{\mu_2 t}, \end{aligned}$$

where the integration constants, c_1' and c_2', are determined by the splicing conditions, namely, that (S_2) must start from where (S_1) left off. Consequently, c_1', c_2' are indirectly determined by the initial values of x_1, x_2.

When the second phase (F_1) begins, if it ever does, the new values of the constants c_1 and c_2 will have to be determined by the new splicing conditions between (S_2) and (S_1), and so forth. It is clear that the problem when handled in this way raises almost insuperable technical difficulties, and one may even ask, as Leontief did, whether it would be possible to predict in *a finite number of steps* the final outcome of the system.[4]

---

[4] An analogy, used by the author elsewhere, may aid in grasping the essence of such a question. It is known, for instance, that the decimal digits of the transcendental number π cannot be determined unless this is done step by step. For numbers such as $7/23$, any decimal digit can be determined in a finite number of steps. The question raised in the text is whether the system has the structure of π, i.e., so that the prediction of any phase requires the *actual* splicing (and knowledge) of the preceding one, or the structure of a rational number, i.e., so that any phase can be computed without necessarily knowing the preceding ones.

It is the purpose of the present chapter to offer a way of answering such a question and to develop a method which can be applied to the study of almost all economic problems where a relaxation phenomenon is present. A more general concept of periodicity, of undoubted importance for economic theory, will also be introduced.[5]

1. Let us think of a system, $(\sum)$, which is subject to two different regimes, R_1 and R_2. Assume that two rules, r_1 and r_2, are also given which govern the switching of the system from regime R_1 to R_2 and vice versa. If from a given initial position, $(\sum_0)$, the system develops under regime R_1,[6] the movement of the system is completely determined up to $t = \infty$.[7]

The evolution of the system may be described by the sequence

(F) $\qquad\qquad\qquad\qquad F_1, F_2, F_1, F_2, \cdots ,$

where F_1 and F_2 represent the phases corresponding to R_1 and R_2. The sequence (F) may be finite or infinite.

Such a scheme constitutes a special type of periodicity, which we shall refer to as *phase-periodicity*. This is a generalized concept of the classical *point-periodicity*. The economic cycles seem to be better described by phase-periodicity than by point-periodicity, since the relevant aspect of the business cycle is the recurrence of the phases and not the repetition, after a constant time-lag, of the *same* values.

Phase-periodicity, as defined above, implies a relaxation phenomenon every time the phase changes. Moreover, it is more general than the relaxation oscillations considered in physics, the latter usually being only point-periodic.

The first problem which arises in connection with a phase-periodic scheme is that of finding out whether or not the sequence (F) is finite, and further, in case (F) is infinite, to determine whether or not the system has an asymptotic movement. If it has, economists would say that the dynamic model tends toward a unique equilibrium.

[5] The author wishes to emphasize that the object of this chapter is not to appraise the merits, from the point of view of economic theory, of the models used here to illustrate the analytical method devised to deal with relaxation phenomena in economics. Moreover, in the case of Leontief's model this would have been impossible because Leontief's contribution is not yet available in print.

[6] This assumption is absolutely necessary. The choice between R_1 and R_2 as the initial regime is therefore supposed to be made according to some outside criteria if the whole evolution is to be considered as having a beginning. This would no longer be necessary if the system were considered as already in movement, in which case the sequence (F) below has no beginning. In some cases, however, a given initial condition may be compatible with only one of the two regimes R_1, R_2.

[7] Provided, however, that situations do not exist where the rule r_1 (or r_2) becomes self-contradictory.

Different types of schemes may be conceived. We shall deal with those which are more likely to be met in economic dynamic models.

2. A simple model to illustrate the relaxation phenomena would be one where capital accumulation during the up-swing period of the business cycle would obey a dynamic law different from that governing capital decumulation during the down-swing. Such an approach would, indeed, be more realistic than that of most dynamic models constructed so far. These assume that both phases are governed by a reversible law.[8]

Let us assume that the aggregate dynamic laws governing the accumulation (or decumulation) of capital during the two phases of the cycle are represented, respectively, by the equations

$$(2) \qquad \frac{dC}{dt} = f_1(C), \qquad \frac{dC}{dt} = f_2(C),$$

thus making the change in capital stock a function of the existing stock.

The problem of describing the evolution of the system has a simple and immediate solution if the system of partial differential equations,

$$(3) \qquad \frac{\partial C}{\partial t} = f_1(C), \qquad \frac{\partial C}{\partial \tau} = f_2(C),$$

is integrable. Let

$$(4) \qquad C = \phi(t, \tau)$$

be the integral of (3), and t_k and τ_k, the lengths of the kth first phase and of the kth second phase, respectively. These lengths are determined by the rules r_1 and r_2. The movement of the system is described in terms of the single function (4):

$$C = \phi \left(\sum_1^n t_i + t, \sum_1^n \tau_i \right) \qquad (0 \leqq t \leqq t_{n+1}),$$

$$(5)$$

$$C = \phi \left(\sum_1^n t_i, \sum_1^{n-1} \tau_i + \tau \right) \qquad (0 \leqq \tau \leqq \tau_n).$$

[8] This point was clearly emphasized by Leontief in his paper. Leontief pointed out the deep significance of the turning point in a business cycle, which goes far beyond the mere formal aspect of changing slope. Use of Leontief's argument is made here solely to illustrate the usefulness of the relaxation concept in economic theory.

In three-dimensional space function (4) will represent a surface and rules r_1 and r_2 will correspond generally to two curves (r_1) and (r_2) (Figure 1). The movement of the system will be described by a path, $C_0, C_1, C_2, \cdots$, on the surface ϕ. Therefore the whole problem of phase-periodicity can be followed by considering the path $c_0, c_1, c_2, \cdots$, on the $t0\tau$ plane.

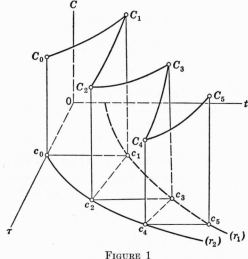

FIGURE 1

It is seen that the value of C at any moment depends only on the lengths of time obtained by summing time separately for each phase. Therefore the complete evolution of the system can be predicted in a finite number of steps.

It is easily seen that the system will tend toward an equilibrium if either one or the other of the following two conditions is fulfilled:

(a) the curves (r_1) and (r_2) meet at a point E, at a finite distance or at infinity (i.e., they are asymptotic);

(b) the two curves (r_1) and (r_2) do not meet, but, for $t = +\infty$,

(6) $$\lim_{\text{along } r_1} \phi = \lim_{\text{along } r_2} \phi.$$

If E is at a finite distance, the equilibrium will be reached over a finite period of time; in all other cases the system will only approach equilibrium.[9]

Economic models can be found which fulfill the integrability condition,

---

[9] Such a conclusion implies evidently that rules r_1 and r_2 never lead to a contradiction. Such would be the case if, in order to go from (r_1) to (r_2) along $c_0, c_1, c_2, \cdots$, it were necessary to move in the negative direction of time.

but they have an exceptional structure and their applicability will therefore be very limited.[10]

3. A two-variable linear model subject to relaxation oscillations can be described in general by the two systems

$$(M) \quad \begin{aligned} \dot{x}_1 &= M_{11}x_1 + M_{12}x_2, \\ \dot{x}_2 &= M_{21}x_1 + M_{22}x_2, \end{aligned}$$

$$(N) \quad \begin{aligned} \dot{x}_1 &= N_{11}x_1 + N_{12}x_2, \\ \dot{x}_2 &= N_{21}x_1 + N_{22}x_2, \end{aligned}$$

each representing one of the regimes R_1 and R_2.

From the first system we obtain

$$(7) \qquad (M_{21}x_1 + M_{22}x_2)\, dx_1 = (M_{11}x_1 + M_{12}x_2)\, dx_2,$$

which represents a one-parameter family of curves, (M), in the plane $x_1 0 x_2$. Through each point of the plane—except the origin of the coordinate system which is a singular point—passes one and only one curve.

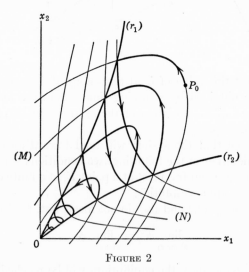

FIGURE 2

Given the initial position of the system, $P_0(x_1^0,\, x_2^0)$, the latter will follow the curve (M) passing through P_0 (Figure 2). If the system starts

[10] As Samuelson, who read the manuscript, further pointed out, in such models the rates of capital accumulation and decumulation at the same level C are in a constant ratio (which obviously must be negative). This follows immediately from the integrability condition of (3): $f_1'(C)/f_1(C) = f_2'(C)/f_2(C)$. Hence $f_1(C) = kf_2(C)$.

from *any* point belonging to the *same* curve (M), it will have the same evolution. This is why the curves (M) will be called *isodromes*.

It is worth stressing that the evolution of the system described by an isodrome is *time-less* but not *sequence-less*. This does not disturb completely the utility of such a description for economic theory, for the latter deals very often with dynamic formulations of this kind. Indeed, many economic statements tell *what* will happen next but do not consider the more delicate question of predicting also exactly *when*.

Equation (7) is not, however, equivalent to (M), for (7) determines only a family of curves and the *isodromes* must have a *direction*. Therefore (7) must be supplemented by information regarding the direction of movement. This can be derived from (M) and formulated in terms of the sign of dx_1 (or dx_2).[11]

The shape of the isodromes (M) depends, as is known, on the nature of the roots, λ_1, λ_2, of the characteristic equation

$$(8) \qquad \begin{vmatrix} M_{11} - \lambda & M_{12} \\ M_{21} & M_{22} - \lambda \end{vmatrix} = 0.$$

In drawing the shapes of the isodromes it is a great help to keep in mind the properties of the straight lines

$$(9) \qquad M_{11}x_1 + M_{12}x_2 = 0, \qquad M_{21}x_1 + M_{22}x_2 = 0,$$

representing the loci of the points for which $dx_1 = 0$, $dx_2 = 0$, as well as those of the lines

$$(10) \qquad (M_{11} - \lambda_1)x_1 + M_{12}x_2 = 0, \qquad (M_{11} - \lambda_2)x_1 + M_{12}x_2 = 0,$$

representing the loci of the points for which the changes in outputs (dx_1, dx_2) are proportionate to the outputs (x_1, x_2). [The lines (10) are not necessarily real.]

A second family of isodromes is determined by (N). If the curves (r_1) and (r_2) are added to the picture, then, from any initial position, the evolution of the system (x_1, x_2) is perfectly determined. This is described in general by a cobweb-like path (Figure 2) with finite or infinite turning points, depending on the particular shapes of the curves here involved and on the initial position.

A simple illustration of the above scheme is the famous cobweb problem of supply and demand. In this case the isodromes (M) and (N) are given, respectively, by the differential equations

$$(11) \qquad dx = 0, \qquad dy = 0,$$

---

[11] The isodromes will not be altered if the right-hand sides of the system (M) are multiplied by the same (arbitrary) function of (x_1, x_2) of constant sign.

where x is price and y is quantity. The rules r_1 and r_2 are represented by the demand and supply curves,

$$(12) \qquad x = D(y), \qquad y = S(x).$$

The direction of movement on the isodromes (M) is toward (r_1), and on (N) toward (r_2).

4. The Leontief model is a particular case of the model considered in the preceding section.

From (F_1) and (F_2) we obtain

$$(13) \qquad \begin{array}{l} \left| \, b \, \right| \dot{x}_1 = \beta_{11} x_1 + \beta_{12} x_2, \\[4pt] \left| \, b \, \right| \dot{x}_2 = \beta_{21} x_1 + \beta_{22} x_2, \end{array}$$

where

$$(14) \qquad \begin{array}{ll} \beta_{11} = b_{22} + a_{12} b_{21}, & \beta_{12} = -(b_{21} + a_{21} b_{22}), \\[4pt] \beta_{21} = -(b_{12} + a_{12} b_{11}), & \beta_{22} = b_{11} + a_{21} b_{12}. \end{array}$$

An alternative formulation of the same system can be made in terms of stocks. The *proper* stock of the commodity G_i in the industry producing G_k is $b_{ki} x_k$. Therefore, X_1 and X_2 being the total stocks,

$$(15) \qquad X_1 = b_{11} x_1 + b_{21} x_2, \qquad X_2 = b_{12} x_1 + b_{22} x_2.$$

Furthermore,

$$(16) \qquad \dot{X}_1 = x_1 - a_{21} x_2, \qquad \dot{X}_2 = x_2 - a_{12} x_1.$$

Eliminating x_1 and x_2, we obtain a system similar to (13), namely

$$(17) \qquad \begin{vmatrix} X_1 & b_{11} & b_{21} \\ X_2 & b_{12} & b_{22} \\ \dot{X}_1 & 1 & -a_{21} \end{vmatrix} = 0, \qquad \begin{vmatrix} X_1 & b_{11} & b_{21} \\ X_2 & b_{12} & b_{22} \\ \dot{X}_2 & -a_{12} & 1 \end{vmatrix} = 0.$$

It is further seen that

$$(18) \qquad \left| \, \beta \, \right| = \left| \, a \, \right| \left| \, b \, \right|.$$

We shall not deal with the case $\left| \, b \, \right| = 0$, where the system (13) is either impossible or indeterminate. But let us consider the special case where $\left| \, a \, \right| = 0$. This leads to

$$(19) \qquad (b_{11} + b_{12} a_{21}) a_{12} \, dx_1 + (b_{22} + b_{21} a_{12}) \, dx_2 = 0,$$

provided $x_1 - a_{21} x_2 \neq 0$. Therefore the (M) isodromes are parallel straight lines. It is seen that the direction of movement depends on the sign of $\left| \, b \, \right|$, except in the case where the initial position of the economic model lies on the straight line $x_1 - a_{21} x_2 = 0$ (or $x_2 - a_{12} x_1 = 0$).

In this case we have $dx_1 = 0$, $dx_2 = 0$. This means that the straight line $x_1 - a_{21}x_2 = 0$ is the locus of static equilibria. If the system is not in static equilibrium from the beginning, the system will tend toward such an equilibrium along an isodrome (19) if $|b| < 0$, or away from static equilibrium if $|b| > 0$. (Figure 3 represents the case $|b| < 0$.) If $|b| > 0$, we have a typical case of unstable static equilibrium.

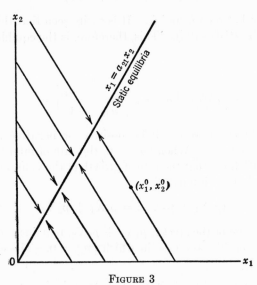

FIGURE 3

Furthermore, if the initial position is not one of static equilibrium, the economic system will not be static, nor will it expand at a constant rate of growth. Nevertheless the rate of interest will be zero. This constitutes a peculiar example of the rate of interest being zero, though the stocks are not constant. Only their total value remains constant.

If i is the instantaneous rate of interest and p_1, p_2 the prices of the two commodities, the equality between prices and average cost leads to

(20)
$$(b_{11}p_1 + b_{12}p_2)i + a_{12}p_2 = p_1,$$

$$(b_{21}p_1 + b_{22}p_2)i + a_{21}p_1 = p_2.$$

As prices must be positive, we have

(21)
$$e(i) = \begin{vmatrix} b_{11}i - 1 & b_{12}i + a_{12} \\ b_{21}i + a_{21} & b_{22}i - 1 \end{vmatrix} = 0$$

and

(22) $(b_{11}i - 1)(b_{12}i + a_{12}) < 0$, $\qquad (b_{21}i + a_{21})(b_{22}i - 1) < 0$;

the last two relations being equivalent if taken together with (21). Let

$$(23) \qquad i_0 = \text{the greatest} \left(-\frac{a_{ik}}{b_{ik}} \right), \qquad i_1 = \text{the smallest} \left(\frac{1}{b_{ii}} \right).$$

As

$$(24) \qquad e(i_0) > 0, \qquad e(i_1) < 0,$$

(21) has a root between i_0 and i_1. It is easily seen that this root is the only one which satisfies (22). This, therefore, is the equilibrium rate of interest.

But

$$(25) \qquad e(0) = |\,a\,| = \begin{vmatrix} -1 & a_{12} \\ a_{21} & -1 \end{vmatrix}.$$

Hence the rate of interest will be positive or negative according to whether $|\,a\,| >$ or < 0. When $|\,a\,| = 0$, the rate of interest is zero.

From (20) it follows that the rate of growth of the value of total stocks is equal to the rate of interest,

$$(26) \qquad (p_1 X_1 + p_2 X_2)i = p_1 \dot{X}_1 + p_2 \dot{X}_2.$$

If $i = 0$, the value of the stocks, $p_1 X_1 + p_2 X_2$, remains constant.

Let us now consider the case in which $|\,a\,| \neq 0$. The characteristic equation of (13),

$$(27) \qquad \psi(\lambda) = |\,b\,|\lambda^2 - (\beta_{11} + \beta_{22})\lambda + |\,a\,| = 0,$$

has the real roots λ_1 and λ_2, since

$$(28) \qquad (\beta_{11} + \beta_{22})^2 - 4|\,a\,|\,|\,b\,| = (\beta_{11} - \beta_{22})^2 + 4\beta_{12}\beta_{21} > 0.$$

There are several alternatives, which shall be examined in turn.

(a) $|\,b\,| > 0$, $|\,a\,| > 0$. This leads to $\lambda_2 > \lambda_1 > 0$. From (28) it follows that

$$(29) \qquad \beta_{ii} - \lambda_1|\,b\,| > 0, \qquad \beta_{ii} - \lambda_2|\,b\,| > 0,$$

and consequently the straight line (δ_k),

$$(30) \qquad (\beta_{11} - \lambda_k|\,b\,|)x_1 + \beta_{12}x_2 = 0$$

or

$$\beta_{21}x_1 + (\beta_{22} - \lambda_k|\,b\,|)x_2 = 0,$$

lies in the positive quadrant only for $k = 1$; it also lies between

$$(31) \qquad \begin{aligned} (\Delta_1)|\,b\,|\dot{x}_1 &= \beta_{11}x_1 + \beta_{12}x_2 = 0, \\ (\Delta_2)|\,b\,|\dot{x}_2 &= \beta_{21}x_1 + \beta_{22}x_2 = 0. \end{aligned}$$

All the isodromes are tangent to (δ_1) in O.   The direction of movement is away from the origin (Figure 4a).

If the initial position belongs to (δ_1),

$$(32) \qquad\qquad \dot{x}_1 = \lambda_1 x_1, \qquad \dot{x}_2 = \lambda_1 x_2,$$

and the system will expand at a constant rate of growth.   In all other cases, sooner or later, one of the outputs, x_1 or x_2, will expand at the expense of the other until this becomes zero.   The dynamic equilibrium is, in Samuelson's sense, unstable [Samuelson, 1947, pp. 266 ff.].

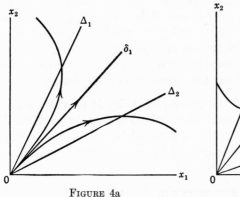

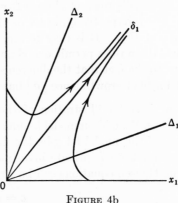

FIGURE 4a   FIGURE 4b

(b) $\left| b \right| < 0, \left| a \right| < 0$.   This leads to $\lambda_2 < \lambda_1 < 0$.   It is seen, in a similar way, that the shape of the isodromes is the same as those of (a), with the exception that the direction of movement is toward the origin.   The economy will end in all cases by contracting toward zero production.   The dynamic equilibrium is stable.

(c) $\left| b \right| < 0, \left| a \right| > 0$.   This leads to $\lambda_2 < 0 < \lambda_1$.   The shape of the isodromes is that shown in Figure 4b.   In all cases the system ends by expanding and tends toward the same equilibrium position represented by a point at infinity on (δ_1).   The dynamic equilibrium is stable.

(d) $\left| b \right| > 0, \left| a \right| < 0$.   This leads to $\lambda_1 < 0 < \lambda_2$.   The shape of the isodromes is similar to that of Figure 4b, but the sense of the movement is reversed.   The dynamic equilibrium is unstable.

Summing up the preceding results shows that (i) the sign of $\left| b \right|$ decides the dynamic stability of the system, and (ii) the sign of $\left| a \right|$ determines the sign of the rate of interest (i.e., whether the system is contracting or expanding).

It is also seen that the existence of a static solution in von Neumann's sense [von Neumann, 1945] (i.e., where the economy will expand (or contract) proportionately in all sectors) is possible only if the initial position lies on (δ_1).

If the system (F_2) is now considered, it is seen that $|b|$ becomes

$$(33) \qquad\qquad b' = -b_{12}b_{21} < 0,$$

and consequently the system will be dynamically stable [cases (b) and (c)]. Furthermore, (13) becomes

$$(34) \qquad \begin{aligned} b'\dot{x}_1 &= \beta_{11}x_1 + \beta_{12}x_2, \\ b'\dot{x}_2 &= -b_{12}x_1 + a_{21}b_{12}x_2. \end{aligned}$$

Consequently Δ_1 in (F_2) is identical with Δ_1 in (F_1).

Leontief's rules of change from (F_1) to (F_2) and vice versa are formulated, respectively, in terms of $\dot{x}_1$ and of the value of x_1 at the beginning of (F_2). It is easy to see, by using the results of (a)–(d) above, that these rules permit one change at most from (F_1) to (F_2). This is due to the fact that the difference between (F_1) and (F_2) does not affect the rate of growth since $|a|$ has the same sign in both phases.

5. A better illustration of the phase-periodicity is provided by the Hansen-Samuelson model [Samuelson, 1939]. For a continuous formulation of this model let y be the flow of national income at the time t; c, consumption; I, private investment; and g, governmental expenditure. The Hansen equations can be written [12]

$$(35) \qquad \begin{aligned} c &= \alpha y - \alpha'\dot{y}, \\ I &= \beta'\dot{c}, \\ y &= I + c + g, \end{aligned}$$

with $0 < \alpha \leqq 1$, and α', β' positive.

We obtain, further,

$$(36) \qquad \begin{aligned} \alpha'\dot{y} &= \alpha y - c, \\ \beta'\dot{c} &= y - c - g, \end{aligned}$$

which, through the simple transformations

$$(37) \quad t = \frac{\alpha'T}{\alpha}, \qquad \beta = \frac{\alpha\beta'}{\alpha'}, \qquad y = Y + \frac{g}{1-\alpha}, \qquad c = C + \frac{\alpha g}{1-\alpha},$$

where T is a new time unit, becomes

$$(38) \qquad \begin{aligned} \alpha\dot{Y} &= \alpha Y - C, \\ \beta\dot{C} &= Y - C. \end{aligned}$$

---

[12] Samuelson's formulation is discontinuous [Samuelson, 1939, p. 76]. It must be remarked that Samuelson's formulation, and therefore (35), does not reveal the source of g [Samuelson, 1939, Table I]. A model in which g is treated in a more explicit way would constitute a better analytical tool. The incidence of tax shifts are considered in the concluding part of this chapter.

This is a linear dynamic model of type (M), the characteristic equation being

(39) $\alpha\beta\lambda^2 + (\alpha - \alpha\beta)\lambda + 1 - \alpha = 0.$

Under the assumption that $\alpha \leqq 1$, the solution of (38) depends on the position of (α, β) with respect to the curve (Figure 5) [13]

(40) $\alpha = \dfrac{4\beta}{(1 + \beta)^2}.$

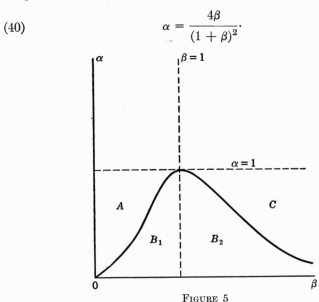

FIGURE 5

The shapes of the isodromes are represented in Figure 6 according to the region where (α, β) lies. The result can be summarized as follows:

Region	Stability *
A	Perfect
$A \cap B_1$	Perfect
B_1	Perfect
$B_1 \cap B_2$	Unstable (cyclic)
B_2	Unstable
$B_2 \cap C$	Partially stable
C	Partially stable

* Stability is considered here in Samuelson's sense (i.e., stability is perfect when any displacement, although shifting the system to another isodrome, will not change the limit toward which the system tends). This limit may be regarded as a possible static solution. The term "partially stable" refers to the case where the system will tend toward the same limit only for some (not all) finite displacements [Samuelson, 1947, p. 262].

[13] Cf. Samuelson [1939, p. 78]. The regions considered here differ somewhat from those used by Samuelson.

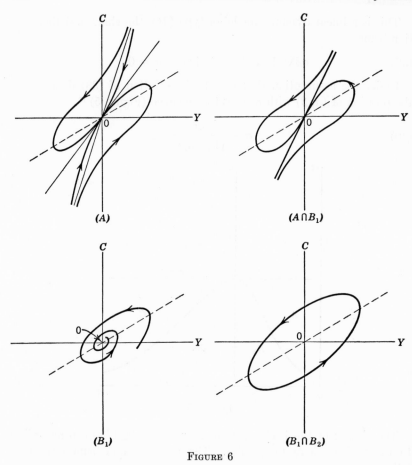

$$(A) \qquad (A \cap B_1)$$

$$(B_1) \qquad (B_1 \cap B_2)$$

FIGURE 6

If we now assume that, soon after income reaches its maximum (i.e., $\dot{Y} = 0$), the propensity to consume, α, increases [Duesenberry, 1948; Modigliani, 1949], or β, "the relation," decreases, or both these things happen simultaneously, there will be a turning point at which a relaxation phenomenon will take place. As an illustration, let us assume that only β decreases from $\beta = 1$ to a point in B_1. The system will become a contracting one instead of a cyclic one. If we assume still further that, as the consumption-income ratio reaches a certain level, the value of β will recover its former value, the system will follow a cobweb path which will lead, generally but not necessarily, to a contraction toward the origin.

Finally, another illustration of the usefulness of the analysis based on isodromes is given by the question whether a fiscal policy aimed at

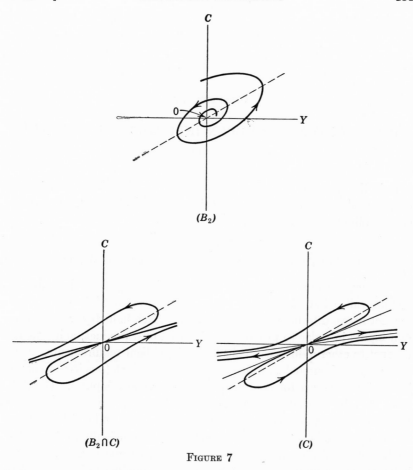

FIGURE 7

decreasing consumption and increasing investment could definitively cure a system having a tendency to consume all its income.   The answer is easily obtained by inspecting the shape of the isodromes in Figure 7. If the assumptions underlying the model and also those regarding the invariability of α and β under changing fiscal policies are accepted, it is seen that in the case of C and $B_2 \cap C$ one shift through taxation may be sufficient definitively to cure the tendency of the system toward disinvesting.   In all other cases the tax must be applied periodically. Furthermore, in order to insure the shifting of the system to a "higher" isodrome by means of only a small tax, the tax must be applied immediately *before* the income reaches its maximum (i.e., before the isodromes reach the straight line $\alpha Y - C = 0$).

Chapter VI

USES OF LEONTIEF'S OPEN INPUT-OUTPUT MODELS [1]

By Harlan M. Smith

It is the purpose of this chapter to explain Leontief's open input-output models, to discuss some of their uses and limitations, and to suggest an alternative model.

1. The Basic Notion of an Input-Output Model

The economy of a country may be divided into any desired number of sectors, called industries, each consisting of firms producing a similar but not necessarily homogeneous product. Each industry requires certain inputs in order to produce a unit of its own product, and sells its product to other industries to meet their ingredient requirements. One "industry" is households, which furnishes its product (services) to other industries in return for consumer goods (household inputs). Government may be treated as an industry which makes payments to other sectors of the economy in return for goods or services and which provides services (its product) the costs of which are met principally by tax levies on the other sectors of the economy. Foreign trade is treated as an industry whose inputs are exports and whose product is imports. Investment is treated, not as a separate industry, but as a portion of the inputs of the several industries.

The transfers of products among the various sectors of the economy can be shown in a table which can be read both vertically and horizontally. Read horizontally, each row shows the disposal of an industry's total product for the given year among other sectors of the economy. Read vertically, each column shows the total inputs used by an industry in the given year in production and investment. Equations (1) represent in generalized form the distribution of each industry's product:

[1] I am indebted to Professors Tjalling C. Koopmans and Paul A. Samuelson for helpful suggestions in the preparation of this chapter.

$$X_1 - x_{21} - x_{31} - \cdots - x_{i1} - \cdots - x_{n1} = 0$$

$$-x_{12} + X_2 - x_{32} - \cdots - x_{i2} - \cdots - x_{n2} = 0$$

$$\cdot \quad \cdot \quad \cdot \quad \cdot \quad \cdot \quad \cdot \quad \cdot \quad \cdot \quad \cdot \quad \cdot \quad \cdot \quad \cdot \quad \cdot \quad \cdot \quad \cdot \quad \cdot \quad \cdot$$

(1)
$$-x_{1i} - x_{2i} - x_{3i} - \cdots + X_i - \cdots - x_{ni} = 0$$

$$\cdot \quad \cdot \quad \cdot \quad \cdot \quad \cdot \quad \cdot \quad \cdot \quad \cdot \quad \cdot \quad \cdot \quad \cdot \quad \cdot \quad \cdot \quad \cdot \quad \cdot \quad \cdot \quad \cdot$$

$$-x_{1n} - x_{2n} - x_{3n} - \cdots - x_{in} - \cdots + X_n = 0.$$

The large X's stand for the total physical outputs of the industries, in units of a dollar's worth of each product in some base year. Each small x indicates the quantity of a product, denoted by the second subscript, used by the industry, denoted by the first subscript.

The relationships between the amounts of various products consumed by each industry and the total output of the industry may be represented by a set of input coefficients,

$$a_{ik} = x_{ik}/X_i.$$

If we assume the input coefficients to be technologically fixed, the economic system may be represented by the following set of linear homogeneous equations:

$$X_1 - a_{21}X_2 - a_{31}X_3 - \cdots - a_{i1}X_i - \cdots - a_{n1}X_n = 0$$

$$-a_{12}X_1 + \quad X_2 - a_{32}X_3 - \cdots - a_{i2}X_i - \cdots - a_{n2}X_n = 0$$

$$\cdot \quad \cdot \quad \cdot \quad \cdot \quad \cdot \quad \cdot \quad \cdot \quad \cdot \quad \cdot \quad \cdot \quad \cdot \quad \cdot \quad \cdot \quad \cdot \quad \cdot \quad \cdot \quad \cdot$$

(2)
$$-a_{1i}X_1 - a_{2i}X_2 - a_{3i}X_3 - \cdots + \quad X_i - \cdots - a_{ni}X_n = 0$$

$$\cdot \quad \cdot \quad \cdot \quad \cdot \quad \cdot \quad \cdot \quad \cdot \quad \cdot \quad \cdot \quad \cdot \quad \cdot \quad \cdot \quad \cdot \quad \cdot \quad \cdot \quad \cdot \quad \cdot$$

$$-a_{1n}X_1 - a_{2n}X_2 - a_{3n}X_3 - \cdots - a_{in}X_i - \cdots + \quad X_n = 0.$$

This system of n equations in n unknowns will have a nontrivial solution only if its determinant, D, vanishes. In that case we can solve for the *relative* values of the variables uniquely if not all the minors of D vanish. Specification of the absolute level of any element of the equations then determines the *absolute* level of all the variables. A more complicated closed system has been developed by Wassily Leontief [1941] to represent the American economy.

2. Open Models and the Concept of Final Demand

In the above we dealt with a closed system which had no exogenous variables. We now examine what may be called *open models* in which certain of the variables are treated as determined outside the models (i.e., certain variables are determined independently of the relationships which define the models and are taken as given so far as the models are concerned).

In two articles [1944, 1946a], Leontief asks what quantity of output and employment in each industry is associated with (and necessary for) the production of a given bill of goods, called *final demand*. Final demand is, in one case, a given quantity of household purchases of various products. If households are represented in equations (1) by the subscript n, the last term on the left side of each of these equations is transferred to the right side and treated as a constant or fixed bill of goods for the production of which certain outputs of other industries are required. In system (2), the last equation is deleted, and the last term on the left side of each remaining equation is replaced by a constant on the right side; thus an open model is obtained. The equation system so obtained is

$$X_1 - a_{21}X_2 - a_{31}X_3 - \cdots - a_{i1}X_i - \cdots - a_{m1}X_m = x_{n1}$$

$$a_{12}X_1 + \quad X_2 - a_{32}X_3 - \cdots - a_{i2}X_i - \cdots - a_{m2}X_m = x_{n2}$$

(2a)

$$-a_{1i}X_1 - a_{2i}X_2 - a_{3i}X_3 - \cdots + \quad X_i - \cdots - a_{mi}X_m = x_{ni}$$

$$-a_{1m}X_1 - a_{2m}X_2 - a_{3m}X_3 - \cdots - a_{im}X_i - \cdots + \quad X_m = x_{nm},$$

where m is short for $n - 1$.

If we do not restrict the choice of the bill of goods $(x_{n1}, \cdots, x_{nm})$, this system can be solved only if the new determinant, D_{mm}, of its coefficients in the left-hand member does not vanish. The solution for $X_1, \cdots, X_m$ is then as follows:

$$X_1 = A_{11}x_{n1} + A_{12}x_{n2} + A_{13}x_{n3} + \cdots + A_{1i}x_{ni} + \cdots + A_{1m}x_{nm}$$

$$X_2 = A_{21}x_{n1} + A_{22}x_{n2} + A_{23}x_{n3} + \cdots + A_{2i}x_{ni} + \cdots + A_{2m}x_{nm}$$

$$X_3 = A_{31}x_{n1} + A_{32}x_{n2} + A_{33}x_{n3} + \cdots + A_{3i}x_{ni} + \cdots + A_{3m}x_{nm}$$

(3)

$$X_i = A_{i1}x_{n1} + A_{i2}x_{n2} + A_{i3}x_{n3} + \cdots + A_{ii}x_{ni} + \cdots + A_{im}x_{nm}$$

$$X_m = A_{m1}x_{n1} + A_{m2}x_{n2} + A_{m3}x_{n3} + \cdots + A_{mi}x_{ni} + \cdots + A_{mm}x_{nm}.$$

The dependence of output and employment on the final demand in each industry is now apparent. The term $A_{12}x_{n2}$ represents that part of industry 1's output which is due to the final demand for x_{n2} units of commodity 2. This magnitude is based on the technical input coefficients of all the industries except households.

Also, employment by industries can be obtained by applying the appropriate (labor) input coefficients to the expressions for total outputs given in (3). Thus employment in industry 1 depends on the items in the bill of goods as follows:

$$x_{1n} = a_{1n}X_1 = a_{1n}A_{11}x_{n1} + a_{1n}A_{12}x_{n2} + \cdots + a_{1n}A_{1m}x_{nm}.$$

Employment in industry 2 is related to items in the bill of goods similarly:

$$x_{2n} = a_{2n}X_2 = a_{2n}A_{21}x_{n1} + a_{2n}A_{22}x_{n2} + \cdots + a_{2n}A_{2m}x_{nm}.$$

Total employment is the sum of such expressions for every industry; summing these expressions and collecting terms yields a coefficient for each element of final demand. For example, the total labor coefficient of x_{n1} is $(a_{1n}A_{11} + a_{2n}A_{21} + \cdots + a_{mn}A_{m1})$. This indicates the contribution to total employment per unit of commodity 1 entered in the final bill of goods, and hence Leontief calls this a total employment coefficient; the direct employment coefficient for x_{n1} is in this case the first term in the parentheses. (For the ith consumption good the direct employment coefficient would be $a_{in}A_{ii}$.) If the final demand for commodity 1 is changed, the change in employment in industry 1 is given by application of the direct employment coefficient and the change in total employment by application of the total employment coefficient. Leontief has computed such coefficients on the basis of 1939 data, the economy being divided into ten industries, plus households (consumption data being the bill of goods), and labor input coefficients being based on actual number of persons employed rather than on value (i.e., wage) figures.

Similarly Leontief investigates the output and employment in each industry dependent on foreign trade. In one model the bill of goods is constituted by total U. S. exports plus domestic investment plus household consumption; in another model, household consumption is excluded from the given bill of goods and treated as a dependent variable along with the inputs and outputs of other industries; in a third model, the bill of goods consists of U. S. domestic and foreign investment (the latter being an export surplus of various products). These models differ from that dealing with final household demand alone in that different sets of equations and hence different sets of input coefficients are discarded in making the computations after the selected inputs have been transferred to the right side of the equations and treated as constants.

3. Limitations of Leontief's Method

Although there are no limits to the number of models which might be constructed on the above lines, there are certain limitations to any such models. In any open models constructed like those of Leontief, a reduction of the bill of goods to zero reduces the outputs and employment of all industries to zero. This does not make very good sense. If, for example, domestic and foreign investment constituted the bill of goods, we would not expect their disappearance to reduce output and employment in all industries to zero. Leontief recognizes this shortcoming of his models and suggests that the use of a linear employment-consumption relationship results in a probable overstatement of the volume of employment dependent on any given bill of goods [Leontief, 1946a]. Leontief could have corrected this defect by introducing a set of constant terms into the household input equations as follows: $x_{ni} = a_{ni}X_n + k_{ni}$. The statistical determination of these constants would be necessary, along with the determination of the input coefficients; this would be a difficult task.

The concept of final demand itself implies a certain limitation of the uses to which the above type of open model may be put. Such a model cannot answer the question, "What is the total effect on output and employment in each and every industry if some one industry makes a new investment for which it uses such-and-such quantities of various products?" Suppose, for example, that industry 1 makes a certain investment the effects of which we wish to investigate. This investment is in the form of an outlay for certain quantities of products of other industries and comes in addition to the outlays for ingredients required for the production of current output of industry 1 with a given productive process. Any manipulations of the input-output model which leave the input of industry 1 in the matrix will treat those inputs as entirely dependent on the output of industry 1 and thus prevent the introduction of an independently determined amount of investment. In order to treat the outlay of that industry as an independent variable, we may transfer the inputs of the industry to the bill of goods and drop the appropriate equation from the system. When this is done, the chosen investment may be made by increases in various items in the bill of goods, and the effects on the outputs of other industries may be computed. However, if the other industries use the product of industry 1 in their productive processes, an increase in their outputs will entail greater current production by industry 1 in order to meet their factor requirements. But, by placing the inputs of industry 1 in the bill of goods, their magnitude was fixed; industry 1 is "not allowed" to increase its inputs further in order to increase its output.   If we repeat the process and insert the newly required inputs as another "independent" increase in the bill of goods, this raises the same problem again when its effects are computed.

The results on other industries of the new investment by industry 1, as given by an open model with the inputs of industry 1 in the bill of goods, may be interpreted in either of two ways.   We may say that the model excludes the "feed-back" effects (i.e., the repercussions which flow from the fact that the expansion of the system requires an increase in the output of industry 1 and hence a further increase in its inputs). The full effect could be obtained from the model only if the correct final input totals of industry 1 were placed in the bill of goods, but these totals are not known in advance merely from the size of the investment to be made.

An alternative interpretation may be given the results of the model. It may be assumed that the increased use of the product of industry 1 by other industries is made possible either by drawing upon inventories of the product or by the use of some inputs by industry 1 for current production instead of for the intended investment purposes.   In such cases, however, the computed employment coefficients do not measure the effect of an investment of a prescribed magnitude since the initial (or intended) investment is offset by disinvestment (or failure to invest) to an extent unknown and dependent on the magnitude of the feed-back effects.   The model gives the total effect of a net investment smaller than that which we wished to introduce, and relates that effect to the bill of goods magnitudes, which magnitudes must be taken to include the feed-back effects on industry 1 of a lesser initial investment by the industry.

In the open model which places the inputs of an investing industry in the bill of goods in order to compute the effects of investment by that industry, then, we must interpret the coefficients which relate items in the bill of goods to output or employment in the several industries as either ruling out the circular effect on the investing industry or as relating part of the final effect to all of it.   Owing to the element of circularity, the model cannot tell us the relationship between some initial stimulus and its final effect, for a further addition to the inputs of the investing industry, consequent upon the response of other industries to the investment purchases, must itself have further effects on the supplying industries.   This fact limits the usefulness of the open models we have discussed; they show only the outputs of various industries associated with a given total quantity of inputs (or total increase in inputs) in the bill of goods.

The concept of final demand is appropriate, however, to a different type of inquiry. We may ask, for example, "What will be the pattern of production and employment associated with any given volume of exports or of household consumption of each product?" Leontief's open models are designed to answer this type of question.

The different open models discussed by Leontief, and the alternative models of the same type which could be constructed, do not, however, yield identical sets of coefficients showing the relationships between output or employment in the various industries and the final demand for each product. The different construction of the several open models (i.e., the transference to the bill of goods of the inputs of different industries and the elimination of different equations and sets of input coefficients) necessarily results in different relationships between a unit of final demand and the output of any industry. Thus, when Leontief investigated the employment associated with a given household demand, household inputs were placed in the bill of goods and the household equation was dropped from the system; when the effects of exports were being investigated, exports were placed in the bill of goods and the foreign trade equation was dropped. But there is no reason why an increase of a unit in final demand for some product should require different amounts of employment in various industries depending on whether that unit of some product was exported or was obtained by households, by investors in one industry or in another, or by government.

The technique of producing the product is the same in any case, so the problem could be regarded as one of investigating the effects of an increase in output of some product without regard to the industry classification of the purchasers of that additional output. Which open model of Leontief's, or of the same type, gives the answer, then, to the question, "How much employment in each industry is associated with a specified increase in the total output of some product?"? Strictly speaking, none of the models answers the question in just this form. Each model tells only how much added employment in each industry is associated with a given final increase in consumption of a product by the sectors of the economy whose inputs constitute the bill of goods of that particular model. Each such result is based on the assumptions which determine uniquely the structure of each model. These are assumptions concerning which industries produce under conditions of fixed input coefficients and concerning the absolute input quantities of the remainder of the economy, the bill of goods containing in each case the inputs of the industry for which the effects of increased outlays are being investigated. Structural steel for a bridge might be used, for example, by the railroads for a railway bridge, by the government for a highway bridge, or might be exported for construction of a bridge in a foreign country. The employment required in the various industries to produce the steel does not really depend on which of these three dispositions is made of the steel. But the input-output models will give three different answers as to the employment effect, for, in the one case, the bill of goods would contain all railroad industry inputs; in another, the government inputs; and in the third, exports; and different equations would be dropped from the system in making the computations in these three cases. This makes the relationship between the increase in the total output of a commodity and the associated increases in employment in the various industries depend on the industry classification of the consumer of the additional output of the commodity in question. Thus, even for the type of question which the open models discussed have been designed to answer, they give answers whose interpretation is severely restrictive.

The problems of circularity and of the interpretation of the results given by different input-output models are essentially problems that were noted in discussions of the theory of the multiplier. Each of the models discussed above makes different assumptions about induced effects,[2] and consequently a different result follows, for a different formula is involved in the computations. Just as each change in the definition of the multiplicand requires the use of a different multiplier, so a change in the definition of the bill of goods requires a different set of employment coefficients to relate items in the bill of goods to total employment in the various industries. However, if what we want to know is the total effect of a given autonomous change in outlays for a certain product by any sector of the economy, then a formula or coefficient which rules out certain induced effects is not useful for the purpose, even if accurately computed on the basis of its own assumptions. It is in the category of what Samuelson has called a "pseudo-multiplier" [Samuelson, 1948].

4. An Autonomous-Expenditure Model

The following open input-output model can be used to escape the limitations of the models discussed thus far. It is characterized chiefly by a bill of goods in which all autonomous expenditures are placed. In order to admit the circular effect explained above and to get coefficients, not varying with the industry classification of the spending unit,

---

[2] Changes in the inputs of an industry due to changes in the industry's output are induced changes; excluding different equations from the matrix in different models is a change of assumptions regarding induced effects.

which relate a given additional input to the total consequent increase in employment in every industry, it is necessary to include every industry and its input coefficients in the matrix used for the computations. However, if the input coefficients of the closed model are used, no industry can increase its investment inputs relative to its output, and an attempt on its part to do so must lead to an infinite rise in all variables of the model. A bill of goods including all autonomous expenditures cannot be added to the closed model except by an appropriate adjustment of the input coefficients.[3]

If the bill of goods is to represent autonomous expenditures (inputs) by any and all industries, adjusted input coefficients may be obtained by classifying the inputs of the base period by whether they were or were not dependent on and required for the production of the current outputs of the industries using them (i.e., by whether inputs represented necessary or autonomous expenditures). The latter may be placed in the bill of goods and the former used to compute input coefficients. However, it is very difficult to make this distinction between autonomous and induced inputs in statistical data. If one is interested in predicting the effects of future changes in certain inputs, the data of some base period are at best a guide to the choice of appropriate input coefficients for the model. It may be possible, therefore, to use supplementary information, such as technological data on input requirements, in estimating the input coefficients applicable to the situation being studied.

There are two industries, in addition to households, which were discussed above, that are not restricted to the same degree as other industries by technological factors in the relationships between their total receipts and their specific outlays. These industries are government and foreign trade; their inputs may be treated as autonomous if so desired. Government expenditures per dollar of total receipts may be rather freely varied by legislative bodies. This provides an argument for excluding government input-output ratios from the model and for placing government inputs in the bill of goods as autonomous. However, some government expenditures may be "automatically" increased under a given set of laws as government receipts rise or fall. For example, unemployment insurance payments may increase as tax receipts fall. Expenditures which vary with government receipts may be treated as induced by dividing the government inputs into autonomous and induced parts and inserting into the matrix the input coefficients applicable to the latter part.

[3] The mathematical reason for this statement lies in the vanishing of D in (2).

Increased imports may not call for immediate increases in exports and in any case may be paid for by equivalent exports of products in any proportions. The justification, if any, for using a particular set of input coefficients for foreign trade, instead of placing exports in the bill of goods, must be that the coefficients indicate the likely increases in exports induced by an increase in imports.

Since some investment may be induced rather than autonomous, investment inputs, by all industries, should be divided between induced and autonomous investment, with the former covered by the input coefficients and the latter in the bill of goods. The bill of goods of this model should then consist of all autonomous expenditures and the minimum household consumption of the various products. The model so obtained would again be described by equations (2a), but the interpretation of the quantities occurring in the right-hand members (bill of goods) is changed as indicated.

A model constructed in this fashion may be said to provide a means of breaking down an aggregate multiplier into specific multipliers, each of which indicates the total effect on output or employment in a specific industry of a given autonomous expenditure on (i.e., increased input of) a specific product. The breakdown is made on the assumptions of fixed input coefficients and unemployment, but the results are invariant with respect to the industry classifications of the spending unit.

CHAPTER VII

ABSTRACT OF A THEOREM CONCERNING
SUBSTITUTABILITY IN OPEN LEONTIEF MODELS

By Paul A. Samuelson

Leontief [1941, 1946a] assumes that total production of each of n outputs, $x_1, \cdots, x_n$, is divided up into final outputs, $C_1, \cdots, C_n$, and into inputs used to help produce (with labor) all the inputs. Hence, for all i,

$$x_i = C_i + \sum_{j=1}^{n} x_{ji} \qquad (i = 1, 2, \cdots, n).$$

Labor, the $(n-1)$th good, can be thought of as the sole "primary factor" or "nonproduced good," and its given total is allocated among all the different industries as follows:

$$x_{n+1} = 0 + \sum_{j=1}^{n} x_{j,\,n+1}.$$

Note that joint products are ruled out, so the x_{ji}'s are functionally independent.

Since Leontief works with so-called "fixed" coefficients of production, it is usually thought that he must try to approximate reality by a produc-

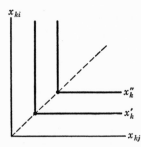

FIGURE 1a—Equal output curves for x_k with fixed coefficients.

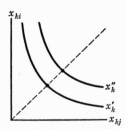

FIGURE 1b—General equal output curves for x_k.

tion function of the form shown in Figure 1a, rather than of the more general form admitting of substitution as shown in Figure 1b. Actually, *all* his theory in its present form is compatible with the more general case of substitutability. With labor the only primary factor, *all desirable substitutions have already been made by the competitive market,* and no variation in the composition of final output or in the total quantity of labor will give rise to price change or substitution. Only the circled points in Figure 1b will ever be observed. The following discussion shows that this is a property of the efficiency frontier always reached under competition.

1. Let each good be subject to a production function, homogeneous of the first order,

$$(1) \qquad x_i = F_i(x_{i1}, x_{i2}, \cdots, x_{i, n+1}) = mF_i\left(\frac{x_{i1}}{m}, \cdots, \frac{x_{i, n+1}}{m}\right).$$

Our equilibrium requires that any C, such as C_1, be at a maximum subject to fixed values of total labor, x_{n+1}, and all other C's; that is,

$$C_1 = F_1(x_{11}, x_{12}, \cdots, x_{1, n+1}) - \sum_{j=1}^{n} x_{j1}$$

is to be a maximum subject to

$$(2) \qquad F_i(x_{i1}, x_{i2}, \cdots, x_{i, n+1}) - \sum_{j=1}^{n} x_{ji} = C_i \qquad (i = 2, 3, \cdots, n),$$

$$0 - \sum_{j=1}^{n} x_{j, n+1} = -x_{n+1},$$

where F_{n+1}, the amount of labor produced, can be set equal to zero. We have the $n(n + 1)$ variables of the form x_{ij} to determine. We assume that with a finite amount of labor some finite quantity of each good is producible.

2. Because of homogeneity or constant returns to scale, the coefficients of production, $a_{ij} = x_{ij}/x_i$, are not constants but are connected by a relation of the form $F_i(a_{i1}, a_{i2}, \cdots, a_{i, n+1}) = 1$. Except for scale, this is shown in Figure 1b. Nevertheless, the following remarkable theorem holds:

THEOREM: *Regardless of the assigned values of* $C_2, C_3, \cdots, C_n, x_{n+1},$ *the optimal coefficients of production will always assume the same constant values, and the resulting production-possibility schedule for society will be of the simple linear form*

$$K_1C_1 + K_2C_2 + \cdots + K_nC_n = x_{n+1},$$

where the K's *are constants independent of the* C's *and* x_{n+1}. *It is also true that relative prices of the form* P_i/P_j *will be similar constants.*

PROOF: Form the Lagrangian expression

$$(3) \quad \lambda_1 C_1 + \lambda_2 (F_2 - \sum_{j=1}^{n} x_{j2} - C_2) + \lambda_3 (F_3 - \sum_{j=1}^{n} x_{j3} - C_3) + \cdots ,$$

and differentiate it with respect to each x_{jk}, treating the λ's as undetermined multipliers with $\lambda_1 = 1$. This gives us

$$(4) \qquad \lambda_i \frac{\partial F_i}{\partial x_{ij}} - \lambda_j = 0 \quad (i = 1, 2, \cdots, n; j = 1, 2, \cdots, n+1).$$

We can eliminate the λ's to get the equations [1]

$$(5) \qquad \frac{\partial F_1}{\partial x_{11}} = 1, \quad \frac{\partial F_1}{\partial x_{1i}} \frac{\partial F_i}{\partial x_{ij}} - \frac{\partial F_1}{\partial x_{1j}} = 0 \quad \begin{matrix} (i = 2, \cdots, n; \\ j = 1, 2, \cdots, n+1). \end{matrix}$$

There are, by (5), $1 + (n-1)(n+1)$ equations to determine our $n(n+1)$ variables x_{ij}. Their economic significance in terms of prices or equivalent marginal rates of substitution is easily expressed. The missing n equations are supplied by the specified C's and x_{n+1}. It may be added that, if we admitted the case of joint production, this simple elimination of the λ's would not be possible.

Since each of the F-functions is homogeneous of order one, each of our partial derivatives must be homogeneous of order zero (i.e., the economic assumption of constant returns to scale implies that all marginal productivities depend on the *proportions* of the inputs alone). Hence the set of equations in (5) may be written so that instead of their involving $(n^2 + n)$ x_{ij}'s they involve only the n^2 *proportions* of inputs of the form $b_{ij} = x_{ij}/x_{i, n+1}$, where i and j now range only from 1 to n.

Equation (5) *determines all the proportions,* b_{ij}, *independently of the* C's *and* x_{n+1}. With proportions always being invariant, it follows that we observe only one invariant set of "coefficients of production," a_{ij}, and the remaining assertions of the theorem are clearly implied.[2]

3. All the above is valid on the assumption that the partial derivatives of equations (5) exist everywhere and define a unique interior solution to

---

[1] Because of the necessary convexity of the F's, each of whose Hessian is required to be negative semidefinite, these necessary first order equations for a maximum are also sufficient. If some x_{ij} does not appear at all in F_i, then we drop the corresponding equation in (4), replacing it by $x_{ij} = 0$. We also make obvious modifications in (5). If a good uses no labor, we must modify our use of b's in a simple and inessential fashion.

[2] I have assumed that the price ratios are the same thing as (marginal) cost ratios, as indeed they will be if something of both goods in question is being produced.

(5). In the usual problems of linear programming, where only a finite number of activities are considered, the functions have corners at which the partial derivatives are undefined, and the optimum solution is defined by boundary inequalities rather than interior equalities of the partial derivatives. Also, we must consider the possibility that more than one set of values satisfy equations (5).

Nonetheless, the theorem remains true; a change in the bill of goods, $C_1, \cdots, C_n$, cannot make substitution profitable, and the frontier of efficiency points remains linear. A sketch of a brief but rigorous proof is as follows: [3]

First, we accept the easily proved fact that the efficiency frontier defined by our maximum problem must be a convex set in consequence of our strong homogeneity assumptions. We then show that through *any* efficient point there passes a linear hyperplane of feasible points. It must follow that the frontier locus is itself a linear hyperplane, for, if it anywhere had a corner or a curved surface, it would be impossible for us to find a hyperplane of feasible points going on all sides of the efficient point in question.

The only problem is to show that through any efficient point, $(C_1^0, C_2^0, \cdots, C_n^0, x_{n+1}^0)$, there does go a hyperplane of feasible points,

$$\sum_1^n \alpha_i (C_i - C_i^0) = x_{n+1} - x_{n+1}^0,$$

for some constant α's. Suppose that there really were absolute constant a_{ij}'s. Then it is a well-known property of Leontief systems [Leontief, 1941, 1946a] that the bill of goods is constrained to follow a linear hyperplane by the equations

$$C_i = x_i - \sum_1^n a_{ji} x_j \qquad (i = 1, 2, \cdots, n),$$

$$-x_{n+1} = -\sum_1^n a_{j,\,n+1} x_j.$$

Consider now an actual efficient point $(C_1^0, C_2^0, \cdots, C_n^0, x_{n+1}^0)$ being produced in the general case of Figure 1b by (x_{ij}^0). These quantities implicitly define a set (a_{ij}^0). Although it may not be obvious that it is *efficient* to stick to these fixed coefficients, the result will certainly be *feasible*. Hence there does exist a set of feasible points along a hyperplane through (C^0, x_{n+1}^0), and the theorem follows.

[3] I believe this argument is closely related to the more elaborate argument of Koopmans [VIII].

Less heuristically, we can easily show that

$$C_i = F_i(t_i x_{i1}, t_i x_{i2}, \cdots) - \sum_1^n x_{ki} t_k,$$

$$-x_{n+1} = -\sum_1^n x_{k,\,n+1}^0 t_k,$$

define, because of the homogeneity property of the F_i, linear parametric equations in terms of the t's; for all the t's equal to one we get $(C_1^0, \cdots, C_n^0, x_{n+1}^0)$, and for all nearby t's we get feasible points on a linear hyperplane.

Chapter VIII

ALTERNATIVE PROOF OF THE SUBSTITUTION THEOREM FOR LEONTIEF MODELS IN THE CASE OF THREE INDUSTRIES

By Tjalling C. Koopmans [1]

In the preceding chapter [VII] Samuelson arrives at an important theorem which shows that Leontief's model of interindustry relationships has a greater generality than a literal reading of its assumptions suggests. In this theorem it is assumed that

(a) each industry produces only one commodity, and

(b) each industry consumes, besides the commodities produced by other industries, only one scarce primary factor (labor), and that factor is the same for all industries.

Assuming, further, constant returns to scale in each industry, Samuelson finds that, even if each industry has a choice of many alternative processes for the production of its commodity, it is compatible with efficiency of production as a whole that each industry uses only one of the processes available to it, and this same process can be used regardless of the commodity composition of the net output of all industries taken together and regardless of the amount of labor available.

In this chapter a proof of this theorem is given which does not require that the alternative processes available to each industry can be subsumed in a production function possessing derivatives. We shall merely assume that the (finite or infinite number of) processes between which choice can be made by each industry have the properties associated in another chapter [III] with the notion of an activity:

(c) all inputs and outputs of a process can be multiplied by a non-negative scale factor (*divisibility*), and

(d) net outputs of different processes available to an industry can be added together to make a new available process (*additivity*).

Assumptions (c) and (d) are also made by Leontief for the (unique) processes characterizing the several industries. Assumption (c) is im-

[1] I am indebted to K. J. Arrow and L. Hurwicz for valuable comments regarding this chapter.

plied in Samuelson's assumption of homogeneous production functions (constant returns to scale), but his counterpart of (d) is the more restrictive assumption of differentiable production functions.

We shall explicitly use two further assumptions:

(e) it is possible for each industry to select a process from among those available to it, and a scalar level of its operation, such that the total net output of all industries is positive for each commodity (except, of course, labor), and

(f) the net output vectors of the alternative processes available to any one industry with a given labor input form a closed and bounded set in the commodity space.

Assumptions (a), (b), (c), and (d) have no economic meaning as a model of production unless Assumption (e) is satisfied, and Assumption (e) is implied in Leontief's model and in Samuelson's discussion of it. An explicit criterion for its validity has been given by Hawkins and Simon [1949] for the present model. In Chapter III, Section 3.6, the same criterion, Postulate C_1, is explored for a more general model. Arrow has proved [IX, Section 3] that a slightly weaker assumption, Postulate C_2 of Chapter III, Section 3.6, together with a further assumption excluding certain degenerate types of technology matrices, implies Assumption (e).

Assumption (f) is sufficient but not necessary for the validity of the theorem. A refinement of this assumption is also given by Arrow [IX].

In the present chapter only the case of three industries will be considered. The proof given here is generalized by Arrow in the next chapter to n industries. It appears in that generalization that the "visual" elements, intentionally employed in the present proof because they aid intuitive understanding, are not essential to the mathematical argument. We now formulate in mathematical terms the theorem to be proved.

THEOREM:[2] *Let there be three closed and bounded convex sets, S_1, S_2, S_3, of points, $y \equiv (y_1, y_2, y_3)$, in three-dimensional space with the following properties:*

(1)
$$\begin{cases} \text{if} \quad a_{(1)} \equiv (a_{11}, a_{21}, a_{31}) \, \epsilon \, S_1, \quad \text{then} \quad a_{11} > 0, \quad a_{21} \leqq 0, \quad a_{31} \leqq 0, \\ \text{if} \quad a_{(2)} \equiv (a_{12}, a_{22}, a_{32}) \, \epsilon \, S_2, \quad \text{then} \quad a_{21} \leqq 0, \quad a_{22} > 0, \quad a_{32} \leqq 0, \\ \text{if} \quad a_{(3)} \equiv (a_{13}, a_{23}, a_{33}) \, \epsilon \, S_3, \quad \text{then} \quad a_{31} \leqq 0, \quad a_{32} \leqq 0, \quad a_{33} > 0. \end{cases}$$

[2] I am indebted to Saunders MacLane for valuable discussions concerning this theorem.

Let there exist three points,[3] $a'_{(1)} \in S_1$, $a'_{(2)} \in S_2$, $a'_{(3)} \in S_3$, *and three scalar weights,* x'_1, x'_2, x'_3, *such that*

(2)
$$
\begin{cases}
y'_1 \equiv a'_{11}x'_1 + a'_{12}x'_2 + a'_{13}x'_3 > 0, \\
y'_2 \equiv a'_{21}x'_1 + a'_{22}x'_2 + a'_{23}x'_3 > 0, \\
y'_3 \equiv a'_{31}x'_1 + a'_{32}x'_2 + a'_{33}x'_3 > 0,
\end{cases}
$$

and

(3) $1 = x'_1 + x'_2 + x'_3,$ $x'_1 \geqq 0,$ $x'_2 \geqq 0,$ $x'_3 \geqq 0.$

Denote by T *the set of those points* y *of the convex hull* $\bar{S}$ *(as defined below) of* S_1, S_2, *and* S_3 *which* (a) *belong to the closed positive octant* P *defined by*

(4) $y_1 \geqq 0,$ $y_2 \geqq 0,$ $y_3 \geqq 0,$

and (b) *are such that no different point,* $y^* \equiv (y_1^*, y_2^*, y_3^*)$, *exists in* $\bar{S}$ *which satisfies*

(5) $y_1^* \geqq y_1,$ $y_2^* \geqq y_2,$ $y_3^* \geqq y_3.$

Then T *is a plane triangle with one vertex on each of the positive coordinate axes, and such that all its points* y *can be obtained through linear combination*

(6)
$$
\begin{cases}
y_1 = a''_{11}x_1 + a''_{12}x_2 + a''_{13}x_3, \\
y_2 = a''_{21}x_1 + a''_{22}x_2 + a''_{23}x_3, \\
y_3 = a''_{31}x_1 + a''_{32}x_2 + a''_{33}x_3,
\end{cases}
$$

of the same three points

(7) $a''_{(1)} \in S_1,$ $a''_{(2)} \in S_2,$ $a''_{(3)} \in S_3,$

with scalar weights, x_1, x_2, x_3, *satisfying*

(8) $1 = x_1 + x_2 + x_3,$ $x_1 \geqq 0,$ $x_2 \geqq 0,$ $x_3 \geqq 0.$

The interpretation of this theorem is as follows. The three sets, S_1, S_2, S_3, incorporate the alternative modes of production available to each industry *at a labor input equal to unity*. The coordinates a_{11}, a_{21}, a_{31} of a "point" $a_{(1)} \in S_1$ specify the positive output (a_{11}) of commodity "1" and the nonnegative inputs $(-a_{21}, -a_{31})$ of commodities "2" and "3" arising from the choice of the process $a_{(1)}$. The sign restrictions in (1) are imposed to satisfy Assumptions (a) and (b). The sets S_1, S_2, S_3 are made convex to satisfy Assumptions (c) and (d), bounded to satisfy Assumption (f), and closed because productive proc-

---

[3] Since no transposition signs are needed in this chapter, the symbols ′ and ″ are used to denote different points.

esses cannot be measured with the absolute accuracy needed to give meaning to the distinction between closed and not closed sets, whereas without the assumption of closedness the theorem would not be valid. The existence of a solution of (2) expresses Assumption (e).

The convex hull $\bar{S}$ of S_1, S_2, S_3 is the set of all points (y_1, y_2, y_3) such that

(9)
$$\begin{cases} y_1 = a_{11}x_1 + a_{12}x_2 + a_{13}x_3, \\ y_2 = a_{21}x_1 + a_{22}x_2 + a_{23}x_3, \\ y_3 = a_{31}x_1 + a_{32}x_2 + a_{33}x_3, \end{cases}$$

for some choice of processes, one for each industry,[4]

(10)
$$a_{(1)} \in S_1, \qquad a_{(2)} \in S_2, \qquad a_{(3)} \in S_3,$$

and some set of levels of operation x_1, x_2, x_3 satisfying (8) so as to absorb all available labor. Since we assume no net inflow of any commodity except labor, the *attainable* [5] point set is the intersection S of $\bar{S}$ and P. The theorem concentrates on the set T of *efficient* [6] points y of S, i.e., those points that cannot be improved upon, in the sense of (5), by any other attainable point y^*. The theorem says that this set T is a plane triangle, and that all its points can be obtained as combinations of the same three processes, $a''_{(1)}$, $a''_{(2)}$, $a''_{(3)}$, one for each industry.

We proceed to the proof of the theorem. The point y' defined by (2) is a point of $\bar{S}$. Now consider the point $y'' = \lambda''y'$, where λ'' is the algebraically largest value of λ for which

(11)
$$\lambda y' = (\lambda y'_1, \quad \lambda y'_2, \quad \lambda y'_3)$$

is contained in $\bar{S}$. (λ'' is finite because $\bar{S}$, as the convex hull of bounded sets, is itself bounded.) Then y'' is on the boundary of $\bar{S}$ and can be made to satisfy

(12)
$$\begin{cases} y''_1 = a''_{11}x''_1 + a''_{12}x''_2 + a''_{13}x''_3 > 0, \\ y''_2 = a''_{21}x''_1 + a''_{22}x''_2 + a''_{23}x''_3 > 0, \\ y''_3 = a''_{31}x''_1 + a''_{32}x''_2 + a''_{33}x''_3 > 0, \end{cases}$$

where

(13)
$$a''_{(1)} \in S_1, \qquad a''_{(2)} \in S_2, \qquad a''_{(3)} \in S_3,$$

for some x'' satisfying (8) if x'' is substituted for x.

[4] There is no need to select more than one process from each S_i because the S_i are themselves assumed to be convex, and therefore the output of any linear combination of processes taken from some S_i is the output of one single process contained in that S_i.

[5] See Chapter III, Definition 5.1. If we allowed some labor to go unused, it would be necessary to replace S by the convex hull $\bar{S}_0$ of $\bar{S}$ and the origin 0. Since this would not add any efficient points, we need not consider this possibility.

[6] See Chapter III, Definition 5.2.

Consider the triangle $\bar{T}$ spanned by $a''_{(1)}$, $a''_{(2)}$, $a''_{(3)}$, i.e., the set of all points (6) for which x satisfies (8). These points belong to $\bar{S}$. The following table indicates that what can be said about the sign configurations of the coordinates of various points or point sets in $\bar{T}$. Here $+$ stands for > 0, $-$ for $\leqq 0$. Since y'' has positive coordinates and is

Vertices			Edges			Internal Point
$a''_{(1)}$	$a''_{(2)}$	$a''_{(3)}$	$\{a''_{(1)}, a''_{(2)}\}$	$\{a''_{(2)}, a''_{(3)}\}$	$\{a''_{(} , a''_{(1)}\}$	y''
$+$	$-$	$-$	$+$	$-$	$+$	$+$
$-$	$+$	$-$	$+$	$+$	$-$	$+$
$-$	$-$	$+$	$-$	$+$	$+$	$+$

contained in the triangle $\bar{T}$, the plane L of $\bar{T}$ does not coincide with a coordinate plane. It follows from the table that the intersections of this triangle with the coordinate side planes must run as indicated by Figure 1 (see dotted lines, with $-$ meaning $\leqq 0$): Within L the intersection of L with

$$y_1 = 0 \text{ separates } y'' \text{ from } \{a''_{(2)}, a''_{(3)}\},$$

(14) $$y_2 = 0 \text{ separates } y'' \text{ from } \{a''_{(3)}, a''_{(1)}\},$$

$$y_3 = 0 \text{ separates } y'' \text{ from } \{a''_{(1)}, a''_{(2)}\},$$

separation meaning strictly that y'' is not on the line $y_1 = 0$ and that no point of $\{a''_{(2)}, a''_{(3)}\}$ is on the same side of $y_1 = 0$ as y'' is, etc.

Denote by

(15) $$y''_{(1)} \equiv (y''_{11}, 0, 0), \qquad y''_{(2)} \equiv (0, y''_{22}, 0), \qquad y''_{(3)} \equiv (0, 0, y''_{33})$$

the three points at which the lines of separation intersect. Now suppose (see Figure 2) that $\bar{S}$ contains any point y''' of P (hence also of S) separated from the origin by L. Then, since S is convex, the entire tetrahedron constructed on the vertices $y''_{(1)}$, $y''_{(2)}$, $y''_{(3)}$, y''' belongs to S, has y'' on its boundary facing the origin, and hence contains a point (3) with $\lambda > \lambda''$, in contradiction to the definition of λ''. It follows that the triangle $T = \{y''_{(1)}, y''_{(2)}, y''_{(3)}\}$ is a part of the boundary of S. We also read from Figure 1 that in (15)

(16) $$y''_{11} > 0, \qquad y''_{22} > 0, \qquad y''_{33} > 0.$$

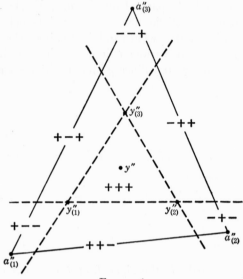

Figure 2 suggests that all points y of T are efficient points. An algebraic argument runs as follows. Let

(17) $$p_1 y_1 + p_2 y_2 + p_3 y_3 = p_1 y_1'' + p_2 y_2'' + p_3 y_3'' = p_0,$$

say, be the equation of the plane L of $\bar{T}$ (and of T), where p_1, p_2, p_3 do not all vanish. Since each of the vertices (15) of T must satisfy this equation if substituted for y, we have

(18) $$p_1 y_{11}'' = p_2 y_{22}'' = p_3 y_{33}'' = p_0.$$

It follows from (16) that we can choose the sign of p_1 such that

(19) $$p_0 > 0, \qquad p_1 > 0, \qquad p_2 > 0, \qquad p_3 > 0.$$

Then S contains no point y^* satisfying

(20) $$p_1 y_1^* + p_2 y_2^* + p_3 y_3^* > p_0$$

because such a point would be separated from the origin by L.

Now let y be a point of T and therefore of P. Any point y^* in $\bar{S}$ satisfying (5) would also have to be in P and therefore in S. But (5) would imply, in view of (19),

(21) $$p_1 y_1^* + p_2 y_2^* + p_3 y_3^* > p_1 y_1 + p_2 y_2 + p_3 y_3 = p_0$$

[unless all three equality signs hold in (5), in which case y^* is not differ-

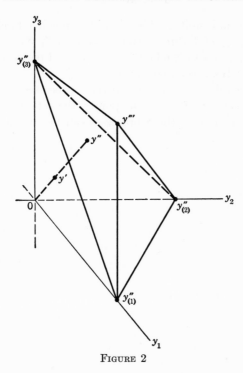

FIGURE 2

ent from y], and we have already seen that S contains no such point y^*. Hence all points y of T satisfy the requirements of the theorem.

Conversely let y' be in S but not in T, and therefore on the same side of L as the origin. The construction (11) already indicated will then lead to a point y'' in $\bar{S}$ such that (5) is satisfied if y'' and y' are substituted for y^* and y, respectively. Hence only points y of T satisfy the requirements of the theorem. This completes the proof of the theorem.

It can be shown that the theorem proved ceases to be true when either (i) more than one scarce primary input is required, or (ii) one of the three industries has joint production (e.g., $a_{11} > 0$, $a_{21} > 0$). Any proof should therefore make use of the restrictions (1) on the signs of the coefficients a_{nk}.

It might be thought that, whenever each of the sets S_1, S_2, S_3 is the convex hull of a smaller set of points representing more "elementary" technological processes, the three points $a''_{(1)}$, $a''_{(2)}$, $a''_{(3)}$ from which the efficient set T is combined might have to be combinations of elementary processes. This, however, need not be the case. To be precise, let an extreme point of a convex set S_k be defined as a point which cannot be represented as a linear combination of other points of S_k with positive weights whose sum is unity. Then it will be possible to choose as basis points $a''_{(1)}$, $a''_{(2)}$, $a''_{(3)}$ of T three extreme points of S_1, S_2, S_3, respectively. A proof of this statement can be based on the first paragraph of Chapter 3, Section 10, of Bonnesen and Fenchel [1934].

It is further easily seen that, while three processes suffice as a basis from which to combine all efficient points, the sets S_1, S_2, S_3 may be such that one or more of these processes can be chosen in more than one way.

CHAPTER IX

ALTERNATIVE PROOF OF THE SUBSTITUTION THEOREM FOR LEONTIEF MODELS IN THE GENERAL CASE

By KENNETH J. ARROW

It is of some interest to state and prove, in a manner which does not involve the use of the calculus, the theorem concerning substitutability in Leontief models stated elsewhere in this volume by Professor Samuelson [VII]. The chief virtue of such restatement is not the generalization to nondifferentiable production functions but the greater clarity given to the importance of the special conditions of the problem. This approach has been developed by Professor Koopmans [VIII] for the case of three outputs; the present chapter seeks to generalize his results.

1. THE ASSUMPTIONS OF THE SAMUELSON-LEONTIEF MODEL

Samuelson's assumptions will be restated here in the terminology of linear programming (see, e.g., Chapter III). We shall let $n + 1$ be the total number of commodities involved; the first n will be termed "products" and the $(n + 1)$th "labor."

ASSUMPTION I: *There is a collection of basic activities, each represented by a vector with $n + 1$ components, such that every possible state of production is represented by a linear combination of a finite number of the basic activities with nonnegative coefficients.*[1] *The collection of basic activities from which such combinations are formed need not itself be finite.*

ASSUMPTION II: *No basic activity has more than one output.*

ASSUMPTION III: *In every basic activity labor is a nonzero input.*

ASSUMPTION IV: *There is a given supply of labor from outside the system, but none of any product.*

---

[1] The restriction to linear combinations of a *finite* number of basic activities is unnecessary. The generalization of a set of nonnegative weights is a *measure* over the space of basic activities. (For the definition of a measure, see Saks [1937, pp. 7–17].) If b stands for a variable basic activity and μ is a measure over the space of basic activities, then any state of production is of the form $\int b \, d\mu$. All subsequent results apply equally well to this more general case, with completely analogous proofs.

155

Assumption I is that of constant returns to scale; II states the absence of joint production in the basic activities; III states that labor appears solely as a primary input; and IV states that no product is a primary input.

In the vector representation of activities, let the $(n + 1)$th component be labor. As usual, inputs will be represented by negative numbers, outputs by positive ones. By an activity of the ith industry we shall understand an activity in which no component other than the ith is positive. Clearly, any linear combination of the basic activities of the ith industry with nonnegative coefficients is itself an activity of the ith industry. Further, let y be any activity. Then, by Assumption I,

$$(1) \qquad y = \sum_k x_k b^k,$$

where $x_k \geqq 0$ and b^k is a vector representing a basic activity.[2] Number the activities b^k in such a way that those with $k = 1, \cdots, n_1$ are basic activities of the first industry, and, in general, those with $k = n_{i-1} + 1$, $\cdots, n_i$ are basic activities of the ith industry, where $n_0 = 0$. Then, from (1),

$$(2) \qquad y = \sum_{i=1}^{n} \sum_{k=n_{i-1}+1}^{n_i} x_k b^k.$$

As noted,

$$\sum_{k=n_{i-1}+1}^{n_i} x_k b^k$$

is an activity of the ith industry. Hence, every activity is expressible as a sum of n activities, one from each industry.

Further, let a normalized activity be one in which the labor input is 1. From Assumption I it follows that every activity of the ith industry is the nonnegative multiple of a normalized activity of that industry, and conversely. Hence every activity is a linear combination of n normalized activities, one from each industry, with nonnegative coefficients. The amount of labor used in any activity is therefore the sum of these coefficients. If, finally, we choose the units of labor so that the total supply of labor available, as guaranteed by Assumption IV, is 1, we may say that any activity y is expressible in the form

$$(3) \qquad y = \sum_{j=1}^{n} x_j a^j,$$

---

[2] In this chapter all vectors are column vectors. For future reference, note that the prime symbol will not denote transposition but will serve to distinguish different column vectors.

where

$$(4) \qquad x_j \geq 0, \qquad \sum_{j=1}^{n} x_j = 1$$

and a^j is a normalized activity of the jth industry. As now defined, all vectors y, a^j have -1 as their $(n + 1)$th component; let us redefine them to have only their first n components.

Note that the set of all normalized activities of the jth industry is a convex set; call it S_j. From Assumption II,

$$(5) \qquad \text{if} \quad a \,\epsilon\, S_j, \quad \text{then} \quad a_k \leq 0 \quad \text{for all} \quad k \neq j.$$

(Here the symbol ϵ means "belongs to"; a_k denotes the kth component of a.) Finally, it follows from Assumption IV that

$$(6) \qquad y \geq 0.$$

(The names and symbols for various partial ordering relations among vectors will be those introduced by Koopmans [III, Section 2.5].)

The set S of feasible points in the product space is that satisfying (3), (4), and (6). The problem is to characterize the set of efficient points [3] of S if the assumption contained in (5) is made.

The set of all points satisfying (3) and (4) will be referred to as the *convex hull of the union* of $S_1, \cdots, S_n$. S is then the intersection of the nonnegative orthant (of Euclidean n-space) with the convex hull of the union of $S_1, \cdots, S_n$.

The following notation and terminology will be used: A will denote a square matrix of order n, a_i^j will be the element in the ith row and jth column of A, and a^j will be the vector which is the jth column of A. A will be said to be *admissible* if $a^j \,\epsilon\, S_j$ for every j. A *weight vector*, x, has the properties $x \geq 0$, $\sum_{j=1}^{n} x_j = 1$. A pair (A, x) is said to be a *representation* if A is admissible, x is a weight vector, and $Ax \geq 0$. A vector y for which there exists a representation (A, x) such that $y = Ax$ is termed *feasible;* this definition agrees with that given in the first sentence of the preceding paragraph.

In the light of (3)–(6), the economic significance of these definitions is obvious. In particular, the set of feasible points, or vectors, is precisely S; a representation is a mode of industrial organization which will achieve a given feasible point. Note that, in view of (5), $a_i^j \leq 0$ for all $i \neq j$.

Two forms of Samuelson's theorem will be established, corresponding to Koopmans' "strong" and "weak" assumptions, respectively [III,

---

[3] For the relevant definition of an efficient point see Chapter III, Section 5.2, considering labor as the only primary commodity.

Section 3.6]. In the first case we assume that it is possible to produce a positive net output of all products; in the second we assume only that some net production is possible.

2. The Substitution Theorem under Strong Assumptions

THEOREM 1: *For each $j = 1, \cdots, n$, let S_j be a convex set in Euclidean n-space such that, if $a \in S_j$, then $a_i \leq 0$ for $i \neq j$. Let S be the intersection of the convex hull of the union of $S_1, \cdots, S_n$ with the nonnegative orthant. If S is a compact set [4] with at least one positive element, then the set of efficient points of S is the intersection with the nonnegative orthant of an $(n - 1)$-dimensional hyperplane the direction coefficients of whose outward normal are all positive.*

LEMMA 1: *If y' belongs to the compact set S, there is an efficient point y'' of S such that $y'' \geq y'$.[5]*

PROOF: Let U be the set of points y such that $y \in S$, $y \geq y'$. U is a compact set, so that the continuous function $\sum_{i=1}^{n} y_i$ attains a maximum in U, say at y''. Since $y'' \in U$, $y'' \geq y'$. If y'' were not efficient, there would be a point $\bar{y}$ of S such that $\bar{y} \geq y''$; but then $\bar{y} \in U$, $\sum_{i=1}^{n} \bar{y}_i > \sum_{i=1}^{n} y''_i$, contrary to the construction of y''.[6]

LEMMA 2: *If A is a (square) matrix such that $a_i^j \leq 0$ for $i \neq j$, and x and y are vectors such that $Ax = y$, $x \geq 0$, $y \geq 0$, $y_i > 0$, then $x_i > 0$.*

PROOF: By hypothesis, $a_i^j x_j \leq 0$ for $i \neq j$, so that $\sum_{j \neq i} a_i^j x_j \leq 0$. Hence $0 < y_i = a_i^i x_i + \sum_{j \neq i} a_i^j x_j \leq a_i^i x_i$. Since $x_i \geq 0$, we must have $x_i > 0$.

LEMMA 3: *Let A be a matrix such that $a_i^j \leq 0$ for $i \neq j$ and for which there exists a vector x such that $Ax > 0$. Then (a) $Ax' \geq 0$ implies $x' \geq 0$; (b) $Ax' \geq 0$ implies $x' \geq 0$.[7]*

PROOF: By Lemma 2, the hypothesis $Ax > 0$ implies $x > 0$. The ratios x'_j / x_j are therefore defined; let

$$(7) \qquad m = \min_j (x'_j / x_j),$$

where j varies from 1 to n, and choose i so that

$$(8) \qquad x'_i / x_i = m.$$

---

[4] That is, closed and bounded.

[5] This lemma has been proved by von Neumann and Morgenstern [1947, p. 593] for the case where S has a finite number of elements.

[6] See Chapter III, Section 2.5, for definitions of "$\geq$" and "$\geq$."

[7] Recall that in this chapter the prime is not used as a transposition sign.

From (7) and the hypotheses,

$$(9) \qquad a_i^j x_j' = a_i^j x_j (x_j'/x_j) \leq a_i^j x_j m \qquad\qquad (j \neq i).$$

Suppose $Ax' \geq 0$. Then, from (8) and (9),

$$0 \leq \sum_{j=1}^{n} a_i^j x_j' \leq a_i^i x_i m + \sum_{j \neq i} a_i^j x_j m = m \sum_{j=1}^{n} a_i^j x_j.$$

By hypothesis, $\sum_{j=1}^{n} a_i^j x_j > 0$, so that $m \geq 0$.   From (7), $x_j' \geq 0$, since $x_j > 0$ for all j, establishing (a).

If $Ax' \geq 0$, then, clearly, $x' \geq 0$ by (a), $x' \neq 0$, so that $x' \geq 0$.

LEMMA 4: *If A is a matrix such that $Ax \geq 0$ only if $x \geq 0$, then A is nonsingular.*

PROOF: If x is such that $Ax = 0$, then $A(-x) = 0$. By hypothesis, $x \geq 0$, $-x \geq 0$, so that $x = 0$. Hence $Ax = 0$ implies $x = 0$, so that A must be nonsingular.

LEMMA 5: *If (A, x) is a representation of $y > 0$, let Q be the set of points $y' \geq 0$ for which there exists a vector x' such that $Ax' = y'$, $\sum_{j=1}^{n} x_j' = 1$. Then every point of Q is feasible.*

PROOF: By hypothesis,

$$(10) \qquad a_i^j \leq 0 \quad \text{for} \quad i \neq j,$$

$$(11) \qquad Ax = y > 0.$$

From (10), (11), and Lemma 3, $Ax' \geq 0$ implies $x' \geq 0$.   Since $\sum_{j=1}^{n} x_j' = 1$, x' is a weight vector.   Therefore (A, x') is a representation, and y' is a feasible point.

LEMMA 6: *If Q is defined as in Lemma 5, there do not exist two points y', y'', in Q such that $y' \geq y''$.*

PROOF: Suppose the contrary.   Let $y' = Ax'$, $y'' = Ax''$, where

$$(12) \qquad \sum_{j=1}^{n} x_j' = 1 = \sum_{j=1}^{n} x_j'',$$

$A(x' - x'') \geq 0$.   By the proof of Lemma 5, A satisfies the hypotheses of Lemma 3, so that $x' - x'' \geq 0$; but then, $\sum_{j=1}^{n} (x_j' - x_j'') > 0$, contrary to (12).

LEMMA 7: *If, for each $k = 1, \cdots, p$, $y^{(k)}$ has representation $(A^{(k)}, x^{(k)})$, and $t_k > 0$, and if $\sum_{k=1}^{p} t_k = 1$, then $y = \sum_{k=1}^{p} t_k y^{(k)}$ is feasible and has a representation (A, x), where $x = \sum_{k=1}^{p} t_k x^{(k)}$, and $a^j = (\sum_{k=1}^{p} t_k x_j^{(k)} a^{(k)j})/x_j$, for all j for which $x_j > 0$.*

PROOF: Define x and a^j as in the hypothesis; for all j such that $x_j = 0$, choose a^j to be any element of S_j. Since the sets S_j are convex, it follows that $a^j \, \epsilon \, S_j$ for each j, so that A is admissible. It is also easy to see that x is a weight vector, that $y = Ax$, and that $y \geq 0$, so that (A, x) is a representation of y.

LEMMA 8: *Let $y > 0$ be an efficient point with representation (A, x), and let T be defined in terms of y in the same way that Q is defined in Lemma 5. Then,* (a) *A is nonsingular;* (b) *every efficient point of S belongs to T.*

PROOF: By the proof of Lemma 5, A satisfies the hypotheses of Lemma 3 and hence is nonsingular by Lemmas 3 and 4.

Let y' be any efficient point. Since there is a positive efficient point, we cannot have $y' = 0$. Since A is nonsingular, there is a vector x' such that $Ax' = y' \geq 0$. By Lemma 3, $x' \geq 0$, and therefore $\sum_{j=1}^{n} x'_j > 0$. Let $t_0 = 1/\sum_{j=1}^{n} x'_j$. Then, $A(t_0 x') = t_0 y' \geq 0$, $\sum_{j=1}^{n} t_0 x'_j = 1$, so that

$$(13) \qquad\qquad t_0 y' \, \epsilon \, T.$$

By (13) and Lemma 5, $t_0 y'$ is feasible. If $t_0 > 1$, then $t_0 y' \geq y'$, which is impossible for an efficient point y'. Hence

$$(14) \qquad\qquad 0 < t_0 \leq 1.$$

The variable point $tt_0 y' + (1 - t)y > 0$ for $t = 0$. Hence we can choose t_1 so that

$$(15) \qquad\qquad t_1 < 0,$$

$$(16) \qquad\qquad y'' = t_1 t_0 y' + (1 - t_1)y > 0.$$

Let $x'' = t_1 t_0 x' + (1 - t_1)x$; then, by the definition of t_0 and the fact that x is a weight vector, $\sum_{j=1}^{n} x''_j = 1$; also, $y'' = Ax''$. From (16) and the definition of T, $y'' \, \epsilon \, T$. By Lemma 5,

$$(17) \qquad\qquad y'' \text{ is a feasible point.}$$

Let $t_2 = (t_1 t_0)/(t_1 t_0 - 1)$, $t_3 = (1 - t_1)/(1 - t_1 t_0)$. From (14) and (15),

$$(18) \qquad\qquad 0 < t_2 < 1,$$

$$(19) \qquad\qquad t_3 \geq 1.$$

From (16),

$$(20) \qquad\qquad t_3 y = t_2 y' + (1 - t_2)y''.$$

From (18), (20), (17), and Lemma 7, $t_3 y$ is a feasible point. If $t_3 > 1$, then $t_3 y > y$, so that y would not be efficient, contrary to hypothesis. Hence, from (19), $t_3 = 1$, which implies that $t_0 = 1$. From (13), then, $y' \, \epsilon \, T$.

PROOF OF THEOREM 1: By hypothesis, there is at least one positive feasible point. By Lemma 1, there is an efficient point $y > 0$. Let T be defined as in Lemma 8. Then every efficient point of S belongs to T. Conversely, let y' be any point of T. If y' is not efficient, there is, by Lemma 1, an efficient point $y'' \geq y'$. Since y'' is efficient, it belongs to T by Lemma 8; but this contradicts Lemma 6. Hence y' is efficient, so that T is precisely the set of efficient points.

T is the intersection with the nonnegative orthant of the hyperplane defined parametrically by the equations $Ax' = y$, $\sum_{j=1}^{n} x_j' = 1$. By Lemma 8, A is nonsingular, so that $x' = A^{-1}y$. Let A_j^i be the element in the jth row and ith column of A^{-1}, and A^i be the ith column. Then the equation of the hyperplane is

$$\sum_{i=1}^{n} \left(\sum_{j=1}^{n} A_j^i \right) y_i = 1.$$

Hence the numbers $\sum_{j=1}^{n} A_j^i$ are the direction numbers of the outward normal to T. For each i, AA^i is a vector all of whose components are zero except for the ith, which is 1. Therefore $AA^i \geq 0$; by Lemma 3, $A^i \geq 0$, so that $\sum_{j=1}^{n} A_j^i > 0$ for all i.

3. THE SUBSTITUTION THEOREM UNDER WEAK ASSUMPTIONS

A generalization of Theorem 1 in which it is assumed only that there is a feasible point $y \geq 0$ (instead of $y > 0$) will be developed in this section. Some new terminology and notation will be needed.

A representation (A, x) will be said to be *trivial* if there is a nonnull set of integers, I, such that $x_i > 0$ for some i in I, and $\sum_{j \in I} a_i^j x_j = 0$ for all i in I. The mode of industrial organization displayed by a trivial representation has the property that there is a collection of industries in which there is some net input of labor and possibly of other commodities and such that the output of any one industry in the group is completely absorbed by the other industries in the group. This group, then, is only a drain on the net resources of the nation. The main result of this section is that any industry which can be used in any system of industrial organization not of the degenerate type just described can yield a positive net output; therefore Samuelson's theorem applies.

LEMMA 9: *Let A be a matrix such that $a_i^j \leq 0$ when $i \neq j$; x and y vectors such that $x \geq 0$, $y \geq 0$, $y = Ax$; I a set of integers (between 1 and n); and i an element of I. Then,* (a) $\sum_{j \in I} a_i^j x_j \geq y_i \geq 0$; (b) *if* $\sum_{j \in I} a_i^j x_j = 0$, *then* $y_i = 0$, *and* $a_i^j = 0$ *for all* $j \in -I$ *such that* $x_j > 0$. (*By* $-I$ *is meant the set of integers between 1 and n not in I.*)

PROOF: From the hypothesis,

$$(21) \qquad a_i^j x_j \leqq 0 \quad \text{for} \quad i \neq j,$$

so that

$$(22) \qquad \sum_{j \, \epsilon \, -I} a_i^j x_j \leqq 0.$$

From (22) and the hypotheses,

$$0 \leqq y_i = \sum_{j \, \epsilon \, I} a_i^j x_j + \sum_{j \, \epsilon \, -I} a_i^j x_j \leqq \sum_{j \, \epsilon \, I} a_i^j x_j,$$

establishing (a). If $\sum_{j \, \epsilon \, I} a_i^j x_j = 0$, then clearly $y_i = 0$, and $\sum_{j \, \epsilon \, -I} a_i^j x_j = 0$, so that, from (21), $a_i^j x_j = 0$ for $j \, \epsilon \, -I$, from which (b) follows.

Lemma 9 is a generalization of Lemma 2.

LEMMA 10: *If $y \geq 0$ has a trivial representation (A, x), then y is not efficient.*

PROOF: By hypothesis, there is a set of integers, I, such that

$$(23) \qquad x_i > 0 \quad \text{for some} \quad i \, \epsilon \, I,$$

$$(24) \qquad \sum_{j \, \epsilon \, I} a_i^j x_j = 0 \quad \text{for all} \quad i \, \epsilon \, I.$$

From (24) and Lemma 9b, $y_i = 0$ for all i in I; since $y_k > 0$ for some k, we must have k in $-I$. By Lemma 2, then, $x_k > 0$ for some k not in I. Together with (1), this shows that $0 < \sum_{j \, \epsilon \, I} x_j < 1$. Let $t = 1/(1 - \sum_{j \, \epsilon \, I} x_j)$, and define $x_j' = 0$ for $j \, \epsilon \, I$, $x_j' = t x_j$ for $j \, \epsilon \, -I$. Then

$$(25) \qquad t > 1,$$

$$(26) \qquad x' \text{ is a weight vector.}$$

Let $y' = A x'$. For i in I, it follows from (24) and Lemma 9b that $a_i^j x_j = 0$ for j in $-I$. Hence

$$(27) \qquad y_i' = \sum_{j \, \epsilon \, I} a_i^j x_j' + \sum_{j \, \epsilon \, -I} a_i^j x_j' = 0 = t y_i,$$

for i in I. For $i \, \epsilon \, -I$, $a_i^j x_j \leqq 0$ for j in I. Therefore

$$0 \leqq y_i = \sum_{j \, \epsilon \, I} a_i^j x_j + \sum_{j \, \epsilon \, -I} a_i^j x_j \leqq \sum_{j \, \epsilon \, -I} a_i^j x_j,$$

so that

$$y_i' = \sum_{j \, \epsilon \, I} a_i^j x_j' + \sum_{j \, \epsilon \, -I} a_i^j x_j' = t \sum_{j \, \epsilon \, -I} a_i^j x_j \geqq t y_i,$$

for i in $-I$, or, with (27),

$$(28) \qquad y' \geqq t y.$$

A is an admissible matrix by hypothesis; x' is a weight vector, by (26); and from (28), (25), and the hypothesis, $y' \geqq 0$, so that y' is a feasible point. Furthermore, from (28), (25), and the hypothesis that $y \geq 0$, it follows that $y' \geq y$, so that y is not efficient.

The proof of Lemma 10 amounts to saying that the industrial organization represented by a trivial representation can always be improved by shutting down the group of industries which yields no net aggregate output and distributing the released labor to the other industries in proportion to the numbers already employed.

We shall also need the following generalization of Lemma 3:

LEMMA 11: *Let A be a matrix such that $a_i^j \leqq 0$ for $i \neq j$ and for which there exists a vector $x > 0$ such that (A, x) is a nontrivial representation. Then* (a) *$Ax' \geqq 0$ implies $x' \geqq 0$; and* (b) *$Ax' \geq 0$ implies $x' \geq 0$.*

PROOF: Since $x > 0$, the ratios x_j'/x_j are defined. Let

$$(29) \qquad m = \min_{j} (x_j'/x_j),$$

and let I be the set of integers such that $x_j'/x_j = m$; I is nonnull. From the hypothesis, $a_i^j x_j < 0$ for i in I, j in $-I$, if $a_i^j \neq 0$. We then have

$$(30) \qquad x_j'/x_j = m \quad \text{for} \quad j \in I,$$

$$(31) \qquad a_i^j x_j' = a_i^j x_j(x_j'/x_j) < m a_i^j x_j,$$

if i is in I, j in $-I$, and $a_i^j \neq 0$. Suppose that for all i in I, $\sum_{j \in I} a_i^j x_j = 0$; since $x_j > 0$ for all j, it would follow that (A, x) is trivial, contrary to hypothesis. Hence, by Lemma 9a, there is some i in I such that

$$(32) \qquad \sum_{j \in I} a_i^j x_j > 0.$$

From (31),

$$(33) \qquad \sum_{j \in -I} a_i^j x_j' < m \sum_{j \in -I} a_i^j x_j,$$

if $a_i^j \neq 0$ for some j in $-I$. Suppose $Ax' \geqq 0$. Then, using (30),

$$(34) \qquad 0 \leq \sum_{j \in I} a_i^j x_j' + \sum_{j \in -I} a_i^j x_j' = m \sum_{j \in I} a_i^j x_j + \sum_{j \in -I} a_i^j x_j'.$$

If $a_i^j = 0$ for all j in $-I$, then, from (32) and (34), it follows that $m \geqq 0$. If $a_i^j \neq 0$ for some j in $-I$, then, from (33) and (34),

$$0 < m \sum_{j=1}^{n} a_i^j x_j.$$

Since $\sum_{j=1}^{n} a_i^j x_j \geq 0$ by the hypothesis that (A, x) is a representation, we must have $m > 0$. Hence, in either case, it follows from (29) that $x' \geq 0$. Part (b) follows from (a) as in Lemma 3.

An integer, i, between 1 and n will be said to denote a *useful industry* if there is some nontrivial representation (A, x) in which $x_i > 0$. Lemma 10 guarantees us that, in the search for efficient points, industries which are not useful can be regarded as nonexistent, so there is no loss of generality in assuming that all numbers denote useful industries.

It is possible that the set of feasible points is empty, in which case Samuelson's theorem naturally has no particular content. Hence we shall assume that there is at least one useful industry.

THEOREM 2: *For each $j = 1, \cdots, n$, let S_j be a convex set in Euclidean n-space such that if $a \in S_j$, then $a_i \leq 0$ for $i \neq j$. Let S be the intersection of the nonnegative orthant with the convex hull of the union of $S_1, \cdots, S_n$. If S is a compact set, and if every number from 1 to n denotes a useful industry, then the set of efficient points of S is the intersection with the nonnegative orthant of a hyperplane the direction coefficients of whose outward normal are all positive.*

PROOF: For each k, let $y^{(k)}$ be a feasible point with a nontrivial representation $(A^{(k)}, x^{(k)})$ such that $x_k^{(k)} > 0$ for each k; the existence of these points follows from the hypothesis that every number from 1 to n denotes a useful industry. Let $y = (\sum_{k=1}^{n} y^{(k)})/n$; by Lemma 7, y is a feasible point with representation (A, x), where $x = (\sum_{k=1}^{n} x^{(k)})/n$, so that $x > 0$, and $a^j = (\sum_{k=1}^{n} x_j^{(k)} a^{(k)j})/nx_j$. Suppose (A, x) is trivial; then, for some set of integers I, $\sum_{j \in I} a_i^j x_j = 0$ for all i in I. From this, it follows that

$$\sum_{k=1}^{n} \left(\sum_{j \in I} a_i^{(k)j} x_j^{(k)} \right) = 0,$$

for all i in I. From Lemma 9a, then, $\sum_{j \in I} a_i^{(k)j} x_j^{(k)} = 0$ for each k and all i in I; in particular, the equation holds for any k in I. Since $x_k^{(k)} > 0$, and therefore $x_i^{(k)} > 0$ for at least one i in I, we would have $(A^{(k)}, x^{(k)})$, a trivial representation, contrary to hypothesis. Hence (A, x) is a nontrivial representation with $x > 0$. All the conditions of Lemma 11 are satisfied, so that, by Lemmas 11 and 4, A is nonsingular.

Let y' be any positive vector. Then there is a vector x' such that $Ax' = y' > 0$. By Lemma 11, $x' \geq 0$; let $t = 1/(\sum_{j=1}^{n} x_j') > 0$. Then tx' is a weight vector, and $ty' = A(tx')$ is a positive feasible point with representation (A, tx'). All the hypotheses of Theorem 1 are then fulfilled, and the conclusion follows.

CHAPTER X

SOME PROPERTIES OF A GENERALIZED
LEONTIEF MODEL [1]

By NICHOLAS GEORGESCU-ROEGEN

1. The model presented by Leontief [1936, 1937, 1941] is based on, among other things, the assumption that each commodity can be produced by one method of production only. This is equivalent to assuming that all factors of production are *limitational*. Because of this, the model will be referred to as the Leontief *limitational model*.

Samuelson and the author have independently considered the possibility of a Leontief model from which the limitationality restriction could be removed. Such a model will be referred to as a Leontief *generalized model*.

This abstract presents the results obtained by the author regarding some properties of the generalized as well as of the limitational model and omits the proofs.[2]

2. In this abstract, a Leontief generalized model is defined by the following assumptions:

ASSUMPTION I: *There are* $n + 1$ *perfectly defined and homogeneous commodities,* $G_1, G_2, \cdots, G_{n+1}$. *The commodity* G_{n+1} *is labor.*

---

[1] The results contained in this chapter may be reproduced in whole or in part for any purpose of the United States Government, under whose contract they have been completed.

These results were presented for the first time on March 22, 1949, at a meeting of the staff of Harvard Economic Research Project. The criticism of Professor W. W. Leontief and of other members of the Harvard Economic Research Project showed to the author the path for an ameliorated formulation of the argument related to the consolidation problem. It is hardly necessary to add that, for any faults the chapter may contain, the author alone is responsible. The facilities of the Institute of Research and Training in Social Sciences at Vanderbilt University extended to the author in preparing the final version are gratefully acknowledged.

[2] The result presented by Samuelson [VII] is identical with Corollary 10.3 below. The proof of 10.3 does not require, however, the existence of derivatives. Alternative proofs which do not require the existence of derivatives have been given by Koopmans [VIII] and Arrow [IX].

165

This assumption contains a relevant economic restriction. A heterogeneous commodity other than labor may be replaced by a number of homogeneous commodities so that the above assumption be fulfilled. This is no longer possible for labor, since the model allows for only one quality of labor.

ASSUMPTION II: *Each commodity, G_k ($k = 1, 2, \cdots, n, n + 1$), can be produced by at least one process with no joint products.* Such processes will be referred to as *elementary processes*.

ASSUMPTION III: *All processes with joint outputs are* derived *processes (i.e., they are obtained by integrating* [3] *two or more elementary processes into which they can again be decomposed).*

This assumption makes legitimate the concept of the industry producing the commodity G_k.

ASSUMPTION IV: *Any elementary processes for G_k ($k \neq n + 1$) require "labor," G_{n+1}, as input.* Labor is, therefore, an *indispensable* factor of production or, in other words, no economic perpetuum mobile free of labor exists.

ASSUMPTION V: *All processes producing G_{n+1} must have at least one input different from zero.*

ASSUMPTION VI: *The elementary processes are linear in terms of input and output flows.* They are, in other words, particular cases of Koopmans' concept of an activity [III].

ASSUMPTION VII: *There is an industry producing only G_k, for any k.*

ASSUMPTION VIII: *Each industry is in competitive long-run equilibrium.*

In a Leontief limitational model, Assumption II is replaced by

ASSUMPTION IIa: *According to the technological information, each commodity G_k can be produced by only one elementary process.*

3. We shall use the notation

$$(1) \qquad P^{(k)}(-a_1^{(k)}, -a_2^{(k)}, \cdots, -a_{k-1}^{(k)}, b_k, -a_{k+1}^{(k)}, \cdots, -a_{n+1}^{(k)})$$

for an elementary process of the industry G_k. The a's are input flows, and the b's are output flows. According to Assumption IV,

$$(2) \qquad b_k > 0, \qquad a_{n+1}^{(k)} > 0, \qquad a_i^{(k)} \geqq 0 \qquad (i \leqq n);$$

for $k \leqq n$, and

$$(3) \qquad b_{n+1} > 0, \qquad \text{at least one} \quad a_i^{(n+1)} > 0$$

for $k = n + 1$.

---

[3] For the definition of integration of processes, see Chapter IV, Lemma 1.

For such a model a technological horizon may be constructed from a given technological information in the manner described elsewhere in this volume [III, IV].

4. The model including the processes producing all G_k ($k = 1, 2, \cdots$, $n + 1$) is a *closed* model. If the processes producing G_{n+1} (labor) are excluded from the model, this is an *open* model with respect to labor. Let H and H' be, respectively, the technological horizons of the closed and of the open model.

The process

(4) $$\pi^{(k)}(0, 0, \cdots, 1, 0, \cdots, 0, -l_k) \quad (k = 1, 2, \cdots, n)$$

will be called a *completely integrated* process of commodity G_k.[4]   If

(5) $$L_k = \text{greatest lower bound of } l_k$$

for all completely integrated processes $\pi^{(k)}$ belonging to H', the process

(6) $$\Pi^{(k)}(0, 0, \cdots, 1, 0, \cdots, 0, -L_k)$$

will be referred to as the *most efficient completely integrated process* of commodity G_k.

Evidently $L_k \geqq 0$. The process $\Pi^{(k)}$ does not necessarily belong to H' if H' is an *open* cone.[5]

5. The following general theorems are valid for an open model:

THEOREM 1: *A necessary and sufficient condition that any bill of goods be produced by labor alone (i.e., with labor as only net input) is that H' should contain at least one completely integrated process for each commodity G_k ($k \neq n + 1$).*

THEOREM 2: *If the conditions of Theorem 1 are fulfilled, and $(x_1, x_2, \cdots, x_{n+1})$ is the space of all commodities, then the linear space*

(7) $$L(x) = \sum_1^n L_k x_k + x_{n+1} = 0$$

is a supporting plane of H'.[6]

---

[4] The position of 1 is determined by the superscript k (i.e., $a_i = 0$ for $i \neq k, n + 1$).

[5] The term *open* has here the meaning used in point set theory and should not be confused with that of the expression "*open* model."

[6] The linear space $L(x) = 0$ will be said to be a supporting plane of H' if

(a) there are vectors of H' which form with $L(x) = 0$ as small an angle as we want;

(b) one of the open halfspaces $L(x) > 0$, $L(x) < 0$ contains no vector of H'.

If H' is a closed cone, the condition (a) is equivalent to: $L(x) = 0$ should contain at least one element of H'.

6. The following theorems have been established for a limitational open model:

THEOREM 3: *If the square matrix* $[a_{ik}]$ *satisfies the conditions*

$$(8) \qquad\qquad a_{ii} > 0, \qquad a_{ik} \leqq 0 \qquad\qquad (i \neq k),$$

and if

$$(9) \qquad\qquad [a_k] = \left[\sum a_{ik}\right] > 0,$$

then the system

$$(10) \qquad\qquad \sum_{k=1}^{n} a_{ik}\lambda_k = A_i \qquad\qquad (i = 1, 2, \cdots, n),$$

where [7]

$$(11) \qquad\qquad [A] \geq 0,$$

admits a solution $[\lambda] \geq 0$.

COROLLARY 3.1: *If condition* (11) *of Theorem* 3 *is supplemented by* $A_i > 0$ *for* $i \leqq \sigma$, *it follows that* $\lambda_i > 0$ *for* $i \leqq \sigma$.

THEOREM 4: *If the square matrix* $[a_{ik}]$ *is nonsingular, and if*

$$(12) \qquad\qquad a_{ii} > 0, \qquad a_{ik} \leqq 0 \qquad\qquad (i \neq k),$$

and

$$(13) \qquad\qquad [a_k] = \left[\sum_{i=1}^{n} a_{ik}\right] \geq 0,$$

then the system

$$(14) \qquad\qquad \sum_{k=1}^{n} a_{ik}\lambda_k = A_i \qquad\qquad (i = 1, 2, \cdots, n),$$

where

$$(15) \qquad\qquad [A] \geq 0,$$

admits a solution $[\lambda] \geq 0$.

COROLLARY 4.1: *If, in Theorem* 4, (15) *is supplemented by* $A_i > 0$ *for* $i \leqq \sigma$, *it follows that* $\lambda_i > 0$, *for* $i \leqq \sigma$.

THEOREM 5: *If one* complete *bill of goods,* $[B^0] > 0$, *can be produced by labor alone, any other bill of goods, whether complete or not, can also be produced by labor alone.*

---

[7] The signs $\geq$ and $\geqq$ are used in the meanings defined in Chapter III, Section 2.5.

This theorem can be stated also in the following form: *The system*

(16)
$$\lambda_i - \sum_{k=1}^{n} \lambda_k a_i^{(k)} = B_i$$

admits a solution $[\lambda] \geq 0$ *for any* $[B] \geq 0$ *if it admits one* $[\lambda^0] > 0$ *for one* $[B^0] > 0$.

Let Γ' be the orthogonal projection of H' upon the linear space $x_{n+1} = 0$. In this space, of coordinates $x_1, x_2, \cdots, x_n$, Γ' is a convex cone. Let also Ω_n^+ be the closed positive orthant of the space $(x_1, x_2, \cdots, x_n)$.

With these notations and under the assumptions of Theorem 5, we have two corollaries.

COROLLARY 5.1:

(17)
$$\Omega_n^+ \subset \Gamma'.$$

In particular, the technological horizon contains a most efficient completely integrated process, $\Pi^{(k)}$, *for each industry* (G_k).

COROLLARY 5.2: Γ' *is n-dimensional, or, in other words,*

(18)
$$\Delta = \begin{vmatrix} 1 & -a_1^{(2)} & \cdots & -a_1^{(n)} \\ -a_2^{(1)} & 1 & \cdots & -a_2^{(n)} \\ \cdot & \cdot & \cdots & \cdot \\ -a_n^{(1)} & -a_n^{(2)} & \cdots & 1 \end{vmatrix} \neq 0.$$

THEOREM 6: *If a complete bill of goods can be produced by labor alone, then*

(19)
$$\Delta_{j_1, j_2, \cdots, j_s}^{j_1, j_2, \cdots, j_s} > 0, \qquad \Delta_{j_1, j_2, \cdots, j_{s-1}, i}^{j_1, j_2, \cdots, j_{s-1}, k} \geq 0,$$

where $0 \leq s \leq n - 2$, $k \neq i$. The Δ's with sub- and superscripts are the classical notations for the minors of Δ in (18).

THEOREM 7: *Necessary and sufficient conditions that the system* (16) *admit a solution* $[\lambda^0] > 0$ *for one* $[B] > 0$ *are given by the* $n - 1$ *inequalities* [8]

(20) $\Delta > 0, \qquad \Delta_1^1 > 0, \qquad \Delta_{1,2}^{1,2} > 0, \qquad \cdots, \qquad \Delta_{1,2,\cdots,n-2}^{1,2,\cdots,n-2} > 0.$

[8] Conditions that the system (16) admit a solution $[\lambda^0] > 0$ have been formulated by Hawkins and Simon [1949]. Theorem 7 differs from the conditions given in that paper by (a) the order of the determinants used (p. 248, Corollary), and (b) the conditions imposed upon $a_i^{(k)}$ (p. 245).

7. The theorems of Section 6 can be easily extended to the generalized open model.

THEOREM 5A: *If one complete bill of goods, $[B^0] > 0$, can be produced by labor alone, any other bill of goods can also be produced by labor alone.*

Under the assumption of Theorem 5A, we have two corollaries.

COROLLARY 5A.1:

(21) $\Omega_n^+ \subset \Gamma'.$

In particular, H' contains at least one completely integrated process, $\pi^{(k)}$, for each G_k.

COROLLARY 5A.2: *Γ' is an n-dimensional cone (i.e., elementary processes, $P^{(1)}, P^{(2)}, \cdots, P^{(n)}$, can be found, belonging to H', such that the corresponding $\Delta \neq 0$).*

THEOREM 7A: *A necessary and sufficient condition that one complete bill of goods, $[B] > 0$, can be produced by labor alone is that a group of primary processes, $P^{(1)}, P^{(2)}, \cdots, P^{(n)}$, belonging to H', can be found such that (20) is fulfilled.*

THEOREM 5B (generalization of Theorem 5A): *If one bill of goods, $(B_1^0, B_2^0, \cdots, B_\sigma^0, 0, 0, \cdots, 0), B_i^0 > 0$ for $i = 1, 2, \cdots, \sigma$, can be produced by labor alone, then any other bill of goods, $(B_1, B_2, \cdots, B_\sigma, 0, \cdots, 0)$, $B_i \geqq 0$ for $i = 1, 2, \cdots, \sigma$, can also be produced by labor alone.*

Under the assumptions of Theorem 5B we have three corollaries.

COROLLARY 5B.1: *H' contains at least one completely integrated process $\pi^{(k)}$ for each commodity G_k.*

If $t \leqq n$ is the maximum number of commodities contained in a bill of goods which can be produced by labor alone, t will be called the *rank of the model.*

COROLLARY 5B.2: *H' contains at least one completely integrated process for t commodities, $G_{\alpha_1}, G_{\alpha_2}, \cdots, G_{\alpha_t}$. H' contains a completely integrated process only for these commodities.*

By a change of notations the commodities mentioned in Corollary 5B.2 may be written $G_1, G_2, \cdots, G_t$. They will be called *elementary commodities.*

COROLLARY 5B.3: *No bill of goods containing nonelementary commodities can be produced by labor alone.*

THEOREM 8: *The rank, t, of the model cannot be equal to $n - 1$ (i.e., either $t = n$ or $t \leqq n - 2$).*

THEOREM 9: *If Γ' is not n-dimensional (i.e., if $\Delta = 0$ for all groups of elementary processes, $P^{(1)}, P^{(2)}, \cdots, P^{(n)}$), the rank of the model $t \leqq n - 2$.*

THEOREM 10: *The greatest lower bound, L, of the amount of labor necessary to produce a bill of elementary goods, $(B_1, B_2, \cdots, B_t, 0, \cdots, 0)$, is given by*

$$(22) \qquad L = \sum_{k=1}^{t} B_k L_k.$$

COROLLARY 10.1: *If $t = n$, and if H' is a closed cone, the minimum amount of labor necessary to produce a bill of goods, $[B] \geq 0$, is given by*

$$(23) \qquad L = \sum_{k=1}^{n} B_k L_k;$$

i.e., the process $P(B_1, B_2, \cdots, B_n, -L)$, which belongs to H', belongs also to the linear space (7).

COROLLARY 10.2: *If $t = n$, and H' is a closed cone, the process*

$$(24) \qquad P(B_1, B_2, \cdots, B_n, -L) = \sum_{k=1}^{n} \lambda_k \overline{P}^{(k)} \qquad ([\lambda] \geq 0),$$

where $\overline{P}^{(k)}$ is an elementary process belonging to (7) and H'.

COROLLARY 10.3: *If $t = n$, and H' is a closed cone, the processes $\overline{P}^{(k)}$ used for producing with the minimum labor a bill of goods, $[B]$, are independent of the bill of goods (i.e., of consumers' demand).*

8. The results presented in the preceding sections are purely technological in nature. They are independent of Assumption VIII, which is not required for the proofs. If we retain the assumptions that $t = n$ and that H' is a *closed* cone, the classical conditions for long-run competitive equilibrium for each industry G_k lead to

THEOREM 11: *Any long-run competitive equilibrium process used by the industry G_k is a $\overline{P}^{(k)}$.* From Corollary 10.3 and Theorem 11, we have immediately

THEOREM 12: *If $t = n$ and H' is closed, then in a generalized open model the long-run competitive equilibrium brings about the optimum allocation of resources (labor).*

THEOREM 13: *If $t = n$ and H' is closed, then*

(25) $$p_k = L_k p_{n+1},$$

where p_k is the long-run competitive equilibrium price of G_k.

If we adopt for each G_k as unit of measurement the quantity produced by one unit of labor in the process $\Pi^{(k)}$, it follows that $L_k = 1$. If labor is taken as *numéraire*, (25) becomes $p_k = 1$, which means that the new unit of G_k is the *dollar's worth*. Relation (23) yields

(26) $$L = \sum_{i=1}^{n} B_i.$$

This relation shows that the natural unit of measurement to be adopted whenever consolidation of industries is contemplated is the dollar's worth of product. This offers a justification for the procedure adopted by Leontief [1941, Chapter 3, pp. 14 ff.].

9. Some of the economic aspects of the above results deserve at this point to be emphasized and accompanied by a few comments. Something will also be added regarding the equilibrium of the closed model.

(a) The model described by the assumptions of Section 2 does not necessarily allow for the production of any bill of goods by labor alone (Corollary 5B.3).

(b) If one bill of goods, $(B_1^0, B_2^0, \cdots, B_\sigma^0, 0, 0, \cdots, 0)$, $B_k^0 > 0$, can be produced by labor alone, any other bill of the same type, $(B_1, B_2, \cdots, B_\sigma, 0, \cdots, 0)$, can also be produced by labor alone (Theorem 5B).

(c) The *rank* of the model (i.e., the maximum number of commodities contained in a bill of goods which can be produced by labor alone) may have any value from 0 to n with the exception of $n - 1$ (Theorem 8).

(d) If the rank of the model is t, there are t elementary commodities, $G_1, G_2, \cdots, G_t$, for which there is achievable a completely integrated process, i.e., a process producing G_k ($k \leq t$) and requiring only labor as input (Corollary 5B.2). It is open, therefore, to the economy to choose to produce only the elementary commodities.

(e) The conditions that the rank of the model be n are those expressed by Theorem 7A.

(f) There is a greatest lower bound to the amount of labor which can produce a given bill of elementary goods (Theorem 10). If the rank of the model is n, and if the technological horizon is closed, this bound is actually reached (Corollary 10.1).

If, however, H' is not closed, all L_k may be zero. In such a case any bill of goods would require only an infinitesimal amount of labor but could not be achieved without it. Labor would then have the role of a catalyst in the roundabout process of production.

(g) If H' is closed, and if the rank of the model is n, the set of elementary processes used by each industry for the optimum allocation of labor is independent of the bill of goods (i.e., independent of demand). Only their scale of production will be influenced by demand (Corollary 10.3).

(h) The long-run competitive equilibrium brings about the optimum allocation of resources (Theorem 12).

(i) If H' is closed, and if the rank of the model is n, the long-run competitive equilibrium prices are proportionate to the amount of labor input in the most efficient completely integrated processes, i.e., proportionate to L_k (Theorem 13). If H' is not closed and all $L_k = 0$, all goods are quasi-free with respect to the wage rate. Their relative prices will be, however, indeterminate.

(j) The long-run static equilibrium of the closed model will be possible only if $H^{(n+1)}$, the technological information of the household—the labor-producing industry—will contain a process,

$$(27) \qquad P^{(n+1)}(-a_1^{(n+1)}, -a_2^{(n+1)}, \cdots, -a_n^{(n+1)}, b_{n+1}),$$

such that $(a_1^{(n+1)}, a_2^{(n+1)}, \cdots, a_n^{(n+1)}, -b_{n+1})$ will be a process contained in H'. Indeed, in this case, there would be equality between the demand and the supply of goods and between the demand and supply of labor.

If $t = 0$, there is no static equilibrium of the closed model. If $t = n$ and H' is closed, (27) must be contained in the linear space (7). If (7) contains no process of $H^{(n+1)}$, static equilibrium is impossible. As enough labor is not forthcoming to produce the demanded bill of goods, the economy will contract down to nil.

If (7) cuts through $H^{(n+1)}$, i.e., if processes of $H^{(n+1)}$ exist on both sides of (7), the supply of labor is greater than that required by the most efficient way of producing some bills of goods. The economy may expand to infinity, or, alternatively, unemployment may appear.

PART TWO

APPLICATIONS OF
ALLOCATION MODELS

Chapter XI

ON THE CHOICE OF A CROP ROTATION PLAN

By Clifford Hildreth and Stanley Reiter

This chapter is concerned with the application of a linear production model to the problem of the selection of a crop rotation plan by an individual farmer. The analysis presented here is static and is relevant to the long-run decision as to which basic rotation and cultivation plan to adopt as a fairly permanent practice. It does not bear on problems of possible year-to-year deviations in plans due to weather or economic conditions experienced in a particular season. For purposes of exposition a number of simplifying assumptions are made. After a simple model has been developed, the effects of relaxing some of the assumptions can be easily indicated.

The farmer is visualized as dealing exclusively in competitive markets. This means that the prices he pays for inputs and receives for outputs are market determined and are independent of his production decisions.

The crops used for illustrations in this chapter are several that are common on Corn Belt farms. A rotation plan is a specification of a sequence of crops to be grown in successive years on a selected parcel of land. A rotation consisting of corn, oats, hay, abbreviated COH, for example, would mean that the parcel was to be planted in corn the first year, oats in the second, hay in the third, corn in the fourth, oats in the fifth, and so forth. This would be called a three-year rotation. A farmer who adopted this rotation would probably divide his cropland into subparcels and start some of his land at each stage of the rotation. This would spread his work more evenly through the year and provide to some degree a hedge against failure of a particular crop in one year. Thus, in considering long-run effects, we regard COH and OHC as the same rotation, but CHO would have to be considered a different rotation (i.e., hay after corn instead of after oats might have a different effect on the soil and might result in different average yields of the three crops).

For simplicity it will be assumed throughout most of this chapter that with each rotation is associated a particular cultivation plan (i.e., a particular sequence of soil treatments). The effect of recognizing that a particular rotation can be carried out with various cultural practices

177

will be briefly considered in Section 3.   It will also be assumed initially that the available land is homogeneous, and effects of relaxing this assumption will also be considered in Section 3.   Our example will be developed in somewhat more detail than would be necessary just to present the practical problem considered.   This will be done in order to illustrate some of the elementary properties of linear production models. These have already been developed by Koopmans [III] and are included here because the crop rotation application seems to be a convenient expository device.

1. The significant consequences of using a particular rotation are the crop yields the rotation will furnish and the input requirements (acres of land, hours of labor, gallons of fuel, etc.) necessary to carry out the rotation.   A rotation may be identified with a vector specifying these quantities.   For convenience we shall think of the quantities that represent a particular rotation as the average annual yields of crops and average annual inputs used for each acre devoted to this rotation (i.e., the rotation vector is normalized on land input).

Each rotation that is considered represents an activity in a linear model.   Each crop produced and each input used is treated as a commodity.   If we first consider only two rotations, say corn every year (CCC) and hay every year (HHH), and assume that land is the only input required, then the model appears as in Table I.[1]

TABLE I

Commodities	Activities	
	Rotation 1 CCC x_1	Rotation 2 HHH x_2
y_1 = corn output	a_{11}	0
y_2 = hay output	0	a_{22}
y_3 = land input	-1	-1

[1] As in Chapter III, a negative coefficient in an activity vector indicates that the associated commodity is used up in the activity.   In this chapter the term "input" is applied to a commodity that is typically used up in the kind of activities being considered, and refers to the negative number whose absolute value measures the extent of this using up.   This differs somewhat from Chapter III, where the term "input" refers to that absolute value rather than to its negative.

We assume first that the input of land is fixed, say $y_3 = -k$ and, therefore, $x_1 + x_2 = k$. Figure 1 then shows the alternative combinations of corn output and hay output that can be obtained by varying the levels x_1 and x_2 of the activities.

If all the land available is devoted to rotation 1, we get the point Q_1 (coordinates ka_{11} and 0); if all the land is devoted to rotation 2, we get the point Q_2 $(0, ka_{22})$. All other points on the line $\overline{Q_1Q_2}$ are obtained by apportioning the land between the two rotations in amounts αk and $(1 - \alpha)k$, where $0 \leqq \alpha \leqq 1$.

If the products cannot be destroyed or thrown away, the line $\overline{Q_1Q_2}$ is the set of all possible combinations of corn and hay from a given land input. It is also the set of efficient points for the given land input since, for every point, one coordinate can be increased only by decreasing the other.

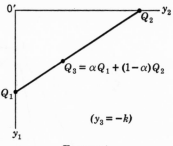

FIGURE 1

If products can be disposed of, the set of possible points is the triangle $\overline{Q_1 0' Q_2}$ since all points on or inside this triangle can be reached, for instance, by producing some combination on the line $\overline{Q_1Q_2}$ and throwing away appropriate quantities of product. However, the efficient point set remains the line $\overline{Q_1Q_2}$.

Let us now permit land input to vary. Then the triangle of Figure 1 is replaced by the cone $\overline{00'Q_1Q_2}$ in the three-dimensional commodity space shown in Figure 2. Figure 1 may then be regarded as the intersection of this cone with the plane $y_3 = -k$. Alternatively, the cone may be regarded as obtained by multiplication out of the origin of the triangle in Figure 1 by a variable nonnegative factor.

If disposal of commodities is ruled out, the efficient point set and the possible point set coincide and consist of the "front" facet of the cone (i.e., the two halflines from 0 through Q_1 and from 0 through Q_2 and the points of the plane angle spanned by these halflines).

If disposal of products is permitted, any combination of corn and hay represented by a point of the cone is possible. However, all such points cannot be efficient for, starting from an interior point, one can obtain more hay (corn) with the same amount of land and without giving up any corn (hay). Alternatively, for any interior point, it is possible to produce that combination of corn and hay with less land. Only those points lying on the "front" facet of the cone are efficient.

The equation of the plane through 0, Q_1, Q_2 determines the rates of substitution or transformation between commodities in efficient production.   In the notation of Table I, the equation of this plane is

(1)
$$y_3 = -\frac{1}{a_{11}} y_1 - \frac{1}{a_{22}} y_2.$$

Thus the marginal rate of substitution of hay for corn is a_{22}/a_{11}, and the marginal rates of transformation are a_{11} between corn and land and a_{22} between hay and land.

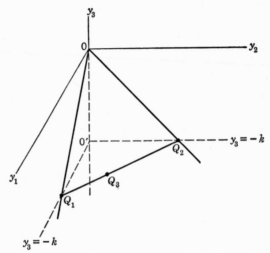

FIGURE 2

It is clear in this simple case that a farmer with a fixed amount of land and these two production alternatives, seeking to maximize the return to his land and entrepreneurship, would choose between corn and hay on the basis of their relative prices.   If the ratio of the price [2] of corn (p_1) to the price of hay (p_2) exceeds the equivalence ratio for hay in terms of corn $(p_1/p_2 > a_{22}/a_{11})$, then corn will be chosen, and conversely for hay.   The case where $p_1/p_2 = a_{22}/a_{11}$ is one of indifference in which corn, hay, and any combination of αk acres of corn and $(1 - \alpha)k$ acres of hay $(0 < \alpha < 1)$ would be equally profitable.

The market price ratio p_1/p_2 determines a family of parallel lines in the (y_1, y_2)-space such that all points on a given line represent combinations of y_1 and y_2 that have equal market value.   Combinations of equal market value are indicated by dotted lines in Figure 3.   The interior angle formed by the intersection of such a line with the positive y_1-axis is $\theta_1 = \arctan(p_1/p_2)$.   The line through the origin perpendic-

[2] For a comparison of the notation for prices in this chapter with that of Chapter III, see footnote 3 of the Introduction (p. 9).

ular to the constant-value lines, $\overline{O'V}$ in Figure 3, has the property that the market value of any point (y_1, y_2) can be measured by the projection of the point on this line.   Thus it may be called the value axis,[3] and it intersects the positive y_2-axis at an angle equal to θ_1.

So long as y_1 and y_2 have positive prices the value axis will lie in the positive quadrant of the (y_1, y_2)-plane. $\overline{O'V'}$, perpendicular to $\overline{Q_1Q_2}$, has the interesting property that all price combinations whose value

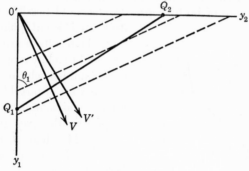

FIGURE 3

axes lie between $\overline{O'V'}$ and the y_1-axis make y_1 the more profitable crop. This is just another way of phrasing the statement above that corn is more profitable if $p_1/p_2 > a_{22}/a_{11}$.

2. The ideas developed so far carry over into somewhat more complex cases quite readily.   Consider the four rotations described in Table II.

TABLE II

Commodities	Activities			
	Rotation 1 CCC x_1	Rotation 2 HHH x_2	Rotation 3 CCH x_3	Rotation 4 CHH x_4
y_1 = corn output	a_{11}	0	a_{13}	a_{14}
y_2 = hay output	0	a_{22}	a_{23}	a_{24}
y_3 = land input	-1	-1	-1	-1

[3] If p_1 and p_2 are measured in dollars, any point (y_1, y_2) that projects to the point $[p_1/(p_1^2 + p_2^2), p_2/(p_1^2 + p_2^2)]$ on the value axis will have a market value of one dollar. This may be regarded as the unit point on the value axis.

Again, assume land input fixed at k acres ($x_1 + x_2 + x_3 + x_4 = k$). The results of raising corn only or hay only are again indicated by points Q_1 and Q_2 in Figure 4. The results of growing two corn crops followed by a hay crop are indicated by Q_3 (coordinates ka_{13}, ka_{23}). Had Q_3 been an interior point of the old set of possible points, say at Q_3', this would have indicated that land reacted unfavorably to alternation of crops. Q_3' would not add to the set of possible points and would not be an efficient point since there are combinations of rotations 1 and 2 that produce more of both crops. Q_3 does add possible points and is itself an efficient point. Q_4 repre-

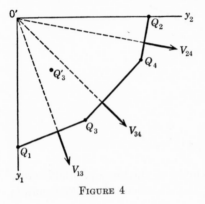

FIGURE 4

sents the results of growing one corn crop and two hay crops on each parcel of land in each three-year period. The new set of possible points is the interior and boundary of the polygon formed by the axes and $\overline{Q_1Q_3Q_4Q_2}$. The broken line $\overline{Q_1Q_3Q_4Q_2}$ is the corresponding set of efficient points and is comparable to a product substitution curve of the usual economic theory. There are now three marginal rates of substitution of hay for corn, one corresponding to each segment of the efficient point set. Along the segment $\overline{Q_1Q_3}$ the rate is $a_{23}/(a_{11} - a_{13})$, along $\overline{Q_3Q_4}$ it is $(a_{24} - a_{23})/(a_{13} - a_{14})$, and along $\overline{Q_4Q_2}$ it is $(a_{22} - a_{24})/a_{14}$. As before, any pair of positive prices for corn and hay give rise to a value axis passing through the origin. $\overline{O'V_{13}}$ is the value axis corresponding to pairs of prices such that $p_1/p_2 = a_{23}/(a_{11} - a_{13})$. At these prices rotations 1 and 3 and all combinations of them are equally profitable.[4] For price combinations such that $p_1/p_2 > a_{23}/(a_{11} - a_{13})$, rotation 1 would be most profitable and the value axis would lie between $\overline{O'V_{13}}$ and the y_1-axis. Similarly, if $a_{23}/(a_{11} - a_{13}) < p_1/p_2 < (a_{24} - a_{23})/(a_{13} - a_{14})$, the value axis lies between $\overline{O'V_{13}}$ and $\overline{O'V_{34}}$ and rotation 3 is the most profitable. Corresponding statements can be made about price ratios in the other two ranges. Thus the three lines perpendicular to segments of the efficient point set classify possible combinations of market prices into four groups, each group containing those price combinations at which a particular rotation plan is most profitable.

[4] Profitability in this context is measured by the total value of the two crops raised. This would include both economic profit and rent.

As in Section 1, if we consider land a variable, the set of possible points becomes a cone and the set of efficient points becomes part of its boundary. This is shown in Figure 5. The efficient point set now has three facets corresponding to the three efficient line segments of Figure 4.

The set of efficient points is conceptually the same as the transformation surface usually employed in the theory of the firm. Marginal rates of substitution and transformation are usually visualized as varying continuously on the transformation surface, whereas, under the assumptions

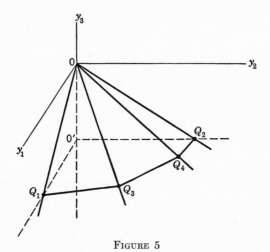

FIGURE 5

employed here, the marginal rates change discontinuously at the edges of facets of the efficient point set and are constant at all points in the interior of a facet. Each of the three "front" facets of the cone in Figure 5 determines a set of marginal rates of substitution and transformation. For example, the equation of the plane through 0, Q_1, Q_3 is

(2)
$$y_3 = -\frac{1}{a_{11}} y_1 - \left(\frac{1}{a_{23}} - \frac{a_{13}}{a_{11}a_{23}} \right) y_2.$$

This determines the marginal rate of substitution of hay for corn as $a_{23}/(a_{11} - a_{13})$ and the marginal rate of transformation between hay and land as $a_{11}a_{23}/(a_{11} - a_{13})$.

3. It may now be useful to consider the following practical situation. A farmer has the use of a certain parcel of land, say k acres, assumed to be homogeneous, and wishes to choose among several rotations. Suppose that data are available from technical experiments to show the average yield of various crops to be expected under each of the alter-

native rotations.[5] Suppose further that the farmer can estimate the various resources that would be required to carry out each rotation. This information could be summarized in a form such as Table III,

Table III

Commodities	Activities			
	Rotation 1 CCC x_1	Rotation 2 HHH x_2	Rotation 3 CCH x_3	Rotation 4 CHH x_4
y_1 = corn output	a_{11}	0	a_{13}	a_{14}
y_2 = hay output	0	a_{22}	a_{23}	a_{24}
y_3 = land input	-1	-1	-1	-1
y_4 = labor input	a_{41}	a_{42}	a_{43}	a_{44}
y_5 = equipment input	a_{51}	a_{52}	a_{53}	a_{54}
y_6 = fuel input	a_{61}	a_{62}	a_{63}	a_{64}

which differs from Table II in that it contains rows for inputs other than land. The coefficients in the last four rows represent inputs used per acre of land cultivated and are therefore negative.

The farmer's profit, π, can be written

$$(3) \qquad \pi = \sum_{i=1}^{6} p_i y_i,$$

where p_i is the price of the ith commodity. His profit if he chooses the jth rotation will be

$$(4) \qquad \pi_j = k \sum_{i=1}^{6} a_{ij} p_i.$$

The difference between profit under the jth rotation and under the lth rotation is

$$(5) \qquad \pi_j - \pi_l = k \sum_{i=1}^{6} (a_{ij} - a_{il}) p_i.$$

For given values of the a's, the equation

$$(6) \qquad \pi_j - \pi_l = 0$$

[5] Such data are available for some rotations on certain types of land; see e.g., Browning, et al. [1948].

is a hyperplane in the 6-dimensional space of all possible commodity prices and divides the space into two sectors, one including those price combinations for which the jth rotation is more profitable ($\pi_j - \pi_l > 0$) and the other including those prices for which the lth rotation is more profitable ($\pi_j - \pi_l < 0$). Such a plane exists for each pair of rotations, and together they would divide the price space into four subsets which we shall refer to as sectors, each sector consisting of those price combinations for which a given rotation is most profitable. On the boundaries of these sectors two or more rotations are equally profitable.

Since, in our example, all planes are parallel to the land-price axis, no information would be lost by considering only a 5-dimensional price space, omitting p_3. The sectors corresponding to the alternative rotations are convex since $\pi_j - \pi_l > 0$ for p, and $\pi_j - \pi_l > 0$ for p^* implies $\pi_j - \pi_l > 0$ for $\alpha p + (1 - \alpha)p^*$, $(0 \leqq \alpha \leqq 1)$. With some approximations, the information in these sectors could be represented in a 2-dimensional figure. Generally speaking, prices paid by farmers for factors of production are more stable than prices of crops raised. An approximate representation might be obtained by inserting average prices for a recent period for p_4, p_5, p_6 and regarding these as constants, thus reducing equations like (6) to lines in the (p_1, p_2)-space.

The equation $\pi_j - \pi_l = 0$ could then be written

$$(7) \qquad (a_{1j} - a_{1l})p_1 + (a_{2j} - a_{2l})p_2 + (c_j - c_l) = 0,$$

where $c_j = \sum_{i=4}^{6} a_{ij}p_i$ ($j = 1, \cdots, 4$) and is regarded as a constant. The six equations like (7) determine boundaries of rotation sectors in the (p_1, p_2)-space as illustrated in Figure 6. The six lines of equal

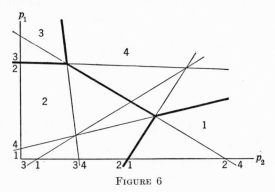

FIGURE 6

profits are shown with the numbers appearing along the coordinate axes showing which two rotations are compared by a particular line. The rotation numbers also show on which side of a line a particular rotation is more profitable.   The four sectors bounded by the heavy lines inside the axes are numbered to show which rotation is most profitable for price combinations in each sector.   The existence of four points at which three lines of equal profits intersect may be regarded as typical.   Whenever we have a point such that $\pi_j - \pi_l = 0$ and $\pi_j - \pi_m = 0$, then it is also true that $\pi_l - \pi_m = 0$ at that point.[6]

The situation represented by Table III is a highly simplified example, but the way in which a number of complexities could be incorporated is clear.   Additional rotations would add columns to the table, additional crops or resources used would add rows.   If the farmer wished to consider alternative cultivation practices for some rotations, each combination of a specific rotation and a specific cultivation practice would represent a distinct activity and would add a column to the table.   However, the procedure for translating the relevant technical information into sets of prices for which particular activities are more profitable would remain unchanged.

If the farmer had more than one type of land, there would be a set of activities for each type of land.   If the quantities of each type of land were regarded as fixed, a separate table could be used for each type and the problems of the best rotation and cultivation plan for each type of land could be considered separately.

4. To shorten the discussion of a few points related to the previous sections, let the model be expressed in matrix form

$$(8) \qquad\qquad y = Ax,$$

where y is the commodity vector whose elements are products produced and resources used as in the previous example. A is a matrix of coefficients of the sort contained in Table III, and x is a vector of levels of activities stating the extent to which each is used.   Let p be the price vector whose elements are the prices of the commodities, y.   Then profit, π, is given by

$$(9) \qquad\qquad \pi = p'y.$$

It is plain that, if the entrepreneur is unrestricted in his selection of x, if prices are independent of his decision, and if one of the activities yields a positive profit, then the entrepreneur can make any desired profit by choosing the appropriate value for x_i, the element of x corresponding to the activity which yields a positive profit.   This situation, of course, is

[6] The four points could be identical, or it could happen that one or more of the rotations are worse than others for all prices, in which case fewer lines and sectors would appear in Figure 4.

not realized in practice.   Any entrepreneur who expanded one or more
activities far enough would encounter some violation of these conditions
for indefinitely large profit.   He would find himself bidding up prices of
resources used, forcing down prices of products sold, exhausting available
resources at least in their more efficient forms, or exhausting his financial
resources.   In any given case it is probable that several of these exist as
potential limits to the expansion of an activity or group of activities.
However, some of the restrictions may be ineffective in that the most
profitable selection of activity levels is the same in a model which includes
them and in a model which excludes them.

In Section 3 it was assumed that the only effective restriction was that
the amount of land available to the farmer was fixed.   In models where
a limitation on one resource is the only effective restriction, the problem
of selecting the optimal collection of activities reduces to the problem of
selecting one activity that yields highest returns per unit of the fixed
resource.   Thus the discussion has been limited to a highly special situation, though it is a situation of some practical interest.

In classical competitive equilibrium theory, profit is eliminated by the
bidding of entrepreneurs for land.   This can be expressed in a linear
model by letting the vector y and the matrix A include only commodities
other than land. $\pi = p'y$ then represents the sum of profits and rent.
If other resources are plentiful and land is scarce, profits will be pushed
to zero and the whole quantity π will be rent.   Furthermore, competition will force each entrepreneur to use the best activity to avoid losses.
The problem of selection of a best activity under these conditions has
been analyzed in Section 3.   Let a_j^* be the column of A corresponding
to a best activity (i.e., $\pi_j = kp'a_j^* \geq \pi_l$ for all l).   The rent per acre
is then equal to $p'a_j^*$.   Similarly, if several types of land exist in an
economy, we could write

$$(10) \qquad\qquad y = [A \ \ B \ \ C \ \cdots]x,$$

where $[A \ \ B \ \ C \ \cdots]$ is a matrix of activities arranged so that activities
using land of, say, type A appear at the left, activities using land of
type B appear next, etc.   Rents for the respective types of land would
then be $p'a_j^*$, $p'b_l^*$, $p'c_m^*$, etc., where b_l^* and c_m^* are columns corresponding
to best activities on land of types B and C, respectively.   The difference
in rent between, say, type A and type B would be equal to $p'(a_j^* - b_l^*)$.
This is the difference in net value productivity and corresponds to the
classical notion of differences in rents being determined by differences in
productivity.

Another interesting question can be explored by considering the hyperplanes in the price space of the form $p'a_i^* = 0$.   Each of these represents

a set of price combinations at which the ith activity would yield zero rent on land of type A. It divides the price space into two sectors, one containing prices at which the activity will yield a positive rent, the other containing prices at which the activity will yield negative rent. If this is done for all activities, the set of prices at which no activity yields a positive rent will either be empty or be a convex set. If it is a nonempty convex set, its boundaries could be considered the price margins of cultivation.

CHAPTER XII

DEVELOPMENT OF DYNAMIC MODELS FOR PROGRAM PLANNING

By MARSHALL K. WOOD AND MURRAY A. GEISLER

The development of dynamic models for program planning will be discussed in the context of military planning problems, as that is the area in which our experience lies. We believe that the techniques discussed in this chapter are applicable to other types of program planning problems, particularly in planning for organizations or economic systems where relationships are largely technological and decision making is highly centralized, as contrasted with those in which decision making is mainly decentralized and relationships depend primarily on individual human reactions. The material presented here is the work of the entire staff of the Planning Research Division, Comptroller, U. S. Air Force.

1. GENERAL PROBLEMS OF PROGRAM PLANNING

It was once possible for a Supreme Commander to plan operations personally. As the planning problem expanded in space, time, and general complexity, however, the inherent limitations in the capacity of any one man were encountered. Military histories are filled with instances of commanders who failed because they bogged down in details, not because they could not eventually have mastered the details, but because they could not master all the relevant details in the time available for decision.

Gradually, as planning problems became more complex, the Supreme Commander came to be surrounded with a General Staff of specialists, which supplemented the Chief in making decisions. The existence of a General Staff permitted the subdivision of the planning process and the assignment of experts to handle each part. The function of the Chief then became one of selecting objectives, coordinating, planning, and resolving conflicts between staff sections.

In judging the acceptability of a planning procedure it is necessary to establish criteria. To be acceptable a plan must embody desired and attainable objectives. It must be consistent in the sense that all parts

189

of the plan must be mutually self-supporting. Furthermore, it must be timely, both with respect to the objectives and assumptions incorporated in it and with respect to the starting date from which its projections are made.

We can picture the staff response to this problem of consistent programming in four stages. In the first stage each agency prepares its own program more or less autonomously for the guidance of its own operations. Staff action is coordinated mainly at the top level. Changes in directives are frequent and programs are built on such information about objectives and related parts of the program as happens to be available. When such a program is put together as of a given cut-off date, it is found to have parts which vary widely in basic objectives. Those parts of the program which are closely related to the basic tactical plan are found to be comparatively up to date, while those parts which are logically several steps removed may represent objectives which are already obsolete.

The second stage marks a recognition by the staff of the need for consistency. It is directed that a single and consistent program shall be developed with objectives and assumptions as of a given date. But frequent directives modifying or totally changing these premises continue to be issued. Since no operator can afford not to reflect the latest changes in his operations, such a heroic effort to attain consistency will have ceased to have operational significance long before completion of the program and its dissemination to the staff and operating commands.

In stage three program consistency is recognized, not as something that can be imposed, but as something that must be built into staff procedures. The program is seen as a logical unfolding of the implications of the stated objectives as determined by the planning factors or operational structure. This procedural approach to the problem of program consistency involves an analysis of the parts of the program in relation to each other. The responsibility of each staff agency to furnish program information to the other staff agencies is specifically defined and a sequence of work established so that prerequisite material is made available as needed in advance of the program step dependent on it. In short, a schedule for programming is set up with deadlines for staff action by all participating agencies. The procedure works best when programming is set up on a recurring basis so that program changes can be withheld and consolidated for dissemination at stated intervals known in advance.

Figure 1 illustrates schematically the application of this procedure to Air Force wartime program scheduling. The entire program was started off with a war plan in which were contained the wartime objectives.

From this plan, by successive stages, as shown by the flow lines, the wartime program specifying unit deployment to the combat theaters, training requirements of flying personnel and technical personnel, supply and maintenance program, etc., was computed. In order to obtain consistent programming the ordering of the steps in the schedule was so

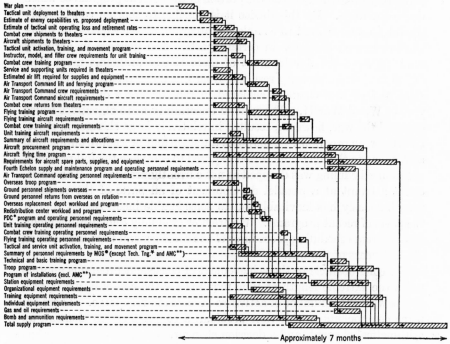

War plan
Tactical unit deployment to theaters
Estimate of enemy capabilities vs. proposed deployment
Estimate of tactical unit operating loss and retirement rates
Combat crew shipments to theaters
Aircraft shipments to theaters
Tactical unit activation, training, and movement program
Instructor, model, and filler crew requirements for unit training
Combat crew training program
Service and supporting units required in theaters
Estimated air lift required for supplies and equipment
Air Transport Command lift and ferrying program
Air Transport Command crew requirements
Air Transport Command aircraft requirements
Combat crew returns from theaters
Flying training program
Flying training aircraft requirements
Combat crew training aircraft requirements
Unit training aircraft requirements
Summary of aircraft requirements and allocations
Aircraft procurement program
Aircraft flying time program
Requirements for aircraft spare parts, supplies, and equipment
Fourth Echelon supply and maintenance program and operating personnel requirements
Air Transport Command operating personnel requirements
Overseas troop program
Ground personnel shipments overseas
Ground personnel returns from overseas on rotation
Overseas replacement depot workload and program
Redistribution center workload and program
PDC* program and operating personnel requirements
Unit training operating personnel requirements
Combat crew training operating personnel requirements
Flying training operating personnel requirements
Tactical and service unit activation, training, and movement program
Summary of personnel requirements by MOS* (except Tech. Tng.* and AMC**)
Technical and basic training program
Troop program
Program of installations (excl. AMC**)
Station equipment requirements
Organizational equipment requirements
Training equipment requirements
Individual equipment requirements
Gas and oil requirements
Bomb and ammunition requirements
Total supply program

◄──────────── Approximately 7 months ────────────►

* Personnel Distribution Command   * Military Occupational Specialty
★ Technical Training   ** Air Materiel Command

FIGURE 1—Schematic diagram of major steps in Air Force wartime program scheduling.

arranged that the flow of information from echelon to echelon was only in one direction, and also the time phasing of information availability was such that the portion of the program prepared at each step did not depend on any following step. The major difficulty with this procedure was that it took too long. Even with the most careful scheduling, it took about seven months to complete the process.

Stage four represents an attempt to cut the time required by a partial sacrifice of consistency for the sake of increased timeliness. This is accomplished by establishing the entire programming procedure on a recurring cyclical basis, with a partial overlap between successive cycles, so that some material pertaining to a program already computed can feed the current sequence as a first approximation for program information which otherwise could only be made available much later. Data extracted from a previous program must be carefully selected, in order to insure that the data used are either for activities which remain fairly stable through successive programs or for activities which exert a comparatively small influence on the portion of the current program to which they contribute. By this device it is possible to shorten considerably the total time required to complete a program, at the expense of somewhat decreased accuracy in certain parts. The increase in accuracy resulting from the development of more timely programs more than offsets the loss in accuracy resulting from this approximation procedure.

Stage four was virtually achieved in the Air Force during the last year of World War II. The general uncertainty as to objectives which followed the war, however, resulted in relatively large changes in objectives between programs. This made the stage four procedure impractical and, owing to the long time period required to complete the full program, program scheduling was dropped as not currently practical. The consequent attempt at a parallel development of all parts of the program simultaneously has inevitably led to considerable inconsistency among the parts of recent programs. We are now gradually reinstituting modified program scheduling procedures of the same general type used during the last years of the war.

The chief obstacle to the achievement of consistent programs appears to be the extreme length of time required for the computation of programs where the number of activities involved is very large. There are three components to this time problem: a communication element, an arithmetical element, and a decision element.

Let us examine each of these in turn. The time required for *communication between staff agencies* can be materially reduced by careful scheduling of the work of each agency and of the flow of program documents between agencies. Where dozens of different staff agencies are involved, however, there is of necessity a considerable lag involved in communication. An agency can seldom be expected to write, type, sign, and transmit a document to another agency in less than a day or two. Even if no time were consumed in actual work, the time lag resulting would be unacceptable. The only cure for this would seem to be centralization of the work; but we have already seen that the complexity and diversity of the information required is such as to preclude successful completion of a program by any one man or small group of men. A procedure is needed whereby the information available in the many staff sections can be brought together in one place in advance of the program problem and then assembled mechanically.

The *arithmetic element* is the simplest to cope with. Once the under-lying structure of the operations involved is analyzed and reduced to a systematic and explicit form, most of the relationships involved are found to be of a simple character which can readily be mechanized. This re-quires a quantitative analysis of the relations among the various items to be programmed. If we are programming gasoline, for example, we need to establish relations between gasoline consumption and flying time based on the statistical records of each. From such systematic studies a set of planning factors can be developed. The complete set of planning factors for one activity, a complex operation, or the Air Force as a whole, expresses the structure of that activity, operation, or the Air Force. The structure thus defined is the planner's basic tool.

In general, structures are not fixed once and for all but require con-stant scrutiny. A distinction must be made between structures which are determined by technological relations and those which have been established by statistical analysis. The technological structure of a single activity may be considered fixed from the outset. If the activity should be redesigned so that the factors involved are changed, it is best to consider that a new activity has been substituted for the old and proceed with the programming accordingly. If, however, we are dealing with structures which are statistical in nature, we must proceed more cautiously. Two or more activities may be lumped together and rela-tions established between the aggregate quantities involved. The pro-portions of these activities entering into the aggregate may be subject to change. Only in the event of stability in the relative importance of the included activities is it useful to program with the aid of statistically determined structures. This is the basic weakness of all programming in terms of aggregates.

The *decision making* involved in the programming process is of two types. The first includes decisions which are required because of initial failure to define objectives in precise terms. Care in the initial state-ment of objectives can eliminate this problem.

The second type of decisions required is that resulting from failure to define adequately in advance the complete range and structure of the *types* of operations or activities to be performed. Decisions respecting changes in the structure of operations should, in so far as possible, be made in anticipation of program computation rather than held up so as to delay it. However, over-all limitations may force changes in the structure of operation which cannot be anticipated. When this hap-pens, it is usually best to complete the program with the structure as initially defined and then to alter the structure in a later revision.

We have been discussing the problems of consistency and timeliness in relation to program planning. Another major deficiency of existing programming procedures is the inability to consider adequately alternative courses of action. In general, there are many possible programs for accomplishing a given objective. The possible variations include not only different combinations of activities in the same time period but also different time phasing of activities. Thus, in addition to choices between, for example, more bombers and fewer fighters in the same time period, there are choices like that of fewer bombers now and more later. The direct consequence of the necessity of making choices with respect to time phasing is a vast increase in the complexity of the planning problem. For now, instead of activities and items which have constant definitions through all time periods, each activity and each item must be particularized for each such period. Thus a B-29 Air Force bomber is not simply a B-29, but a B-29 available in a certain time period. A Pilot Training School is not a continuous activity, but a series of distinct activities in a succession of time periods.

These complexities have been spelled out to indicate a whole range of planning problems which, because of the present difficulties of computing alternative programs, receive little or no consideration. *So much time and effort is now devoted to working out the operational program that no attention can be given to the question whether there may not be some better program that is equally compatible with the given conditions.* It is perhaps too much to suppose that this difference between programs is as much as the difference between victory and defeat, but it is certainly a significant difference with respect to the tax dollar and the division of the total national product between military and civilian uses.

Consideration of the practical advantages to be gained by comparative programming, and particularly by the selection of "best" programs, leads to a requirement for a technique for handling all program elements simultaneously and for introducing the maximization process directly into the computation of programs. Such a technique is now in prospect.

2. FORMULATION OF THE MATHEMATICAL MODEL

As discussed in Chapter I, we are attempting to solve these problems by the construction of a mathematical model of Air Force operations which can be manipulated with a large scale digital electronic computer or, as an interim measure, with the punched card electrical accounting equipment now available. In constructing the mathematical model of Air Force operations we have used the special finite model discussed in Chapter II. An Air Force program then consists of a schedule giving the magnitudes or levels of each of these activities for each of a number of time periods within the larger general time interval covered by the program.

Each of the activities has certain requirements for real estate, equipment, supplies, personnel, funds, collectively referred to hereafter as *items*. The interrelationships between activities and the equations expressing them are perhaps best explained through the medium of an example. For this purpose a simplified model of the Berlin airlift has been chosen.

Consider first the actual flying operation itself. It produces supplies in Berlin; it requires aircrews, aircraft, and runways for its operation; it consumes funds for gasoline and for pay of aircrews and ground personnel. It also uses up part of the aircraft inventory as a result of crashes and normal wear and tear. Thus there are two types of coefficients for each item, called *input* coefficients and *output* coefficients. The coefficients for all items together completely define the activity. The input coefficients define the amounts of each item required at the beginning of a unit time period or consumed during the time period to permit unit amount operation of the activity; the output coefficients define the amounts of each item left over at the end of a unit time period or produced during the time period as a result of unit amount operation of the activity.

The input coefficient is obtained as the sum of the capital equipment, the attrition, and the consumption, all of which must be on hand at the beginning of the time period. The output coefficient is the sum of the capital equipment (which normally equals its input value) and the production per unit of the activity, both of which are available at the end of the time period. The capital equipment consists of items which are utilized by the activity in carrying on operations but which remain essentially unchanged at the end of the operation. Real estate, aircraft, and operating personnel are usually in this category.

The derivation of the input and output coefficients is illustrated in Table I. The coefficient for the 95,000 tons of supplies delivered in Berlin has been put into the consumption column and given a minus sign, instead of being shown in the production column, because, under the rule just described, the output is considered one time unit later than the input, whereas the delivery of supplies by air is a continuous process which involves a negligible time lag in terms of the size of time units being used. This time lag is the essential distinction between the input and output coefficients as they are used here, rather than an implication of direction of flow which might be inferred from the words.

The unit "crew capacity" has been used and treated as a consumption item in place of using "crews" as a capital equipment item because the loss of crews as a result of the operation is not a function primarily of the amount of flying but of the age distribution of the crews in terms of the length of time they have been flying the airlift. In this example a policy of retiring airlift crews to other less exacting jobs after six months of flying the airlift is assumed. This is reflected in activities V and VI and in items 3 and 4 in Table II. Item 4, "new crews," represents

TABLE I. COMPUTATION OF INPUT AND OUTPUT COEFFICIENTS

ACTIVITY II—FLYING THE AIRLIFT *

Items	Unit of Measure	Required at the Beginning of Time Period				Available at End of Time Period		
		Capital Equipment	Attrition	Consumption	Total Input Coefficient	Capital Equipment	Production	Total Output Coefficient
Supplies in Berlin	Thousands of tons			−95	−95			
Runways	Number of runways	1			1	1		1
Crew capacity	Number of crews			134	134			
Aircraft	Number of aircraft	39	5		44	39		39
Money	Millions of dollars			8.7	8.7			

* Unit of activity: 10,000 flights; unit of time: three months.

crews which have just started their six-month tour of duty on the airlift; item 3, "experienced crews," represents crews which have completed half of their six-month tour. One hundred one crews of either type will produce 100 units of crew capacity; if experienced crews are used (activity V), no crews will be left as they are retired from the airlift, whereas 100 experienced crews will remain if new crews are used (activity VI). New crews for activity VI must be procured from "training new crews" (activity VIII). In training, an average of 67 new crews acting as instructors at the beginning of the three-month period will produce 1,000 new crews. Actually the production may be weekly during the period, but it is shown in this simplified model as if it all occurred at the end of the three-month period. It is further seen that 44 aircraft are required on the airlift to operate 10,000 flights in a three-month period. Thirty-nine of these aircraft are required for the continuous operation, and 5 extra are required as replacements for aircraft which crash or are worn out during the operation.

The unit coefficient in activity I, "supplying Berlin," merely provides that the amount of supplies delivered to Berlin will be expressed in thousands of tons. Activity II, "flying the airlift," will deliver during the period 95,000 tons of supplies for 10,000 flights. Operating and support costs for this will be $8,700,000, as seen by the coefficient of 8.7 on the money row under activity II. The input coefficient of unity against the runways item of activity II means that each runway is capable of supporting 10,000 flights during a three-month period. The companion output coefficient of unity indicates that the runway is still available for use at the end of the time period.

In order to increase the level of activity beyond that which can be supported by the available runways in Berlin, additional runways will have to be constructed. (It is here assumed that there is an excess of runway capacity at the western termini of the airlift.) Activity III, "constructing runways in Berlin," is constrained to take on integral values, as can be seen from the restrictions on the variables given under Table II. A look at the coefficients of activity III shows that, in order to construct one runway in Berlin, 2,000 tons of supply (e.g., steel matting, traffic control equipment, bulldozers, etc.) as well as $1,230,000 will be consumed during the three-month period. At the end of the three-month period, one runway will be ready for use.

The purpose of activity IV, "slough-off of unused runway capacity," is to use up any part of a runway which may not be used because the airlift activity is not composed of units of exactly 10,000 flights. As long as activity II provides an integral number of runways, we will never, by this device, be creating programs which utilize a portion of a runway.

Thus far the individual activities have been described. It is pertinent now to discuss the equations which interrelate these activities. Table II may be considered a table of detached coefficients from which the equations shown below can be derived. The basic rule is to multiply the outputs of each activity per unit of activity by the level of the activity in a given time period and sum for each equipment item. This gives the total available as inputs for the next time period; accordingly, each sum of inputs for period t is equated to the corresponding sum of outputs for period $t - 1$.

Equation (1) states that the tonnage supplied to Berlin, $x_1^{(t)}$, in any period equals the amount shipped in, $95x_2^{(t)}$, less the amount used to construct new airfields in Berlin, $2x_3^{(t)}$. It should be noted that all output coefficients for this equipment item are zero; hence no activity level for the previous period appears in this equation.

TABLE II. HYPOTHETICAL MODEL OF BERLIN AIRLIFT: FLOW COEFFICIENTS OF BASIC ACTIVITIES FOR THREE-MONTH PERIOD †

Item	I Supplying Berlin (per thousand tons)		II Flying the Airlift (per ten thousand flights)		III Constructing Runways in Berlin (per runway)		IV Slough-off of Unused Runway Capacity (per runway)		V Using Experienced Crews (per hundred crews)	
	I‡	O‡	I	O	I	O	I	O	I	O
1. Supplies in Berlin * (thousands of tons)	1		-95							
2. Runways in Berlin (number of runways)					2	1	1	1		
3. Experienced crews (number of crews)			1						101	
4. New crews (number of crews)									-100	
5. Crew capacity * (number of crews)			134							
6. Aircraft (number of aircraft)			44	39						
7. Money (millions of dollars)			8.7		1.2					
Symbol for Quantity of Activity during tth Time Period	$x_1^{(t)} \geq 0$		$x_2^{(t)} \geq 0$		$x_3^{(t)} = 0, 1, 2, \cdots$		$x_4^{(t)} \geq 0$		$x_5^{(t)} \geq 0$	

* See footnote ‡.

† The figures shown in this table are illustrative and are not to be used in planning.

‡ I represents total *input* (per unit of activity) at the beginning of period, O represents *output* at end of period. However, for starred items it is flow during a three-month period where + means flow consumed by the activity and − means flow produced by the activity.

Item	Activities VI Using New Crews (per hundred crews)		VII Slough-off of Unused Crew Capacity (per hundred crews)		VIII Training New Crews (per thousand crews)		IX Storing of Unused Aircraft (per aircraft)		X Exogenous Supply $(t-1)$th Period	
	I	O	I	O	I	O	I	O	I	O
1. Supplies in Berlin * (thousands of tons)										
2. Runways in Berlin (number of runways)										
3. Experienced crews (number of crews)		100								
4. New crews (number of crews)	101				67	1,000				$C^{(0)}$
5. Crew capacity * (number of crews)	−100		100							
6. Aircraft (number of aircraft)					47	43	1	1		$A^{(t-1)}$
7. Money (millions of dollars)			.024		2.9					$B^{(t-1)}$
Symbol for Quantity of Activity during tth Time Period	$x_6^{(t)} \geqq 0$		$x_7^{(t)} \geqq 0$		$x_8^{(t)} \geqq 0$		$x_9^{(t)} \geqq 0$		$x_{10}^{(t)} \geqq 1$	

Equations Represented by Table II:

(1) $x_1^{(t)} + 2x_3^{(t)} = 95 x_2^{(t)}$

(2) $x_2^{(t)} + x_4^{(t)} = x_2^{(t-1)} + x_3^{(t-1)} + x_4^{(t-1)}$

(3) $101 x_5^{(t)} = 100 x_6^{(t-1)}$

(4) $101 x_6^{(t)} + 67 x_8^{(t)} = 1{,}000 x_8^{(t-1)} + C^{(0)} \delta_1^{(t)}$

(5) $134 x_2^{(t)} + x_7^{(t)} = 100 x_5^{(t)} + 100 x_6^{(t)}$

(6) $44 x_2^{(t)} + 47 x_8^{(t)} + x_9^{(t)} = 39 x_2^{(t-1)} + 43 x_8^{(t-1)} + x_9^{(t-1)} + A^{(t-1)}$

(7) $8.7 x_2^{(t)} + 1.2 x_3^{(t)} + 0.024 x_7^{(t)} + 2.9 x_8^{(t)} = B^{(t-1)}$

$(\delta_1^{(t)} = 1$ if $t = 1$, and $\delta_1^{(t)} = 0$ if $t \neq 1)$

Equation (2) states that the number of runways available for use in the tth period, $(x_2^{(t)} + x_4^{(t)})$, is equal to the number in use in the $(t - 1)$th period, $(x_2^{(t-1)} + x_4^{(t-1)})$, plus the number constructed, $x_3^{(t-1)}$.

Equation (3) states that the level of experienced crew activity during the tth period is equal to output of experienced crews from new crew operations of the previous period.

Equation (4) states that the new crews produced in training during $t - 1$, $1{,}000x_8^{(t-1)}$, are shared between training, $67x_8^{(t)}$, and overseas operations of new crews, $101x_6^{(t)}$, during the tth period. $C^{(0)}$ represents the initial availability of new crews at the start of the operation.

Equation (5) states that the crew capacity produced by activities V and VI must be equal to or greater than the amount used in airlift operations. The level $x_7^{(t)}$, being nonnegative, assures this condition. It will be noted that crews, even if not used, must be paid, fed, housed, and administered. Their nonuse costs \$24,000 per crew for three months. This takes care of continuing expenses that are incurred if bad weather sets in and curtails operations; this is the reason why $x_7^{(t)}$ appears in equation (7).

Equation (6) states that the input requirements of aircraft during the tth period for activities of training, airlift, or storage is equal to the output of these activities for the previous period plus any new procurement of aircraft, $A^{(t-1)}$.

Equation (7) states that the amount of money required for support of all activities equals the amount of money, $B^{(t-1)}$, made available from outside the system.

It will be noted that each of these equations relates the activities of a time period to the activities of the preceding time period. The activities of the first time period are related to the initial inventories of items on hand through the exogenous supply activities. If the program being constructed is to cover several time periods, there will be as many sets of these equations as there are time periods. Thus, if we represent a single set of these equations by a rectangle, we may represent the complete set of equations for a program of four time periods as in Figure 2.

The coefficient matrix of each set of equations is characteristically rectangular, as is the complete matrix obtained by putting together the matrices for the several time periods comprising a complete program. That is, there are more activities than there are items. Remember that the variables in the equations are the levels or magnitudes of the various activities and that there is one equation for each item. This corresponds to the obvious fact that, given certain quantities of various items, there are, in real situations, usually many different sets of actions which can be performed, completely using these items.   In the airlift model being considered, a decision must be made in each time period as to whether any of the tonnage flown into Berlin will consist of construction materials and, if so, how much.   By choosing to build a runway in any particular time period, at some loss of supplies in the current time period, we may get increased deliveries in the next time period (provided that aircraft, crews, or money is not in short supply).   To prepare a program it is necessary to provide some statement of objectives which will permit

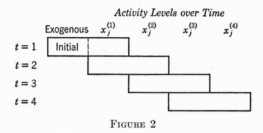

Activity Levels over Time

FIGURE 2

us to select from among the many possible solutions satisfying the system of equations *that particular solution* which best accomplishes our objectives.

In the case of the airlift example, we might have a definite schedule of net tonnages available in Berlin which we desired to meet over several successive time periods.   We would then specify the levels of activity I for each of the time periods involved and would seek that solution, consistent with the delivery of these tonnages, which would minimize the cost, that is, the exogenous supply of money, $B^{(t-1)}$, summed over all time periods, so that $B^{(0)} + B^{(1)} + \cdots + B^{(t-1)} = \min$.

Alternatively, we may have a definitely limited supply of aircraft or money and seek to maximize the tonnage supplied to Berlin.   We then have $x_1^{(1)} + x_1^{(2)} + \cdots + x_1^{(n)} = \max$.

Thus, when we apply this objective concept to the above discussion concerning the choice of use of tonnage between runway construction and supplying Berlin, the solutions obtained from our formulation of the problem do not necessarily provide optima within each time period but do give the optimum over all time periods of the program.   Therefore these solutions would provide for some sacrifice of supplies to Berlin in a given time period for later benefit through availability of added runway capacity, so that, over *all* time periods of the program, maximum tonnage would be delivered to Berlin.

3. THE TRIANGULAR MODEL

Computing techniques are now available for solution of small linear programming problems. (See Chapters XXI, XXIV, and XXV.) However, for accurate over-all Air Force planning, the size of the required model is such that conventional punched card computing equipment, or even the interim electronic computer being built for the Air Force by the National Bureau of Standards, is not sufficiently powerful to cope satisfactorily with the problem of choosing the optimum activities and activity levels over time.

In order to obtain a programming procedure which would be immediately useful with presently available computing equipment, we have

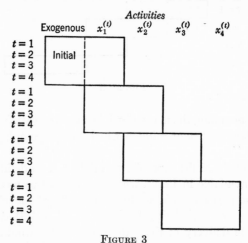

FIGURE 3

been forced to use a determinate and hence less general formulation of the programming problem that parallels closely the staff procedure illustrated in Figure 1. We have called this a triangular model because in it the matrix of detached coefficients, when arranged as in Table III and omitting the "initial" part, assumes a triangular form, with all coefficients above and to the right of the principal diagonal being zero. Thus the activities and items are so ordered that the levels of any one activity over time depend only on the levels of the activities which precede it in the hierarchy. This means that in the computation of the program we successively work down the hierarchy, at each step solving completely for the levels of each activity in each of the time periods before proceeding to the next activity, as shown by Figure 3.

This computation is very much like that found in the solution of a set of n simultaneous equations in n unknowns when the set is reduced to one equation in one unknown, and the values of the successive variables then are obtained by the process of back solution. Obviously the triangular model does not permit answering some of the questions answered by the rectangular model discussed above. Like the staff procedure described earlier, this triangular model permits generation of the resource requirements to support a given set of quantitatively stated objectives, but it will not permit the determination of the maximum amount of a qualitatively stated objective which can be attained with a given resource availability. In this sense the triangular model is less general than the rectangular model. Even in the generation of resource requirements for a given set of objectives, the triangular model will not

TABLE III. TRIANGULARIZATION OF BERLIN AIRLIFT MODEL

Item		Airlift Flying $x_1^{(t)}$	Resting Weary Crews $x_2^{(t)}$	Training New Crews $x_3^{(t)}$	Procuring Aircraft $x_4^{(t)}$
Supply shipped by airlift	In	-1			
	Out				
Weary crews	In		1		
	Out	125			
Active crews	In	130		0.05	
	Out		1	1.00	
Aircraft	In	50		0.06	
	Out	49		0.05	1
Money	In	9,000	5	10.00	200

Equations

(1) $$\alpha_{1,0}^{(t)} = x_1^{(t)},$$

(2) $$125x_1^{(t-1)} = x_2^{(t)},$$

(3) $$\alpha_{3,0}^{(t)} + 130x_1^{(t)} - x_2^{(t-1)} + 0.05x_3^{(t)} = x_3^{(t-1)},$$

(4) $$\alpha_{4,0}^{(t)} + 50x_1^{(t)} - 49x_1^{(t-1)} + 0.06x_3^{(t)} - 0.05x_3^{(t-1)} = x_4^{(t-1)},$$

(5) $$9,000x_1^{(t)} + 5x_2^{(t)} + 10x_3^{(t)} + 200x_4^{(t)} = \text{money required in } t\text{th period};$$

where $\alpha_{1,0}^{(t)}$ = program of tonnages to be delivered in t = 1, 2, 3, and 4 (i.e., 1.5, 1.6, 1.8, and 2.0); $\alpha_{3,0}^{(t)}$ = inventory of crews initially available for airlift (i.e., 200, 0, 0, 0); $\alpha_{4,0}^{(t)}$ = inventory of aircraft initially available for airlift (i.e., 25, 0, 0, 0).

necessarily yield optimum solutions if there are real choices between alternative production processes. To illustrate the triangular model let us consider a somewhat modified presentation of the Berlin airlift model. If we assume that the airlift program is generated by the supply tonnages to be airlifted into Berlin in successive time intervals, the first activity will be "airlift flying," designated by $x_1^{(t)}$ as shown in Table III. Equation (1) expresses the relationship that the values of $x_1^{(t)}$ will be successively equal to the supply tonnage values, designated by $\alpha_{1,0}^{(t)}$ specified for each time period. These values of $\alpha_{1,0}^{(t)}$ are shown at the end of Table III. Table IV gives the values of $x_1^{(t)}$ obtained from the program

TABLE IV. THEORETICAL BERLIN AIRLIFT PROGRAM

Time Period	Airlift Flying $x_1^{(t)}$	Resting Weary Crews $x_2^{(t)}$	Training New Crews $x_3^{(t)}$	Storing Aircraft	Procuring Aircraft $x_4^{(t)}$	Money
First	1.5	0	10	16	0	$13,600
Second	1.6	188	49	3	0	15,830
Third	1.8	200	62	1	10	19,820
Fourth	2.0	255	37	0	..	22,095

values established for this problem, if the specified activities stay level at the value specified in the last time period.

The next activity whose levels can be determined is "resting weary crews," designated by $x_2^{(t)}$, because it depends solely on the values of $x_1^{(t-1)}$. This is shown by equation (2). The two activities involved in equation (2) are separated by one time period, because in this model the crews retire after one time period of flying the airlift, and therefore the crews resting in the current time period are derived from those flying the airlift in the previous time period. Table IV shows the values for $x_2^{(t)}$ obtained by application of equation (2). It is to be noted at this point that we can, and have, solved for the levels of activities $x_2^{(t)}$ over all time periods before we go on to the next activity. This ordering of the computational steps is an advantage in program development because, when appropriate computing equipment is used, it permits the study of the program levels as they are being generated, so that errors in the program or impossible programs may be detected before the whole program is generated.

The third activity in this model is "training new crews," designated by $x_3^{(t)}$. It depends on the levels of the previous two activities and also on its own level in the previous time period. This is so because we must train instructors in the previous time period in order to have sufficient instructors available in the current time period. This is a usual dynamic condition encountered in economic and similar planning problems, and the simultaneous equations involved are solved by iteration. A further aspect of the third equation is that there has been introduced an initial stock of aircrews from which we can draw before starting the training activity. The levels of this activity, based on the airlift supply program, are given in Table IV.

The fourth activity, "procuring aircraft," designated by $x_4^{(t)}$, comes at this position in the model because it depends on $x_1^{(t)}$ and $x_3^{(t)}$. Substitution of the determined values of these two activities in equation (4) readily gives the values for $x_4^{(t)}$ shown in Table IV. It is to be noted that the value for $x_4^{(4)}$ is not given in this table because $x_4^{(4)}$ depends on $x_1^{(5)}$, which was not specified in the program under discussion.

It will be noted that, in the formulation of the equations for the airlift model, each item was uniquely related to the single activity which produces it. This means that the slough-off and storing activities were not included in the structural equations.

However, in the computation of the program it is necessary to include the storage and slough-off activities, as shown by the inclusion in Table IV of the activity "storing aircraft." A need for establishing this activity occurs because the inventory of aircraft available at the start of the program is greater than required by the levels of the activities utilizing aircraft. Hence the surplus of aircraft must be stored, and an activity for accomplishing this is created. Thus, although the triangular model usually specifies explicitly only the producing activities, the complete system has implicit within it additional activities which may store or dispose of surplus or unutilized equipment. Thus, in point of fact, in computing a program we may require two to three times as many activities as items.

The last equation in Table III, (5), is used not to determine the level of an activity but to determine the value of an item designated as "money." No activity is associated with the item money in this model because the activity involved, that of appropriating money, is exogenous to the Air Force. Consequently the last equation involves only input coefficients (i.e., equipment flowing toward each activity requiring money).

Table IV thus gives the program of *required* support activities generated by this model, which must be attained if the tonnage deliveries are to be satisfied. The model has been so arranged that a determinate and unique statement of these requirements is obtained. This is definitely a more limited approach to the programming problem, motivated largely by the need to stay within computing capabilities. In some cases arbitrary decisions must be made to establish the necessary hierarchy of activities, and this is a definite drawback of the procedure. However, in the practical job of fitting Air Force operations into a mathematical model, it has not been found difficult to fit the triangular arrangement, nor has it been necessary to distort materially the true relationships in doing so. In general, we find that there is only one major type of productive activity for each type of item; this is the principal prerequisite of the triangular model. There is, of course, no a priori reason to assume that other economies will be equally adaptable to formulation in a triangular model.

Computationally, however, the triangular model yields a tremendous advantage over all known alternatives. With this formulation we have been able to solve programming problems involving 100 activities and 36 time periods in one day by using present punched card equipment, obtaining answers which are realistic and useful. In the more general formulation this would be represented by 3,600 equations in 3,600 unknowns.

One other significant advantage of the triangular model which should be noted is that it frees us completely from the necessity of using linear relationships between inputs and activity levels. In the illustration given above we have used linear relationships because the relationships appear to be fundamentally linear. However, in computing solutions with the triangular model the levels of each activity over time are completely determined by the levels of the preceding activities in the model, and consequently we may use any functional relationship between activity levels and input requirements which seems appropriate to the facts, provided only that the function used determines uniquely the inputs from the activity levels. In the succeeding section on the reformulation of the model with flow coefficients an example is given in which arbitrary function tables are used in lieu of input coefficients.

One of the difficulties with the triangular model is that complete specification of the objective activities and complete specification of the initial status are quite likely to set up an overdetermined set of equations in which no solution is possible. Another difficulty is that the triangular system has little slack in the time dimension; every requirement must be met exactly on time, unless there is a stored surplus remaining from the initial status. The model makes no provision for the anticipatory creation of temporary surpluses in order to meet future peaks in demand. Thus it may require rapid and erratic fluctuation in production, or it may require continued rapid expansion of production at rates in excess of those which experience indicates can be attained.

In order to overcome these difficulties we have tried to relax somewhat the rigidity of the triangular model and to introduce certain limited elements of optimization. Thus we have modified the formulation to specify the levels of the objective activities for a time span starting with some future date, rather than with an actual current status. This eliminates the possibility of setting up an overdetermined set of equations, provided that we place no restrictions on rates of change of activity levels within the period prior to the starting date of the program. Such overdetermination is almost certain to occur in a determinate system when both the initial status and the objectives are completely specified quantitatively. This also conforms much better to the usual formulation of the peacetime programming problem in the military establishment, in which the objectives to be attained are removed by a substantial time interval from the current status. The problem is then to define the status to be attained at some future date that will be consistent with the accomplishment of stated objectives after that date. In doing this we also generate a detailed program for accomplishing objectives after that date.

This relaxation of the conditions of the problem not only eliminates the probability of overdetermination but also creates a certainty of underdetermination. To arrive at a solution we must now impose some further conditions on the rates of change in the levels of the production activities after the future date for which we wish to define an initial status.

In most types of production activities, whether pilot training, aircraft production, or gasoline refining, there appear to be inherent limitations on the maximum rates of expansion which can be attained. Extensive analysis of World War II experience, together with industrial planning studies made since the war, has indicated statistically that for most industries or activities the highest expansion possible is for output to increase, as an approximation, by a constant geometric rate from the production level on the date the expansion is initiated, after a time lag of varying length. For example, the pilot-training establishment might approximately double its rate of output every five months, after a lag equal to the length of the production pipeline, or about ten months. Similarly the aircraft industry might double its output every eight months, after a lag of about one year. This type of relationship seems to hold equally well for smaller components, such as production of landing gear struts, propellers, engines. In other words, it appears that in most production processes we may assume that the maximum percentage rate of production expansion at any given time after the start of the program is a constant which depends on the type of activity but is relatively independent of the initial production level.

Figure 4 illustrates schematically the problem under consideration. The cumulative program requirements curve is characteristically S-shaped, being first concave upward and later concave downward.

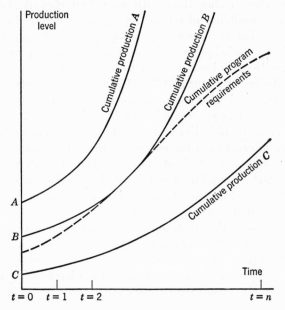

FIGURE 4—Determination of minimum production level at $t = 0$ consistent with cumulative program.

The family of alternative cumulative production curves, A, B, and C, are characteristically concave upward, each representing a different initial production rate. It is clear that curve B is the most efficient production curve because curve A more than meets the requirements of the program whereas curve C does not satisfy the program requirements during a portion of the period. Curve B is characterized by being tangent to the cumulative program curve, and it is obvious that beyond the point of tangency the production rate need only be maintained so as to just meet the program. A further property of curve B is that it minimizes the amount of storage necessary before the cumulative production meets the cumulative program. This storage is necessary because the program, in the initial stages, expands more rapidly than production.

In order to fit the production curves to the program requirements, we must know either the initial production rate or the initial inventory.

Since, under the new formulation of the problem, the initial point of the program is removed by a time span from the present, we do not yet know either.   We do, however, know both the initial position and the production rate at the present.   If we are willing to make an assumption of, say, linear increase or decrease in the production rate between the present and the initial program date, the determination of either the inventory or the production rate at the initial program point will determine the other.   This is made clear by Figure 5.

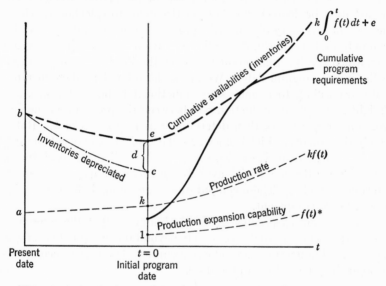

$$k \int_0^t f(t)\,dt + e$$

Cumulative program requirements

Cumulative availablities (inventories)

b

Inventories depreciated

e

d

c

$kf(t)$

Production rate

k

a

Production expansion capability $f(t)*$

1

Present date

$t = 0$
Initial program date

t

*$f(t)$ = standard production growth function starting from unit production rate at $t = 0$.

FIGURE 5—Determination of inventory and production rate at initial program date.

The ordinate on the chart is the quantity of the item concerned; the abscissa is the time dimension and is measured from an origin in the center of the chart, which is the assumed initial program date.   The left side of the chart represents the interval between the present date and the assumed initial program date.   The lower two broken lines are production rates; the upper two are inventories or cumulative availabilities; and the solid line is the cumulative program requirement. The problem, then, given the cumulative production requirement curve (solid line), the present inventory, b, and production rate, a, and the basic production expansion capability function, $f(t)$, which is plotted from a unit initial production rate at $t = 0$, is to find the inventory, e, and production rate, k, at the initial program date, and the cumulative availability curve (heavy broken line) on the right side over the period after the initial program date.

The cumulative availability curve (heavy broken line) on the right side is the sum of the initial inventory, e, at $t = 0$, and the cumulative availability from production, which is $k \int_0^t f(t)\, dt$. Obviously, if either e or k is known, the other can be determined. Since neither is known a priori, we must introduce another condition. We know the initial inventory, b, at the present time; it is a simple matter, when we know the attrition or depreciation rate on the item, to calculate c, which is the present inventory discounted to the initial program date. We have then only to determine d, the additional inventory at the initial program date which results from production over the interval from the present to the initial program date. We know the present production rate, a; if we are willing to assume some functional form, as for instance a straight line, for the production rate between the present and the initial program date, we may then determine d as a function of k. But e is merely the sum of c, which is known, and d; and so we may get an expression for e in terms of k, or vice versa. Substituting this back into the expression for the cumulative availability curve, we may then uniquely determine e and k. These computations can be made by conventional punched card equipment.

An interesting by-product of this technique is that the same fitting procedure can be repeated successively beyond the first point of tangency in order to obtain a smooth production curve. This is also accomplished through the punched card procedure.

4. REFORMULATION WITH FLOW COEFFICIENTS

The duration of the activities of the Air Force varies over a considerable range of values, from a single instant to several years. It is therefore difficult to fit these activities into a discrete model based on fixed time intervals, and it is also clear that some loss in accuracy must result if we are constrained to retain the concept of fixed time lengths in developing the coefficients for the model. To obviate this difficulty we have reformulated the basic concepts underlying the construction of the coefficients for the models. The items or commodities entering into the model are now considered in terms of stocks and flows. *Stocks* are the inventories of the various items or commodities required by the activity to be on hand as long as that activity continues. Thus the personnel manning a training base, or the aircraft within a group, are stocks of equipment required to be on hand in order for the training and combat activities, respectively, to operate. The *flow* coefficients describe the rates at which the commodities involved in an activity are continuously consumed or produced by the activity per unit period of its operation. Thus gasoline consumed in aircraft flights, or unserviceable engines produced as the result of aircraft activity, are examples of flow in our structure. Capital equipment in this formulation is always treated as stock. Noncapital items may occur as either stock or flow. Thus gasoline is required in both forms, first as stock in terms of an inventory to cover lead-time in distribution and second as flow to be consumed in flying activities. Attrition or depreciation on capital equipment may be considered a flow.

Continuing this type of formulation, we find that we are released from the use of fixed time periods in the initial formulation of the coefficients of the model. Setting up a basic time length of sufficiently small duration so that the activities can be accurately expressed in terms of the unit time lengths, we can introduce both the stocks and flows into the model by means of flow coefficients. All inputs of stocks are considered equivalent to flows toward the activity (indicated by a plus sign attached to the coefficient), taking place during one unit time period in advance of the time they are required to be on hand. All releases or outputs of stocks from an activity are considered equivalent to flows away from the activity (indicated by a minus sign attached to the coefficient), taking place during one unit time period in advance of the time they can be released or are produced. All flows are shown as rates of item inputs $(+)$ or outputs $(-)$ per unit volume of activity per unit time period with two time coefficients identifying the times at which the flow is to begin or end. Thus we are adopting the concept of a continuous model in the underlying formulation of the coefficients. This permits continuous balancing of requirements and availabilities over time, establishing storage as required if an overage exists, and establishing procurement or production as required if a shortage occurs.

5. Example of Dynamic Model with Flow Coefficients

As an illustration of the procedure used here for presenting the data under this kind of formulation, an illustrative but fictitious example of an Air Force model has been set up and is shown in Table V. Consider the first activity in Table V, "operation of bomber wing." The item produced by this wing is called a "wing operation unit," with dimensions of flying hours, or sorties, etc. The coefficient of -1 associated with the item shows that one wing operation unit is produced by the activity each week. The time coefficients, from 0 to 1, associated with this item, show that the output of this unit by the activity takes place during one

TABLE V. HYPOTHETICAL TRIANGULAR MODEL OF AN AIR FORCE OPERATION SHOWING FUNDAMENTAL RELATIONSHIPS AND COEFFICIENTS *

Activities

Items	Operation of Bomber Wing Time From/To	Operation of Bomber Wing Amount‡	Training of Bomber Wing Time From/To	Training of Bomber Wing Amount	Training of Bomber Crews Time From/To	Training of Bomber Crews Amount	Training of Technicians Time From/To	Training of Technicians Amount	Procurement of Bomber Aircraft and Spare Engines Time From/To	Procurement of Bomber Aircraft and Spare Engines Amount	Overhaul of Engines Time From/To	Overhaul of Engines Amount	Procurement of Bomber and Engine Parts Time From/To	Procurement of Bomber and Engine Parts Amount	Procurement of Gasoline and Oil Time From/To	Procurement of Gasoline and Oil Amount
Wing operation unit	0 1	-1														
Bomber wing	-5 -4 -4 -3	-1 -1	60 61	1												
Bomber crews	-5 -4 -4 -3	52 -50	-1 0 0 61 60 61	5 1 55	-1 0 0 61 60 61	20 5 -120										
Technical personnel	-5 -4	45	-1 0 0 61 60 61	1,050 50 -1,050	-1 0 0 61 60 61	445 40 -445	-1 0 0 25 24 25	8 1 -108								
Bomber aircraft	-6 -5 -5 -4	20 -15	-4 -3 -3 58 57 58	5 1 5	-4 -3 -3 58 57 58	10 2 10			-1 0	-1						
Serviceable engines	-4 -3 -3 -2	12 -10	-3 -2 -2 61 60 61	20 1 20	-3 -2 -2 61 60 61	30 2 30			-1 0	-5	4 5	-1				
Bomber aircraft and engine parts	-5 -4 -4 -3	50 -48	-3 -2 -2 59 58 59	25 5 25	-3 -2 -2 59 58 59	45 25 45			-1 0	-2	0 5	1	-1 0	-1		
Gasoline and oil	-4 -3 -3 -2	10 -7	-2 -1 -1 60 59 60	5 44 5	-2 -1 -1 60 59 60	30 80 30									-1 0	-1
Funds	0 1	5	0 61	5	0 61	4	0 25	3	-25 -24	2	0 5	1	-15 -14	§	-5 -4	1

* This presentation is purely hypothetical, and the sole purpose of presentation is for illustration of technique.
† Time is measured in weeks.
‡ The amounts all represent unit physical quantities (i.e., "technical personnel" is measured in terms of persons, etc.).
§ Function table coefficients used.

week, which is the basic time period in which the program is computed. All the other items appearing under the bomber wing operation activity are required to generate this one wing operation unit, and their time coefficients are measured with reference to "zero" time as the origin.

The second item is called "bomber wing"; it is a major stock item required by the first activity. It is therefore shown as a flow over the unit time period previous to its requirement by the first activity. The -5 and -4 indicate that there is a passage of four weeks between the completion of training of a bomber wing (accomplished by the second activity) and its availability for use by the first activity. This means that, in order to have a bomber wing available as input into the first activity, the second activity must have produced the bomber wing four weeks previously, and the time coefficients of -5 and -4 provide the time link between the first and second activities. Obviously we could have inserted intermediate shipping activities between the training of a wing and its availability for operation, which would obviate the necessity for showing the lead time in the first activity. The second coefficient attached to the bomber wing item shows that the item is not consumed by the activity but is an output at the end of the week's activity, available for reuse in the next time period. Thus, the bomber wing is a capital item. The item "bomber crews" is shown as a stock input and then as a stock output one time period later, the difference in the amounts representing the attrition of crews brought about through operation of the activity. It should be noted that the crew capital equipment of a bomber wing (in this example) is 50 crews, so the input coefficient is the sum of the capital plus attrition requirements for the week. The fourth item is called "technical personnel" (i.e., the mechanics, electronics personnel, cooks, etc., needed to support the crews and aircraft). They are shown only as an input because the technical personnel capital equipment is incorporated in the equipment item "bomber wing," and so only an input of replacements to cover attrition during the week is necessary in order to have the required amount of capital on hand. As before, the -5 and -4 time coefficients indicate a four-week delivery time between the completion of training of the technical personnel and their availability for use in the wing.

The comments on the items "bomber aircraft" and "serviceable engines" parallel those given above for the item on crews. The input, or positive, coefficient shows the number of serviceable engines required as stock and as consumption to cover replacement of worn-out engines. The output coefficient shows the number of engines left over as stock at the end of the week's operation. The same comments as made on serviceable engines apply to the next two equipment items, "bomber aircraft and engine parts" and "gasoline and oil." Finally, the equipment item "funds" is shown as an input coefficient, and it covers costs which can best be associated with this activity. Thus the cost of pay and allowances of the personnel are reflected, but not the cost of aircraft procurement, which in this model can better be handled under the "procurement of bomber aircraft and spare engines" activity itself.

It will be noted that each activity is associated with an item which it produces. The amount of production of each item required of the

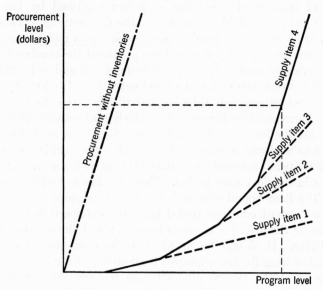

FIGURE 6—Nonlinearity of coefficients resulting from aggregation of four supply items with disproportionate inventories.

producing activity determines its level. To make this clear, let us consider the following equation, by means of which the level of the activity "training of bomber wing" in any time period can be established. Let x_1 be "operation of bomber wing" activity, and x_2, "training of bomber wing" activity. Since the sum of the flows in any time period must equal zero, the following relationship must be satisfied by the levels of x_1 and x_2:

$$1x_1^{(t+5)} - 1x_1^{(t+4)} - 1x_2^{(t-60)} = 0,$$

where t takes on integral values. Comparable equations may be developed for the other activities in this model. The simplicity of the flow formulation, and its flexibility, can best be appreciated by study of these functional relationships among the activities in a model such as the one illustrated.

It will be noted that the coefficient for the activity "procurement of bomber and engine parts" related to the funds is footnoted, because, in developing these coefficients, we aggregate the individual items and parts and express their aggregate value in dollars to avoid dealing individually with hundreds of thousands of items. Through this aggregation we have succeeded in reducing the problem to one of dealing with about 100 classes of items. However, in doing this we find that the coefficient describing the dollar amount of procurement of items required per unit of consumption of this item changes with the level of consumption because, in many cases, the amount of inventory on hand is significant and disproportionate among the several items aggregated together. As a result, we introduce function tables into the computing procedure, in which the procurement coefficients in the structure change with the level of required consumption (i.e., level of program). The kind of function table required is schematically illustrated in Figure 6. In this figure we have four equipment items. The inventory of each equipment item is expressed in terms of the number of program levels it can support, called normalized inventory. The items are then ranked from the smallest to the largest normalized inventory (expressed in program units, such as flying hours, personnel). Item 1 is the item which has the smallest normalized inventory and hence must be procured first. Item 2 is next in order, and so on. The envelope outline of the curve, shown as a solid line, constitutes the nonlinear function which must be handled as a function table.

Chapter XIII

REPRESENTATION IN A LINEAR MODEL OF NONLINEAR GROWTH CURVES IN THE AIRCRAFT INDUSTRY

By Marshall K. Wood [1]

In attempting to represent the aircraft industry in the discrete linear model described in Chapters I, II, and XII, two characteristics appeared which did not, at first glance, seem to lend themselves to representation in the linear model. The first of these is the fact that there appears to be a limit to the rate at which the industry can grow over time, even if there are no shortages of the materials necessary for the production process. This fact was mentioned in Chapter XII and used in the formulation of the dynamic triangular model. In general, it appears that production can expand in geometric ratio, i.e., that the levels of production in successive time periods may equal, but not exceed, the successive terms in the series 1, $(1 + \alpha)$, $(1 + \alpha)^2$, $(1 + \alpha)^3$, $\cdots$, $(1 + \alpha)^{t-1}$, where α represents the proportional increase in production during a unit time period. This general form of the expansion curve was actually observed during World War II and also may be derived, with slightly different coefficients, from studies of future production capabilities made by aircraft manufacturers since the war.

It may be conjectured that this limitation on the growth rate is not in fact a characteristic of the industry but arises as a result of the cumulative effect of shortages of labor, equipment, materials, etc., which in turn may be produced by activities with constant input coefficients. It may well be true that, if all the tangible and intangible elements of the production process were defined in sufficient detail, and if their input coefficients were evaluated with accuracy, then it would not be necessary to introduce this growth rate limitation explicitly into the model. However, until all these factors can be evaluated with greater detail and accuracy than is now possible, it appears necessary to introduce the limiting growth rate as a separate side condition in the model.

This may be done entirely within the framework of the linear model.

[1] Acknowledgment is made to George B. Dantzig, U. S. Air Force, and T. E. Harris, The RAND Corporation, for invaluable mathematical assistance in preparing this chapter.

To do this, we first create an artificial item which we may call "management capacity" for want of a better name. This item is not observable or definable as such, and it is evaluated by reference to experienced expansion rates or production planning studies. We then formulate the model of the aircraft production activity given in Table I.

TABLE I

Item	Input at Beginning of Period	Output at End of Period
I. Aircraft	0	1
II. Management capacity	1	$1 + \alpha$

If the item management capacity appears in no other activity, it will immediately be seen that the level of the activity whose coefficients are given above must increase over time at the rate 1, $(1 + \alpha)$, $(1 + \alpha)^2$, $(1 + \alpha)^3$, $\cdots$, since the output of each period becomes the input of the following period. If we then introduce a disposal activity, constrained to be nonnegative, with a single coefficient of -1 for management capacity, the levels of the aircraft production activity must be equal to or less than the series 1, $(1 + \alpha)$, $(1 + \alpha)^2$, $\cdots$. Furthermore, we have insured that in no time period shall the level of the activity exceed the level in the previous time period by a ratio greater than $1 + \alpha$. By appropriate selection of α we may fit any desired geometric expansion curve.

The second major problem encountered in representing the aircraft industry in the linear model is the observed fact that labor costs per unit of output appear to decrease in inverse geometric ratio to the cumulative quantity produced. At first glance this seems impossible to represent in the linear model. However, the conditions under which this relationship is observed, and the conditions under which planning studies have indicated that it will occur, are conditions of expansion of production at the maximum possible rate.

Suppose then that, for purposes of creating the mathematical model, we arbitrarily split the production process into two nonnegative activities, P and Q, the sum of whose inputs and outputs are to equal the total inputs and outputs, respectively, of the aircraft production activity, with the selection between the two activities to be made on the basis of the minimization of cost, subject to the restriction imposed by the linear model. These two production activities may be called "high cost production" and "low cost production," respectively. It need not be assumed that they are physically separable or identifiable, although it is possible that they are. The subdivision of the production process into these two activities is here made only for mathematical convenience in formulating the model. We may then set up the model with the input and output coefficients given in Table II. The coefficients are restricted

TABLE II

	Activities			
Items	P—High Cost Production		Q—Low Cost Production	
	Input at beginning of period	Output at end of period	Input at beginning of period	Output at end of period
I. Aircraft	0	1	0	1
II. Management capacity	1	a	1	a
III. Production experience	0	1	b	c
IV. Manpower cost	1	0	d	0

as follows: $a > 1$, $d < 1$, $c \geqq ba$, where $a = 1 + \alpha$ in the previous model.

Item III, here called "production experience," is another artificial item (like item II) which is not physically identifiable or measurable and is created here for convenience in order to make the model conform to the observed characteristics. Since we have retained the same coefficients of 1 and a for item II in both activities, it is clear that the sum of the two activities is still limited to an expansion rate of 1, a, a^2, a^3, $\cdots$, a^{t-1}. It is necessary to restrict $c \geqq ba$ in order to insure that the ratio of output to input for item III, c/b, does not impose a more severe restriction on the total growth rate of production than is imposed by the output-input ratio, $a/1$, for item II. We must, of course, add to the model another disposal activity with a single coefficient of -1 for item III, as we did above for item II.

Turning now to the question of cost, we see that the two activities P and Q have differing manpower costs (item IV) per unit of production. Since activity Q produces at lower cost than activity P (i.e., $d < 1$), and since we are seeking a minimum cost solution, the solution will always contain as large a proportion of activity Q as is permitted by the basic equations.

Substituting the above coefficients in the basic equations of the linear system [see II], and imposing the additional condition that the total production $(P + Q)$ expand over time at the maximum rate possible from a rate of 1 at $t = 1$, we have:

$$(1) \qquad P_t + Q_t = a^{t-1}, \qquad Q_t = a^{t-1} - P_t,$$

where P_t and Q_t are the levels of activities P and Q, respectively, at time t. This is the general limitation on the rate of growth of total production, as discussed above. Furthermore,

$$(2) \qquad Q_t = \frac{P_{t-1} + cQ_{t-1}}{b}.$$

This is the condition imposed by the input and output coefficients for item III, plus the stipulation that Q shall always be as large as possible in relation to P (minimum cost). Finally,

$$(3) \qquad Q_1 = 0.$$

This results from the fact that the initial inventory of item III is zero at $t = 1$, and that activity Q can only be used after some of this item is produced through the operation of activity P.

Putting $t = t - 1, t - 2$, etc., in (1), substituting in (2), and solving simultaneously, we have

$$(4) \qquad Q_t = \frac{a^{t-1} - f^{t-1}}{b(a - f)},$$

where $f = (c - 1)/b$.

The cost of production is given by

$$(5) \qquad C_t = P_t + dQ_t.$$

By substituting (1) and (4) in (5), and letting $e = (d - 1)/b$, we have

$$(6) \qquad C_t = a^{t-1} + e\frac{a^{t-1} - f^{t-1}}{a - f}.$$

The cumulative production is

$$(7) \qquad \sum_{i=1}^{t} (P_i + Q_i) = \frac{a^t - 1}{a - 1}$$

It is now desired to select the coefficients b, c, and d so that the unit manpower cost of production will be in inverse geometric ratio to the cumulative production. For example, let us take the unit manpower cost inversely proportional to the cube root of the cumulative production. Then the cumulative manpower cost will be proportional to the two-thirds power of the cumulative production. Then we desire that

$$(8) \qquad \sum_{i=1}^{t} C_i = \left(\frac{a^t - 1}{a - 1}\right)^{\frac{2}{3}}$$

for a given value of a over a range of t.

It is apparent that we are more concerned about accuracy in the total cost function for the entire production run of an aircraft model than in the precise costs for individual time periods within the production run. We may therefore elect to fit the function precisely for, say $t = 25$, assuming a monthly unit time interval and a total production run of about two years. It will also be desirable to fit the cumulative cost function for one intermediate time period, say $t = 15$. After meeting those restrictions, it is still possible to select arbitrarily the values of a and d, representing respectively the rate of increase of total production per time period and the minimum manpower cost per unit of production as the amount of production becomes infinitely large. We may select $a = 1.1$, assuming a monthly time interval, as representing an upper bound to the rate of increase of total production at 10 per cent per month. We may then select d at 0.17, representing a minimum unit manpower cost of about one-sixth that of the first article. Proceeding then to evaluate b and c, for $t = 15$ and $t = 25$, we find $b = 3.6$ and $c = 3.95$. With these values the fraction of production at the high cost level just about reaches zero at the end of the twenty-fifth period. A

TABLE III

t	$\left(\dfrac{\text{Cumulative}}{\text{Production}}\right)^{\frac{2}{3}}$	Cumulative Cost	High Cost Fraction $P_t/(P_t + Q_t)$
1	1.0	1.1	1.00
5	3.3	4.1	0.23
10	6.3	6.9	0.05
15	10.0	10.0	0.01
20	14.9	14.5	0.00+
25	21.3	21.6	0.00+

larger value of d would make this fraction reach zero before the end of the twenty-fifth period; then some changes would have to be made in the model.

Table III compares the resulting values of the two-thirds power of the cumulative production and the cumulative cost and shows how the high cost fraction of production changes with time. It is seen that the cumulative cost as computed from the model is a very good fit to the two-thirds power of the cumulative production and is well within the error of the empirical data.

It should also be noted that the unit manpower cost under this formulation has a minimum equal to the value selected for the coefficient d as the cumulative production becomes very large, whereas the commonly used "two-thirds power law" implies that the unit manpower cost approaches zero as the cumulative production becomes very large. It is believed that the former is intuitively a more reasonable assumption.

CHAPTER XIV

A MODEL OF TRANSPORTATION [1]

By Tjalling C. Koopmans and Stanley Reiter

In this chapter we shall apply the model developed in Chapter III to the problem of efficient utilization of movable transportation equipment. After discussing the characteristics of an efficient solution to this problem, we shall indicate how marginal rates of substitution between flows of transported goods on various routes can be derived.

For the sake of definiteness we shall speak in terms of the transportation of cargoes on ocean-going ships. In considering only shipping we do not lose generality of application since ships may be "translated" into trucks, aircraft, or, in first approximation,[2] trains, and ports into the various sorts of terminals. Such translation is possible because all the above examples involve particular types of movable transportation equipment.

The models treated here will be "simplified" in several respects. First, they are static models. We describe the joint output of shipping operations as a set of cargo flows, to be referred to as the transportation *program*, which is assumed to be unchanged in quantity over time. (By measuring cargo flows on each route in shiploads, we need not preclude changes in commodity composition of cargo.) Second, we assume that all ships are of the same type and therefore completely interchangeable in each of their uses.

1. A Model with Two Ports

1.1. *Commodities and activities.* The model which we consider first is further simplified in that we assume only two ports, P and Q. The technology matrix for this model is given in Table I. At each port two

---

[1] The theory presented in this chapter was originally developed by the former author partly during, but mostly after, his association as statistician with the (British-American) Combined Shipping Adjustment Board and with the British Merchant Shipping Mission in Washington during World War II. The responsibility for this chapter rests, of course, with the authors. For a nonmathematical exposition of this model see T. C. Koopmans [1947], where another illustrative example is also given.

[2] The case of railroad equipment is complicated by the "decomposability" of trains, particularly in regard to locomotives.

TABLE I. TECHNOLOGY MATRIX FOR A TWO-PORT MODEL

Commodities	Unit	Symbol	Port P Loading $\bar{x}_P$	Port P Discharging x_P	Port Q Loading $\bar{x}_Q$	Port Q Discharging x_Q	Port P to Q Sailing loaded $\bar{x}_{PQ}$	Port P to Q Sailing empty x_{PQ}	Port Q to P Sailing loaded $\bar{x}_{QP}$	Port Q to P Sailing empty x_{QP}
Final:* Cargo transportation										
From P to Q	Shiploads per month	y_{PQ}				1				
From Q to P	Shiploads per month	y_{QP}		1						
Intermediate:* Net appearances of loaded ships										
At P for Q	Ships per month	0	1				-1			
At P from Q	Ships per month	0		-1					1	
At Q for P	Ships per month	0			1				-1	
At Q from P	Ships per month	0				-1	1			
Net appearances of empty ships										
At P	Ships per month	0	-1	1				-1		1
At Q	Ships per month	0			-1	1		1		-1
Primary:*										
Availability of shipping	Ships	$\bar{z}$	$-l_P$	$-d_P$	$-l_Q$	$-d_Q$	$-\bar{s}_{PQ}$	$-s_{PQ}$	$-\bar{s}_{QP}$	$-s_{QP}$
Capacity of port P	Berths	z_P	$-k_P$	$-m_P$						
Capacity of port Q	Berths	z_Q			$-k_Q$	$-m_Q$				

Activities †

* For the concepts final, intermediate, and primary commodities, see Chapter III, Section 1.

† In units of ships per month.

activities,[3] "loading cargo" and "discharging cargo," are defined. For each *route*, i.e., for each ordered pair of ports (in the present case there are two routes) two activities are defined, "sailing with cargo from P to Q," and "sailing in ballast (i.e., without cargo) from P to Q." Each activity is given by a column of coefficients as in Table I. If a *commodity* (associated with a row in Table I) is not involved in a given activity, the coefficient in that row and column is zero; if the commodity is an input, its coefficient in the given activity is negative; if the commodity is an output of the given activity, its coefficient is positive. The net output of a commodity by an activity is assumed to be equal to the coefficient of that commodity multiplied by the *amount* ($\bar{x}_P$, x_P, etc.) of that activity.

The list of commodities, and the units in which commodities and activities are measured, can be read from Table I. We may point out explicitly, however, that the coefficients indicated by the letters l, d, $\bar{s}$, s, appearing in the "shipping" row of Table I have the dimension "time," measured in months. Thus l_P denotes the fraction of a month required to load a ship at port P. Since all activities are measured in units of "ships per month" we have, in the case of the first activity,

$$(1.1) \qquad (\bar{x}_P \text{ ships/month})(l_P \text{ months}) = \bar{x}_P l_P \text{ ships}$$

tied up at any instant of time (more precisely: on the average for a long period of time) in loading at port P. This is the correct dimension of z, the total fleet in use. Similarly, the port capacity coefficients k, m, have the dimension "berth-months per ship."

1.2. *Partial reduction of the technology matrix.* We shall explore what vectors of cargo flows are possible in this model, while further simplifying the model as we go on. Note that we must have

$$(1.2) \qquad \bar{x}_P, \ x_P, \ \bar{x}_Q, \ x_Q, \ \bar{x}_{PQ}, \ x_{PQ}, \ \bar{x}_{QP}, \ x_{QP} \geqq 0,$$

since no activity can be carried out "in reverse." (Sailing empty from P to Q is not the negative of sailing empty from Q to P because both activities require the employment of ships.)

Since our model is static, we do not permit accumulation (or decumulation) of stocks of idle ships, loaded or empty, in ports. This is expressed by requiring all net output flows of intermediate commodities to be zero. We shall call a set (y_{PQ}, y_{QP}, $\bar{z}$, z_P, z_Q) of net commodity flows a *possible point* in the commodity space if the flows in question can be accomplished

---

[3] For the concepts "activity" and "commodity" see Chapter III, Section 1.4. Our use of these concepts here implies that we ignore the indivisibility of individual ships.

by nonnegative activity levels satisfying this requirement. We note that, for all possible points,

(1.3) $y_{PQ}, y_{QP} \geqq 0,$ $\bar{z}, z_P, z_Q \leqq 0,$

since the coefficients of final commodities in Table I are all nonnegative and those of primary commodities are all nonpositive.

For some purposes, such as the analysis of what can be done in a limited period with a given fleet and given port facilities, it is useful to regard the flows $\bar{z}, z_P, z_Q$ of primary commodities as subject to given capacity limitations,

(1.4a) $\bar{z} \geqq \zeta,$ $\zeta < 0,$

(1.4b) $z_P \geqq \zeta_P,$ $z_Q \geqq \zeta_Q,$ $\zeta_P, \zeta_Q < 0.$

Any possible point in the commodity space falling within these limitations will be called an *attainable point*.

Before writing out the net output equations for all commodities, we shall utilize the equations for the loaded ship appearances to simplify the technology matrix. These equations are equivalent to

(1.5) $\bar{x}_P = \bar{x}_{PQ} = x_Q;$ $\bar{x}_Q = \bar{x}_{QP} = x_P.$

Each pair of equations (1.5) requires that three activities be carried out in equal amounts. Since these activities are so tied to one another, nothing will be changed except the appearance of the technology matrix if we define one new activity, "transporting cargo from P to Q" to include unit amounts of "loading at P," "sailing with cargo from P to Q," and "discharging cargo at Q," and if similarly we define another activity, "transporting cargo from Q to P." The coefficients of the new activities, as given in Table II, are the sums of the corresponding coefficients of the component activities,

(1.6) $t_{PQ} = l_P + \bar{s}_{PQ} + d_Q,$ $t_{QP} = l_Q + \bar{s}_{QP} + d_P.$

We have thus performed a partial *reduction* [III, Section 3.10] of the technology matrix. Each condensation of activities in this reduction replaces three inequalities of the form $x \geqq 0$ by one such inequality, the three x's being the amounts of the component activities and the new restrictions, $\bar{x}_{PQ} \geqq 0, \bar{x}_{QP} \geqq 0,$ referring to the amounts of the new activities. Table II gives the partially reduced technology matrix.

As it now stands, the model contains three primary commodities. If capacity limits, $\zeta, \zeta_P, \zeta_Q,$ on their inflows are introduced by (1.4a), (1.4b), any of these limits can, and at least one must, constitute an

TABLE II. PARTIALLY REDUCED TECHNOLOGY MATRIX A FOR A TWO-PORT MODEL

Commodities			Activities *			
			Route P to Q		Route Q to P	
			Trans-porting cargo	Sailing empty	Trans-porting cargo	Sailing empty
	Unit	Sym-bol	$\bar{x}_{PQ}$	x_{PQ}	$\bar{x}_{QP}$	x_{QP}
Final:						
Cargo from P to Q	Shiploads per month	y_{PQ}	1			
Cargo from Q to P		y_{QP}			1	
Intermediate: Net appearances of empty ships						
At P	Ships per month		0	−1	−1	1	1
At Q			0	1	1	−1	−1
Primary: Availability of shipping	Ships	$\bar{z}$	$-t_{PQ}$	$-s_{PQ}$	$-t_{QP}$	$-s_{QP}$

* In units of ships per month.

effective restriction on the set of attainable points.[4] We shall now simplify our model by assuming that port facilities are known to be so plentiful relative to shipping that the two restrictions under (1.4b) do not exclude any point in the commodity space attainable under the restriction (1.4a).

If, on the other hand, no explicit capacity limits are introduced, we shall still confine ourselves to situations in which supply of the services of port facilities is no problem. Since we are thus no longer interested in these primary commodities, we have in Table II omitted the port capacity rows of Table I. This leaves us with three variables of interest, y_{PQ}, y_{QP}, and $\bar{z}$. Our problem has thus been reduced to finding the possible point set in the space of these three commodity flows.

[4] Since, as is easily seen from Figure 1, Postulates B and D_2 of Chapter III, Section 3, are satisfied. See also Lemma 5.8.1 of the same chapter.

From Table II we obtain the following net output equations:

(1.7a) $\quad y_{PQ} = \quad\quad \bar{x}_{PQ},$

(1.7b) $\quad y_{QP} = \quad\quad\quad\quad\quad\quad \bar{x}_{QP},$

(1.7c) $\quad 0 = - \quad \bar{x}_{PQ} - \quad x_{PQ} + \quad \bar{x}_{QP} + \quad x_{QP},$

(1.7d) $\quad 0 = \quad\quad \bar{x}_{PQ} + \quad x_{PQ} - \quad \bar{x}_{QP} - \quad x_{QP},$

(1.7e) $\quad \bar{z} = -l_{PQ}\bar{x}_{PQ} - s_{PQ}x_{PQ} - l_{QP}\bar{x}_{QP} - s_{QP}x_{QP}.$

Since (1.7c) implies (1.7d), we can omit (1.7d) from consideration.[5]

1.3. *Leg-of-voyage and round-voyage activities.* At this point we must decide on a choice of coordinates in the activity space. One possibility is to operate in terms of the levels $\bar{x}_{PQ}$, x_{PQ}, $\bar{x}_{QP}$, x_{QP} of the "elementary" activities so far introduced while observing the restriction (1.7c). Another possibility is to complete the reduction of the technology matrix by introducing new "composite" activities, chosen in such a way that a combination of elementary activities at the levels $\bar{x}_{PQ}$, x_{PQ}, $\bar{x}_{QP}$, x_{QP} will at the same time be a combination of the new activities (at non-negative levels) *if and only if* the restriction (1.7c) is satisfied. We can then operate with nonnegative combinations of the new activities without further restraints.

When $\bar{a}_{PQ}$, a_{PQ}, $\bar{a}_{QP}$, a_{QP} are written for the column vectors of coefficients in the technology matrix A of Table II, such a new set of activities is defined by

(1.8) $\quad a_{(1)} = \bar{a}_{PQ} + \bar{a}_{QP}, \quad\quad a_{(2)} = \bar{a}_{PQ} + a_{QP}, \quad\quad a_{(3)} = a_{PQ} + \bar{a}_{QP},$

$$a_{(4)} = a_{PQ} + a_{QP}.$$

These activities represent the four different types of round voyages described in Table III. The unit of each of these activities is a rate of flow of one ship per month on the round voyage in question.[6]

---

[5] The two restrictions (1.7c) and (1.7d) are equivalent because we have a closed model with no activities that introduce or remove ships: one intermediate commodity row in Table II is the negative of the other. For that reason, for any constant levels of the activities, net appearances at port P are equal to the negative of net appearances at port Q. Since, in addition to requiring constant levels of all activities, our model classifies empty ship appearances as intermediate commodities, and thus prohibits accumulation (or decumulation) of ship inventories at any port, net appearances at both ports are required to be zero, and the two conditions expressing this are dependent.

[6] The use of round-voyage coordinates instead of leg-of-voyage coordinates corresponds to the use of loop currents instead of branch currents in the analysis of electrical networks. See Electric Circuits [1943], pp. 124–133. In Section 2.11 below we discuss the analogy with electrical networks further.

TABLE III. COMPLETELY REDUCED TECHNOLOGY MATRIX $\bar{A}$ FOR A TWO-PORT
MODEL

Commodities			Activities *			
			Transporting cargo both ways	Transporting cargo P to Q, returning empty	Sailing empty P to Q, returning with cargo	Sailing empty both ways
	Unit	Symbol	x_1	x_2	x_3	x_4
Final: Cargo from P to Q	Shiploads per month	y_{PQ}	1	1		
Cargo from Q to P		y_{QP}	1		1	
Primary: Shipping	Ships	$\bar{\bar{z}}$	$-t_{PQ} - t_{QP}$	$-t_{PQ} - s_{QP}$	$-s_{PQ} - t_{QP}$	$-s_{PQ} - s_{QP}$

* In units of ships per month.

Since each new activity, regarded as a combination of the elementary "leg-of-voyage" activities, satisfies (1.7c), any combination of the new activities does. It follows further from (1.8) that any combination of the new activities with nonnegative levels, x_1, x_2, x_3, x_4, say, is a combination of the old activities with the nonnegative levels given by

$$(1.9) \quad \bar{x}_{PQ} = x_1 + x_2, \quad x_{PQ} = x_3 + x_4, \quad \bar{x}_{QP} = x_1 + x_3,$$
$$x_{QP} = x_2 + x_4.$$

Conversely, for each set of nonnegative levels of the leg-of-voyage activities satisfying (1.7c) we can select nonnegative levels, x_1, x_2, x_3, x_4, of the round-voyage activities satisfying (1.9). One choice is given by

$$(1.10) \quad x_1 = \bar{x}_{QP}, \quad x_2 = \bar{x}_{PQ} - \bar{x}_{QP}, \quad x_3 = 0, \quad x_4 = x_{PQ}$$
$$\text{if} \quad \bar{x}_{PQ} \geqq \bar{x}_{QP};$$
$$x_1 = \bar{x}_{PQ}, \quad x_2 = 0, \quad x_3 = \bar{x}_{QP} - \bar{x}_{PQ}, \quad x_4 = x_{QP}$$
$$\text{if} \quad \bar{x}_{QP} \geqq \bar{x}_{PQ}.$$

In general, additional choices of the levels of the round-voyage activities can be derived from (1.10) by the transformation

(1.10a)
$$x_1^* = x_1 + \delta, \qquad x_2^* = x_2 - \delta,$$
$$x_3^* = x_3 - \delta, \qquad x_4^* = x_4 + \delta,$$

with such values of $\delta \neq 0$, if any, that the levels $x_1^*, \cdots$, remain non-negative. The transformation (1.10a) consists in a trivial reshuffling of leg-of-voyage activities between ships in making up complete round voyages.

The vectors $a_{(1)}, \cdots$, defining the round-voyage activities, constitute the completely reduced technology matrix, $\bar{A}$, shown in Table III. They are frame vectors of the cone of all possible points in the space of the commodities y_{PQ}, y_{QP}, $\bar{z}$, as shown in Figure 1. (The term "possible" is used here in the meaning given to it in Chapter III, Section 4.1, i.e., possible without regard to availability limits on shipping or port capacities but under the restriction that ships circulate in a stationary flow pattern.)

In the case of n ports the number of round-voyage activities, $a_1, \cdots$, becomes large more quickly, with increasing n, than the number of leg-of-voyage activities, $\bar{a}_{PQ}, \cdots$. Accordingly, the degree of indeterminacy in their levels, $x_1, \cdots$, for given possible commodity flows, $y_{PQ}, \cdots$, $\bar{z}$, increases. Nevertheless it would seem that, for the purpose of specifying the entire possible point set, and its entire subset of efficient points (as defined below), the round-voyage coordinates, $x_1, \cdots$, are the proper ones to use. It would then be necessary to select those round-voyage activities, $a_{(k)}$, associated with frame vectors and, from these, select the subsets that can occur simultaneously in an efficient activity combination.

We have found leg-of-voyage coordinates, $\bar{x}_{PQ}, \cdots$, more useful, in the n-port case, to treat the more limited problem of deriving local properties of the efficient point set (i.e., properties in the neighborhood of one efficient point, as defined below). For this reason, in preparation for the n-port case, we shall in the present two-port case demonstrate the analysis of the efficient point set in terms of leg-of-voyage coordinates. It may be added that in dynamic models round-voyage coordinates lose their usefulness, whereas leg-of-voyage coordinates, properly dated, remain appropriate.

1.4. *Possible points and efficient points in the commodity space.* Equations (1.7a–e), in which the activity levels, $\bar{x}_{PQ}, \cdots$, are restricted to nonnegative values, define the set of (technologically) *possible* points in the space of the commodity flows $(y_{PQ}, y_{QP}, \bar{z})$. It follows from the analysis of Section 1.3 that this set is a convex polyhedral cone (A) spanned by the vectors $a_{(1)}$, $a_{(2)}$, $a_{(3)}$, $a_{(4)}$, as shown in Figure 1. In preparation for the analysis of the n-port model, we shall obtain the same result in leg-of-voyage coordinates.

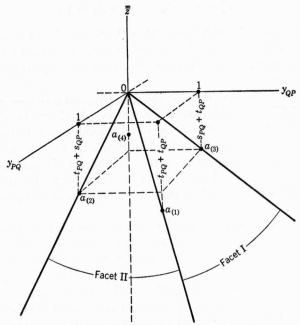

FIGURE 1—The possible cone in a two-port model.   (Note: $\overline{0a}_{(4)} = s_{PQ} + s_{QP}$.)

For the purposes of the present analysis, a possible point $a = (y_{PQ}, y_{QP}, z_0)$ is called *efficient* (without reference to the availability limit ζ on shipping) if $-z_0$ represents the minimum amount of shipping required to carry out the program $y \equiv (y_{PQ}, y_{QP})$, i.e., if there exists no possible point (y_{PQ}, y_{QP}, z) with $-z < -z_0$. This is an asymmetric definition, logically different from the definition adopted in Chapter III, Section 4.2. According to the latter definition, a point $a = (y_{PQ}, y_{QP}, z_0)$ would be called efficient if there existed no possible point $a^* = (y^*_{PQ}, y^*_{QP}, z^*)$ such that

(1.11) $y^*_{PQ} \geqq y_{PQ}, \qquad y^*_{QP} \geqq y_{QP}, \qquad z^* \geqq z_0,$

except the point $a^* = a$ itself. This says that, starting from an efficient point, no commodity flow can be increased (algebraically) without decreasing another commodity flow.

We shall show below that these two definitions, logically different, are equivalent under the assumptions of the present model. For that reason we can afford to utilize the former, asymmetric, definition in analyzing the efficient point set in Figure 1. For reasons of exposition we shall present this analysis independently of the general theory [III], referring to the theorems from which our results would also follow only after these results have already been obtained.

We shall therefore address ourselves to the following question: Given a program, $y = (y_{PQ}, y_{QP})$, what is the maximum value, $\bar{z} = \bar{z}_0$, of the nonpositive variable $\bar{z}$ such that $(y, \bar{z}) = (y_{PQ}, y_{QP}, \bar{z})$ is a possible point? The answer to this question will also help us to delineate the possible point set without using round-voyage coordinates.

We simplify the equations (1.7a–e) that define the possible point set, by eliminating $\bar{x}_{PQ}$ and $\bar{x}_{QP}$. This leaves us with the system

$$(1.12a) \qquad 0 = -y_{PQ} - x_{PQ} + y_{QP} + x_{QP},$$

$$(1.12b) \qquad -\bar{z} = t_{PQ}y_{PQ} + s_{PQ}x_{PQ} + t_{QP}y_{QP} + s_{QP}x_{QP},$$

$$(1.12c) \qquad y_{PQ} \geqq 0, \qquad y_{QP} \geqq 0, \qquad x_{PQ} \geqq 0, \qquad x_{QP} \geqq 0,$$

where it is known that

$$(1.13) \qquad t_{PQ} > s_{PQ} > 0, \qquad t_{QP} > s_{QP} > 0,$$

because of the definitions of the quantities involved.

From the given program $y = (y_{PQ}, y_{QP})$ we obtain

$$(1.14) \qquad x_{PQ} - x_{QP} = y_{QP} - y_{PQ} = \text{a given number.}$$

Starting with any set of values x_{PQ}, x_{QP} satisfying (1.14), we see readily that (1.14) is preserved if we diminish both x_{PQ} and x_{QP} by the same amount.[7] Hence, in view of (1.13), $\bar{z}$ is maximized by diminishing x_{PQ} and x_{QP} by the largest amount that does not violate (1.12c). We distinguish two cases.

CASE I: $y_{QP} - y_{PQ} \geqq 0$. Then efficiency requires

$$(1.15) \qquad x_{QP} = 0, \qquad \text{and hence} \qquad x_{PQ} = y_{QP} - y_{PQ} \geqq 0.$$

Substituting this in (1.12b) we obtain, with reference also to (1.12c),

$$(1.16) \qquad \begin{aligned} -\bar{z}_0 &= (t_{PQ} - s_{PQ})y_{PQ} + (t_{QP} + s_{PQ})y_{QP} \\ &\text{when} \qquad y_{QP} - y_{PQ} \geqq 0, \quad y_{PQ} \geqq 0, \end{aligned}$$

a set of conditions defining what in anticipation we shall call facet I of the efficient point set.

---

[7] This diminution is a simple case of what will be called a circular transformation in Section 2.4.

The economic meaning of the foregoing reasoning is obvious and trivial. If the traffic with cargo from Q to P exceeds that in the opposite direction, the most efficient routing of ships in a continuing program requires the excess of shipping arising at P to be moved back in ballast to fill the deficit at Q, with no other movements in ballast taking place ($x_{QP} = 0$). Moreover, since it is always possible under (1.14) to waste tonnage by adding equal positive amounts to x_{PQ} and x_{QP}, we find that in Case I all points (y_{PQ}, y_{QP}, $\bar{z}$) satisfying

$$-\bar{z} \geqq (t_{PQ} - s_{PQ})y_{PQ} + (t_{QP} + s_{PQ})y_{QP},$$

(1.17)

$$y_{QP} - y_{PQ} \geqq 0, \qquad y_{PQ} \geqq 0$$

are possible points.

CASE II: $y_{QP} - y_{PQ} \leqq 0$. Now efficiency requires

(1.18) $x_{PQ} = 0$,   and hence $x_{QP} = y_{PQ} - y_{QP} \geqq 0$.

We must send a number of empty ships from Q to P just sufficient to permit carrying out the transportation program. Sending empty ships from P to Q would, obviously, be inefficient. Substituting in (1.12b), we obtain

$$-\bar{z}_0 = (t_{PQ} + s_{QP})y_{PQ} + (t_{QP} - s_{QP})y_{QP}$$

(1.19)

$$\text{when} \quad y_{QP} - y_{PQ} \leqq 0, \quad y_{QP} \geqq 0,$$

which defines what we shall call facet II of the efficient point set. Moreover, all points (y_{PQ}, y_{QP}, $\bar{z}$) satisfying

$$-\bar{z} \geqq (t_{PQ} + s_{QP})y_{PQ} + (t_{QP} - s_{QP})y_{QP},$$

(1.20)

$$y_{QP} - y_{PQ} \leqq 0, \qquad y_{QP} \geqq 0$$

are possible.

We shall now demonstrate how the conditions (1.17) and (1.20) enable us to visualize the efficient facets I and II in relation to the entire possible point set. At the same time we shall show that facets I and II together constitute the entire efficient point set, also by the symmetric definition (1.11).

We note that the Cases I and II considered above exhaust all possibilities for the two nonnegative variables y_{PQ} and y_{QP}. Since (1.16) and (1.19) represent minimum values of $-\bar{z}$ for given values of y_{PQ}, y_{QP}, it follows that all possible points satisfy either (1.17) or (1.20), and some satisfy both conditions. Moreover, in Case I, (1.17) implies the first condition (1.20) because then

$$(t_{PQ} - s_{PQ})y_{PQ} + (t_{QP} + s_{PQ})y_{QP} - (t_{PQ} + s_{QP})y_{PQ}$$

(1.21)

$$- (t_{QP} - s_{PQ})y_{QP} = (s_{PQ} + s_{QP})(-y_{PQ} + y_{QP}) \geqq 0.$$

Similarly, in Case II, (1.20) implies the first condition (1.17).   It follows that the possible point set is fully described by the following four inequalities:

$$y_{PQ} \geqq 0, \qquad y_{QP} \geqq 0,$$

(1.22) $$0 \geqq (t_{PQ} - s_{PQ})y_{PQ} + (t_{QP} + s_{PQ})y_{QP} + \bar{z},$$

$$0 \geqq (t_{PQ} + s_{QP})y_{PQ} + (t_{QP} - s_{QP})y_{QP} + \bar{z}.$$

The possible point set is therefore an intersection of halfspaces, each having the origin in its boundary, hence a convex polyhedral cone. Since possible points can be found in the boundary of each of these halfspaces, the cone as shown in Figure 1 has four two-dimensional facets, of which two fall in coordinate planes.   The remaining two facets, I and II, constitute the set of efficient points by either definition, asymmetric or symmetric, because by (1.13) all coefficients in the last two inequalities (1.22) are positive.   Hence, if (1.16) or (1.19) holds in a point $a = (y_{PQ}, y_{QP}, \bar{z}_0)$ an increase in any one or more of the coordinates of a destroys the possibility of that point.   On the other hand, any possible point a not satisfying (1.16) or (1.19) permits some increase to its $\bar{z}$-coordinate, say, without destroying its possibility.

We note that the present analysis in leg-of-voyage coordinates has led us to a characterization of the possible cone as an intersection of halfspaces, while the analysis of Section 1.3 in round-voyage coordinates has led us to an equivalent characterization as a convex hull of halflines, $(a_{(1)}), \cdots , (a_{(4)})$.   This equivalence is discussed more generally by Gale [XVII].

1.5. *The efficient point set as a transformation function.*   The conditions for efficiency can be summarized in the statement that it is inefficient for ballast traffic in both directions to be positive.   Therefore

(1.23) $$\text{either} \quad x_{PQ} = 0 \quad \text{or} \quad x_{QP} = 0.$$

Thus, facet I of the efficient point set [less the halfline $(a_{(1)})$ common to both facets] may be characterized as the set of efficient points for which $x_{PQ} > 0$, and hence $x_{QP} = 0$.   Similarly, facet II [less the halfline $(a_{(1)})$] can be characterized as the set of efficient points for which $x_{QP} > 0$, and hence $x_{PQ} = 0$.   Thus, to anticipate a bit, an efficient facet may be identified with the empty shipping route(s) in use for all points on the relative interior [III, Section 2.4; XVIII, Definition 31] of that facet. We also observe that the efficient point set in Figure 1 represents a transformation function (production function) defined everywhere in the range of its variables and expressed, for instance, as the minimum shipping requirements,

(1.24) $-\bar{z}_0 = \min(-\bar{z}) = f(y_{PQ}, y_{QP})$,

of a given program. The derivatives of this function and the ratio thereof,

(1.25) $-\dfrac{\partial \bar{z}_0}{\partial y_{PQ}}, \quad -\dfrac{\partial \bar{z}_0}{\partial y_{QP}}, \quad \dfrac{\partial \bar{z}_0}{\partial y_{QP}} \Big/ \dfrac{\partial \bar{z}_0}{\partial y_{PQ}}$,

where they exist, represent the marginal cost, in terms of shipping employed, of a unit increase in the program items y_{PQ} and y_{QP}, respectively, and the marginal rate of substitution expressing the opportunity cost of a unit increase in y_{QP} in terms of a compensating decrease in y_{PQ}. On facet I the marginal rates of substitution (1.25) take the values

(1.26) $t_{PQ} - s_{PQ}, \quad t_{QP} + s_{PQ}, \quad (t_{QP} + s_{PQ})/(t_{PQ} - s_{PQ})$.

Thus the marginal cost of transporting an additional shipload per month from Q to P on facet I, in the proper units, is given by

(1.27) $-\dfrac{\Delta \bar{z}_0}{\Delta y_{QP}} = \dfrac{(t_{QP} + s_{PQ})\text{ ships}}{1\text{ ship per month}} = (t_{QP} + s_{PQ})\text{ months},$

where Δ denotes corresponding finite increments in the variable following it. This marginal cost coefficient equals the full turn-around time of a ship returning empty because on facet I the preponderant cargo movement is in the direction y_{QP} (i.e., the direction in which loaded traffic is being increased). No return loads are available for the additional ships, and the time cost of their return trip must be charged to the increment in outgoing cargo movements.

On the other hand, the cost of transporting an additional shipload monthly from P to Q on facet I is

(1.28) $-\dfrac{\Delta \bar{z}_0}{\Delta y_{PQ}} = \dfrac{(t_{PQ} - s_{PQ})\text{ ships}}{1\text{ ship per month}} = (t_{PQ} - s_{PQ})\text{ months}.$

This is the time cost of reallocating a ship from sailing in ballast from P to Q to transporting cargo from P to Q. We may regard t_{PQ} in (1.28) or t_{QP} in (1.27) as the *direct cost* of the additional transportation commitment, occasioned by the operations with cargo, and $-s_{PQ}$ in (1.28) or s_{PQ} in (1.27) as its *indirect cost*, occasioned by the change in location of the ship resulting from its loaded movement.

Similarly, on facet II, the rates of substitution (1.24) are

(1.29) $t_{PQ} + s_{QP}, \quad t_{QP} - s_{QP}, \quad (t_{QP} - s_{QP})/(t_{PQ} + s_{PQ})$.

The marginal rates of substitution, (1.26) and (1.29), are applicable both to *finite increases* and *finite decreases* in cargo flows, *within the facet in question*. In particular, the marginal cost coefficient for an increase in the preponderant cargo flow (y_{QP} in Case I) applies to indefinitely large increases as long as we rule out port congestion. The marginal cost coefficient for a decrease in the lesser cargo flow (y_{PQ} in Case I) applies until that flow is reduced to zero and is therefore restricted in its applicability only by the *feasibility limit* ($\Delta y_{PQ} \geqq -y_{PQ}$ in Case I) to the decrease in question. The marginal cost coefficient for an increase in the lesser flow, and for a decrease in the preponderant flow, are subject to *applicability limits* that are reached at the relative boundary [III, Section 2.4; XIX, Definition 32] of the facet in question, where the two cargo flows have become equal. From a point, $y_{PQ} = y_{QP}$, on the halfline ($a_{(1)}$) common to facets I and II, the marginal cost of a unit increase in one of the cargo flows exceeds the marginal saving from a unit decrease in that flow.

1.6. *Efficiency prices.* Although the foregoing analysis is complete for the two-port model, it may be useful to indicate an equivalent characterization of the efficient point set which will be helpful in analyzing the n-port model. The coefficients of y_{PQ}, y_{QP}, $\bar{z}_0$ in equation (1.16) of facet I are the coordinates

$$(1.30) \qquad p_{PQ} = t_{PQ} - s_{PQ}, \qquad p_{QP} = t_{QP} + s_{PQ}, \qquad p_z = 1,$$

of a vector p normal to that facet. They have been interpreted as efficiency prices [III, Sections 4.7, 5.12] associated with each efficient point of facet I. It has been proved generally for linear models of production such as those considered here [III, Theorems 4.3, 5.11] that a possible point a in the commodity space is efficient if and only if there exists an associated price vector p (subject to certain sign restrictions on its components) such that each activity in the technology has a nonpositive profitability, while each activity engaged in, in order to realize the commodity flow vector $a = \sum_k a_{(k)} x_k$, has a zero profitability

$$(1.31) \quad \begin{cases} \text{(a)} & p'a_{(k)} \leqq 0 \quad \text{for all } k, \\ \text{(b)} & p'a_{(k)} = 0 \quad \text{if } x_k > 0. \end{cases}$$

The sign restrictions relevant to the present case are that p shall have positive components for all desired (final or primary) commodities, i.e., all commodities entering in the definition of efficiency, and represented in our case by the flows y_{PQ}, y_{QP}, $\bar{z}$:

$$(1.32) \qquad p_{PQ} > 0, \qquad p_{QP} > 0, \qquad p_z > 0.$$

No sign restriction is involved for the prices of intermediate commodities, here represented by the flows y_P and y_Q. In the presence of intermediate commodities with net flows restricted to zero, the criterion stated as applied to the original technology is equivalent to that applied to the reduced technology from which intermediate commodities have been eliminated [III, Theorem 5.11].

In the present example, it is most easily verified from the reduced matrix in Table III that conditions (1.31) and (1.32) indeed admit all points, a, of facets I and II, and no other points. The vector p of *efficiency prices* defines a halfspace, $p'a^* \leq 0$, containing all possible points, a^*, and having the efficient point a in its bounding plane. This bounding plane necessarily contains the facet having a in its relative interior.[8] If normalized by

$$(1.33) \qquad\qquad p_z = 1,$$

the vector p is therefore uniquely determined, at the same value (1.30), for all points, a, of the relative interior of facet I. Similarly it uniquely equals

$$(1.34) \qquad p_{PQ} = t_{PQ} + s_{QP}, \qquad p_{QP} = t_{QP} - s_{QP}, \qquad p_z = 1$$

on all relative interior points, a, of facet II. It is not uniquely determined at any point a of the common relative boundary of two two-dimensional facets, but may be given the value specific to either facet, or a positive linear combination of these two values [subject to the sign restriction (2.32) which enters when one of the two facets is not an efficient facet]. Thus the efficiency prices define marginal rates of substitution wherever they are uniquely determined.

1.7. *The efficiency price on the location of ship appearances.* The equivalent application of criteria (1.31) and (1.32) to the technology matrix of Table II leads to the determination of efficiency prices on the intermediate commodities (ship appearances) which will play an important role in the n-port model. On the relative interior of facet I, where we have

$$(1.35) \qquad \bar{x}_{PQ} > 0, \qquad x_{PQ} > 0, \qquad \bar{x}_{QP} > 0, \qquad x_{QP} = 0,$$

the conditions (1.31) now become

$$(1.36) \qquad \begin{aligned} p_{PQ} - p_P + p_Q - t_{PQ} &= 0, \\ -p_P + p_Q - s_{PQ} &= 0, \\ p_{QP} + p_P - p_Q - t_{QP} &= 0, \\ p_P - p_Q - s_{QP} &\leq 0. \end{aligned}$$

---

[8] The definition of relative interior referred to above implies that the facet having a in its relative interior is the facet spanned by those vectors $a_{(k)}$ for which $x_k > 0$ in (1.31). See Gerstenhaber [XVIII, Theorem 1].

These conditions are solved, within the sign restrictions (1.32) and subject to the normalization (1.33), by (1.30) and by any p_P, p_Q such that

$$(1.37) \qquad p_Q = p_P + s_{PQ}.$$

We note that the efficiency prices, p_P and p_Q, of ship appearances in P and Q permit the following general expressions for the marginal cost coefficient for an increase in a cargo flow. From (1.27) and (1.37) we derive

$$(1.38) \qquad -\frac{\Delta \bar{z}_0}{\Delta y_{PQ}} = t_{PQ} + p_P - p_Q, \qquad -\frac{\Delta \bar{z}_0}{\Delta y_{QP}} = t_{QP} + p_Q - p_P$$

for finite variations within facet I. Since these expressions are symmetrical in the two ports, they apply also to finite variations within facet II if we remember that on that facet we must replace (1.37) by

$$(1.39) \qquad p_P = p_Q + s_{QP}.$$

By (1.38) the indirect cost of an increase in a transportation commitment by one shipload a month, accomplishable within any one efficient facet, is found to equal the decrease in the efficiency price attached to the location of a ship, resulting from the change in location required by the fulfilment of the new transportation commitment. For that reason the prices p_P and p_Q have also been called the *economic potential* of the location of a ship in P and Q, respectively.[9]

1.8. *Efficient points under capacity restrictions.* In the foregoing analysis the input $-\bar{z}$ of shipping has been regarded as a variable entering into the definition (1.11) of efficiency. Alternatively, in the definition of efficiency, the third condition (1.11) can be replaced by the requirement that both the would-be efficient point a and the possible point a^* be attainable, i.e., satisfy the capacity restriction (1.4a) arising from a given size of fleet. In this case the attainable point set is the pyramid $0A_1A_2A_3A_4$ indicated by Figure 2a, and the efficient point set consists of the two line segments A_1A_2 and A_1A_3. Figure 2b gives the corresponding attainable $(0A_1A_2A_3)$ and efficient $(A_1A_2$ and $A_1A_3)$ point sets in the two-dimensional "program space" of the variables y_{PQ}, y_{QP}.

The foregoing analysis of efficiency prices remains valid in the present case, provided that the assumption that the limits to port capacities are never reached is maintained. The only difference is that efficiency now requires that the quantity $\bar{z}_0$, previously a freely choosable nonpositive

---

[9] The reader may wish to exercise himself in the application of this concept to models with three or four ports.

variable, now equals the given constant ζ. Therefore the interpretation of efficiency prices, when unique, as marginal rates of substitution in efficient operation now applies only to offsetting variations in y_{PQ} and y_{QP}. Further interpretations of the efficiency prices are given in the n-port case in Sections 2.8, 2.9, and 2.10.

If port capacities ζ_P, ζ_Q actually restrict the attainable point set by (1.4b), the foregoing analysis of efficiency prices applies only in those efficient points (if any) in which neither of the equality signs in (1.4b)

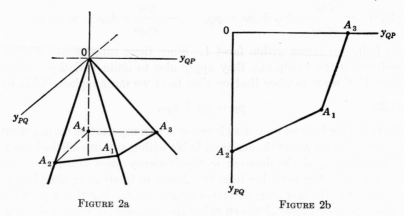

FIGURE 2a   FIGURE 2b

applies. If one or both equality signs in (1.4b) apply in an efficient point, the efficiency prices associated with such a point, if unique, contain allowances for rent arising from the use of scarce port facilities.

2. A MODEL WITH n PORTS

2.1. *The routing of empty ships.* A generalization to n ports of the technology matrix of Table II is given in Table IV. This table contains a cargo transportation activity and an empty sailing activity for each route (i.e., for each ordered pair of ports). The units of measurement of activities and commodities have been changed to correspond to an example described in Section 2.2 below.

As in the two-port case, we begin by assuming a desired transportation program. Let us treat this program as if it were given to a central shipping authority whose job it is to perform the indicated transportation, unchanged from month to month, at minimum cost in terms of shipping continually in use.

The given transportation program will determine the levels of all activities relating to the movement of cargo. This leaves the shipping authority free to choose only the levels of activities involving movements

TABLE IV.   PARTIALLY REDUCED TECHNOLOGY MATRIX FOR AN n-PORT MODEL

Commodities	Unit	Symbol	Transporting cargo							Sailing empty			
			from 1 to 2 $\bar{x}_{12}$	from 1 to 3 $\bar{x}_{13}$	...	from 1 to n $\bar{x}_{1n}$	from 2 to 1 $\bar{x}_{21}$	from 2 to 3 $\bar{x}_{23}$	... from n to n−1 $\bar{x}_{n,(n-1)}$	from 1 to 2 x_{12}	from 1 to 3 x_{13}	... from 1 to n x_{1n}	from n to n−1 $x_{n,(n-1)}$
Final: Cargo transported	1 million tons of cargo per month												
From 1 to 2		y_{12}	1										
From 1 to 3		y_{13}		1									
...		...											
From 1 to n		y_{1n}				1							
From 2 to 1		y_{21}					1						
From 2 to 3		y_{23}						1					
...		...											
From n to n − 1		$y_{n,(n-1)}$							1				
Intermediate: Net appearances of empty ships	1 million tons of cargo-carrying capacity per month												
At 1		0	−1	−1		−1				−1	−1		
At 2		0	1				−1	−1		1			
At 3		0		1				1			1		
...		...											
At n − 1		0							1				1
At n		0				1			−1			1	−1
Primary: Shipping	1 million tons of cargo-carrying capacity	$\equiv z$	$-t_{12}$	$-t_{13}$		$-t_{1n}$			$-t_{n,(n-1)}$	$-s_{12}$	$-s_{13}$	$-s_{1n}$	$-s_{n,(n-1)}$

* In millions of tons of cargo or cargo carrying capacity per month.

of empty ships. Thus the problem of finding the efficient point corresponding to a given transportation program is equivalent to finding a
routing plan for empty ships such that the total cost of the given program, in terms of shipping in use, is minimized.

These statements, obvious in themselves, are verified if we write the
net output equations associated with the technology matrix of Table IV
in the matrix form [10]

$$(2.1) \qquad a \equiv \begin{bmatrix} y \\ 0 \\ \bar{z} \end{bmatrix} = \begin{bmatrix} I & 0 \\ B & B \\ -t' & -s' \end{bmatrix} \begin{bmatrix} \bar{x} \\ x \end{bmatrix} \equiv A\bar{x} \qquad (y \geqq 0, \ \bar{x} \geqq 0).$$

From the first set of rows we find the loaded movements $\bar{x}$ determined
by the program y,

$$(2.2) \qquad\qquad y = I\bar{x} = \bar{x}.$$

We further read from the last (single) row

$$(2.3) \qquad \bar{z} = \bar{z} + z, \quad \text{with} \quad \bar{z} \equiv -t'\bar{x} = -t'y, \quad z \equiv -s'x,$$

where, analogous to (1.13), we have

$$(2.4) \qquad\qquad t > s > 0.$$

We thus find that, in order to minimize shipping employed, $-\bar{z}$, in a
given program, y, we must minimize shipping employed in empty movements, $-z$, by proper choice of the routing plan x so as to balance the
loaded movements $\bar{x}$. To achieve this balancing x must satisfy the
restrictions

$$(2.5) \qquad\qquad Bx + b = 0, \quad \text{with} \quad b \equiv B\bar{x},$$

following from the second set of rows in (2.1).

The matrix B, a submatrix of the given technology matrix A, is found
by reference to Table IV. To visualize the conditions (2.5), it will be
useful to write them equivalently in indicial form,

$$(2.6) \qquad x_{ij} \geqq 0, \quad \sum_{j=1}^{n} x_{ij} - \sum_{j=1}^{n} x_{ji} = b_i,$$

$$\text{where} \quad b_i \equiv \sum_{j=1}^{n} \bar{x}_{ji} - \sum_{j=1}^{n} \bar{x}_{ij}, \qquad (i = 1, \cdots, n).$$

(It is convenient here to think of x_{ii}, $\bar{x}_{ii}$ as equal to zero for all i, and not
represented in the vectors x, $\bar{x}$.) The elements of b defined in (2.6) are

---

[10] We employ the notations for inequalities between vectors introduced in Chapter
III, Section 2.5.

the net surpluses of empty ships arising in the various ports from the performance of loaded movements. These are actual surpluses in all ports receiving more shiploads than they dispatch, deficits in all ports in the reverse situation. Because the net surpluses are generated by loaded movements, and because our model of shipping technology disregards ship losses at sea, the sum of all net surpluses vanishes, as is easily verified directly from (2.5). If

$$(2.7) \qquad\qquad e' \equiv [1 \quad 1 \quad \cdots \quad 1]$$

is a row vector with all its n elements equal to 1, the remark just made is expressed by the property

$$(2.8) \qquad\qquad\qquad e'B = 0$$

of the matrix [11] B, which through (2.5) leads to

$$(2.9) \qquad\qquad\qquad e'b = \sum_i b_i = 0.$$

From the nature of our problem it is intuitively obvious that for every program y there exists at least one routing plan x that minimizes shipping employed in empty movements. To argue this point mathematically, we note first that every program y is possible (i.e., can be performed if enough shipping $-\bar{z}$ is available and port capacities are unlimited). A particular routing plan which is always available [12] is

$$(2.10) \quad x_{ij} = \bar{x}_{ji}, \quad \text{so} \quad -z = \sum_{i,j} s_{ij}\bar{x}_{ji} = \sum_{i,j} s_{ij}y_{ji} \equiv -z_0, \text{ say.}$$

This routing plan consists in returning all ships empty by the routes reverse to those traveled with cargo. Although in general this routing plan will be inefficient, it permits us to remark that, if we do not have, for all $i, j, i \neq j$,

$$(2.11) \qquad x_{ij} \leqq -z_0/s_{ij}, \quad \text{where} \,^{13} \quad 0 < -z_0/s_{ij} < \infty,$$

the function $-z = s'x$ will exceed the value $-z_0$ reached in (2.10). For the purpose of finding the minimum of the linear function $s'x$ subject to the restrictions (2.5), therefore, we can confine x to the closed and bounded convex polyhedral set S given by (2.5) and (2.11). We state without proof that on such a set a linear function reaches a minimum.

---

[11] It may be noted that B is of rank $n - 1$ and can by permutation of columns be given the form $[-C \quad C]$. It follows that b is subject to no other restrictions than (2.9), even though $\bar{x}$ is restricted to be nonnegative.

[12] Another type of "feasible solution" is employed by Dantzig [XXIII] as initial value in an iterative method to find an optimal x.

[13] Using (2.4) and excluding the trivial case $y = 0$, $z_0 = 0$, where $x = 0$ minimizes $-z$.

TABLE V. NET RECEIPTS OF DRY CARGO IN OVERSEAS TRADE, 1913 *

Area	Representative Port	Received Annually, $12\sum_j y_{ji}$	Dispatched Annually, $12\sum_j y_{ij}$	Annual Net Receipts, $12b_i$	Monthly Average of Annual Net Receipts, b_i
Baltic countries, Norway, Germany, Netherlands, Belgium, Great Britain, and Ireland	Rotterdam	151.30	156.72	− 5.42	−0.46
France, Spain, and Portugal	Lisbon	38.48	23.63	14.85	1.24
Mediterranean, except France, Spain, and Portugal	Athens	32.42	13.86	18.56	1.55
Black Sea countries	Odessa	1.70	13.25	−11.55	−0.96
West Africa	Lagos	2.76	1.34	1.42	0.12
South and East Africa	Durban	2.93	1.77	1.16	0.10
Arabia, Iran, and India	Bombay	6.49	9.95	− 3.46	−0.29
Malaya, Siam, Indochina, Philippines, and Indonesia	Singapore	4.75	4.93	− 0.18	−0.02
Japan, China, and Asiatic Russia	Yokohama	5.39	3.35	2.04	0.17
Australia and New Zealand	Sydney	3.37	6.30	− 2.93	−0.24
Pacific Coast of United States and Canada	San Francisco	2.60	2.37	0.23	0.02
Atlantic and Gulf Coast of United States and Canada	New York	12.78	28.18	−15.40	−1.28
Mexico, Caribbean, North Coast of South America, and Brazil	St. Thomas	12.04	7.80	4.24	0.35
Remainder of South America	La Plata	12.26	15.82	− 3.56	−0.30
Total		289.27	289.27	0.00	0.00

* Source: *Der Güterverkehr der Weltschiffahrt*, Statistisches Reichsamt, Berlin, 1928. All figures are in millions of metric tons.

This minimum may be reached in a single point, x, or in all points of a closed and convex polyhedral set, S_{min}. No local minima higher than this absolute minimum can exist because of the convexity of S. For proofs of these statements we refer to Chapter III, Sections 5.6, 5.8.

2.2. *An example with data for* 1913. We shall employ an example [14] constructed from data showing world movements of dry cargo in 1913. Table V gives the computation of the net surplus vector b from the given program. Although the data represent shipments between areas, we shall assume for simplicity that the entire traffic of an area goes through its representative port. The sailing times, s_{ij}, defined on that basis can be derived from Table VI. Assuming that a ship in ballast (allowing

TABLE VI. DISTANCES BETWEEN REPRESENTATIVE PORTS *

	Lisbon	Athens	Lagos	Durban	Yoko-hama	San Francisco	St. Thomas
Rotterdam	1.1						
Odessa		0.7					
Bombay	5.2	3.7	8.1	4.1	5.4	9.8	8.3
Singapore	7.2	5.7	9.0	4.9	2.9	7.3	10.2
Sydney	10.6	9.0	12.7	6.2	4.3	6.4	8.8
New York	3.0	4.8	4.9		9.7	5.2	1.4
La Plata	5.3	7.1	4.3	4.6	13.2	8.7	4.6

* All figures are in 1,000 nautical miles. Assuming vessel speeds in ballast (with allowance for time spent fueling) to correspond to 5,000 nautical miles per month, the coefficients s_{ij} are found by dividing the figures in this table by 5.

for time spent in refueling) sails 5,000 nautical miles in one month, the coefficients s_{ij} are obtained by dividing the figures in Table VI by 5. Furthermore, while the data were actually generated in a market situation, we shall assume them to be given to our hypothetical central shipping authority as the desired transportation program. Finally, we proceed as if these numbers represented constant rates of flow through time.

The unit of cargo flows is a million tons per month. The unit of flows of shipping, loaded or empty, is the flow of ships that if loaded would carry a unit flow of cargo. In this choice of units, we have disregarded the slight dependence of a ship's carrying capacity on the length of the loaded voyage, arising from the necessity to carry fuel.

[14] A similar example based on data for 1925 is contained in Koopmans [1947].

2.3. *Possible graphs of empty shipping routes.* Any vector x satisfying (2.6), and hence representing a possible routing plan for empty ships in relation to the program y, defines a set of routes (i, j) on which a positive flow of empty ships, $x_{ij} > 0$, is prescribed. The figure consisting of all these routes (as "arcs") plus all ports in the technology (as "vertices") is, according to topological terminology, a *linear graph* [König, 1936]. It will be called the graph $G = G(x)$ of ballast traffic associated with the possible routing plan x.

Map 1 gives a possible graph of ballast traffic for the program of Table V. Amounts x_{ij} that satisfy condition (2.6) are indicated alongside each route, the net surpluses b_i with each port.

2.4. *Conditions for an efficient graph.* A routing plan, x, possible in relation to a program, y, is called efficient if it minimizes the amount (2.4) of shipping absorbed in empty movements. A graph, $G(x)$, associated with an efficient routing plan, x, is likewise called efficient. A general theorem [III, Theorem 4.3, as extended in Theorem 5.9], already quoted, states that the existence of a vector p of prices, satisfying conditions similar to (1.36) as well as certain sign restrictions, is necessary and sufficient for the efficiency of a point (2.1) and, hence, of a routing plan x in relation to a program y. We shall here establish the validity of this criterion by reasoning specific to the present transportation model. The shortest road to that end will be the heuristic exploration of the consequences of conditions (1.36), should they be satisfied at a point a arising by (2.1) from a routing plan x.

In the present notation, and normalizing by $p_z = 1$, the conditions (1.36) are, for cargo-carrying activities,

$$(2.12) \quad \begin{cases} \text{(a)} & p_{ij} - p_i + p_j - t_{ij} \leq 0 \quad \text{for all } (i, j), \\ \text{(b)} & p_{ij} - p_i + p_j - t_{ij} = 0 \quad \text{if } \bar{x}_{ij} > 0, \end{cases}$$

and, for empty movements,

$$(2.13) \quad \begin{cases} \text{(a)} & p_j \leq p_i + s_{ij} \quad \text{for all } (i, j), \\ \text{(b)} & p_j = p_i + s_{ij} \quad \text{if } x_{ij} > 0. \end{cases}$$

We shall concern ourselves first with the conditions (2.13) on the p_i, which, as prices of intermediate commodities, are not subject to any sign restrictions. In Map 2 we shall attempt to determine for all ports values p_i that satisfy the conditions (2.13) corresponding to the graph G_{1913} of Map 1. Since conditions (2.13) are invariant under addition of the same constant to all p_i we may arbitrarily choose

$$(2.14) \quad\quad\quad p_{\text{Athens}} = 0.$$

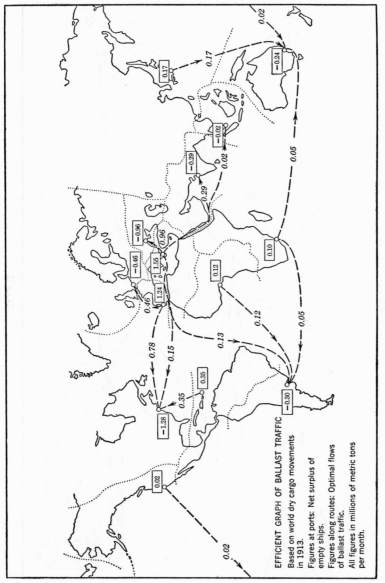

EFFICIENT GRAPH OF BALLAST TRAFFIC

Based on world dry cargo movements in 1913.

Figures at ports: Net surplus of empty ships.

Figures along routes: Optimal flows of ballast traffic.

All figures in millions of metric tons per month.

MAP 1

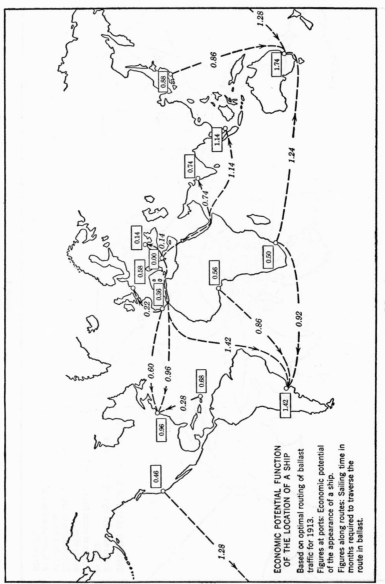

ECONOMIC POTENTIAL FUNCTION
OF THE LOCATION OF A SHIP

Based on optimal routing of ballast
traffic for 1913.
Figures at ports: Economic potential
of the appearance of a ship.
Figures along routes: Sailing time in
months required to traverse the
route in ballast.

MAP 2

Application of (2.13b), with reference to Table VI for the values of s_{ij}, now leads successively to the values of p_i in all ports connected with Athens by a chain of routes,

$$(2.15) \qquad \begin{aligned} p_{\text{LaPlata}} &= p_{\text{Athens}} + 1.42 = 1.42, \\ p_{\text{Durban}} &= p_{\text{LaPlata}} - 0.92 = 0.50, \end{aligned}$$

etc., as exhibited in Map 2. The procedure is formalized as follows.

We shall exclude graphs which contain both a route (l, m) and its reverse (m, l). Such graphs would in any case be inefficient. Let a chain C contained in the graph G be defined as a sequence of routes of G,

$$(2.16) \quad (i, j) \text{ or } (j, i), \; \cdots, \; (l, m) \text{ or } (m, l), \; \cdots, \; (p, q) \text{ or } (q, p),$$

connecting successive ports in a sequence,

$$(2.17) \qquad\qquad i, j, \; \cdots, \; l, m, \; \cdots, \; p, q,$$

of ports, no two of which are the same. This chain is said to lead from port i to port q. With reference to the routes of a given chain, C, we define [15]

$$(2.18) \quad \begin{cases} v_{lm}^{C} = 1 & \text{if } (l, m) \, \epsilon \, C \text{ and } l \text{ precedes } m \text{ in (2.17)}, \\ v_{ml}^{C} = -1 & \text{if } (m, l) \, \epsilon \, C \text{ and } m \text{ follows } l \text{ in (2.17)}. \end{cases}$$

Then repeated application of (2.13b) is equivalent to the rule

$$(2.19) \quad p_q = p_i + \sum_{(g, h) \, \epsilon \, C} v_{gh}^{C} s_{gh}, \qquad C \subset G, \qquad C \text{ leads from } i \text{ to } q.$$

In order to ascertain whether and when this procedure gives determinate p_i-values in all ports, we must explore the two possibilities of contradiction and of indeterminacy. To begin with possible contradiction, let us define a circuit, O, contained in G in a manner similar to a chain, except that we require the first and last port to be the same $(q = i)$, all other ports to be different. The notion of a circuit includes the sense (from left to right) in which the sequence (2.16) (with $q = i$) is traced, and constants v_{gh}^{O} are defined as in (2.18) with reference to that sense.

In a graph that contains no circuits, (2.19) cannot lead to a contradiction. If a graph G contains a circuit O with successive ports $(i, j, k, \cdots, p, i)$, contradiction will arise unless

$$(2.20) \qquad\qquad \sum_{(g, h) \, \epsilon \, O} v_{gh}^{O} s_{gh} = 0.$$

This is easily seen to be also a necessary condition for the efficiency of G.

[15] The symbol ϵ denotes "is a route of"; the symbol $\subset$, "is contained in."

If the left-hand member of (2.20) were negative, a *circular transformation*,

(2.21)
$$x_{gh}^* = x_{gh} + \mu v_{gh}^O \quad \text{if} \quad (g, h) \, \epsilon \, O,$$
$$x_{gh}^* = x_{gh} \text{ on all other routes } (g, h),$$

of the flows of empty shipping, with a positive *modulus* μ, would decrease the expression (2.4) for the shipping engaged in these movements by the positive amount

(2.22)
$$s'x - s'x^* = -\mu \sum_{(g, h) \, \epsilon \, O} v_{gh}^O s_{gh}.$$

The meaning of this transformation is that, tracing the circuit in the sense $i, j, k, \cdots, p, i$, an amount μ is added to the flow of empty ships on all routes traced in the direction of that flow and an amount μ is subtracted from the flow on all routes traced in a direction opposite to that flow. This can always be done within the restriction $x^* \geqq 0$ by taking a sufficiently small value of μ, since the graph $G = G(x)$ contains only routes of positive flows $x_{ij}, \cdots$. Similarly, if the left-hand member of (2.20) were positive, a sufficiently small negative modulus μ would define a possible transformation such that (2.22) is positive. Finally, by considering each of the four cases (omitting superscripts O)

(2.23)
$$v_{ij} = v_{jk} = 1; \quad v_{ji} = v_{kj} = -1; \quad v_{ij} = 1, \quad v_{kj} = -1;$$
$$v_{ji} = -1, \quad v_{jk} = 1;$$

it is easily seen that, with either sign of μ, the transformed routing plan x^* satisfies the restrictions (2.6) for every port j whenever the original plan x does.

A circuit $O = (i, j, \cdots, i)$ contained in a graph G is called *neutral* if (2.20) is satisfied. It is easily seen that, if all circuits contained in a graph G are neutral, no contradiction can arise in defining p_i-values in all ports. Since, in particular, any circuit contained in an efficient graph is a neutral circuit, no contradiction in the evaluation of p_i-values for all ports by (2.19) can arise if the graph G is indeed efficient.

Indeterminacy of one or more p_i can arise if the graph G is not *connected*, i.e., if there exists at least one pair of ports i, q not connected by a chain $(i, j, \cdots, q)$ in G. We shall come back to this case in Section 2.5, and we assume here that G is indeed connected.

We have thus established that, if G is a possible and connected graph containing only neutral circuits (if any), conditions (2.13b) permit a unique determination of p_i-values for all ports from a prescribed value in one port. We shall prove further that, under these assumptions, conditions (2.13a) are both necessary and sufficient for the efficiency of G.

To show the necessity, assume that

(2.24) $$p_j > p_i + s_{ij}$$

for some (i, j). To illustrate the argument in Map 2, let i = Durban, j = Singapore, and assume that $s_{ij} = 0.60$ instead of the value 0.98 following from Table VI. Then, by adding the route (Durban, Singapore) to G_{1913} to make G^*_{1913}, we give rise to a circuit (Durban, Singapore, Athens, La Plata, Durban) in G^*_{1913} because Singapore and Durban are already connected by a chain in G before the new route is added. The saving in shipping from a circular transformation on this circuit with positive modulus μ equals, by (2.22) and (2.19),

(2.25) $$-\mu(s_{\mathrm{Du, Si}} - s_{\mathrm{Ath, Si}} + s_{\mathrm{Ath, LP}} - s_{\mathrm{LP, Du}})$$
$$= -\mu(s_{\mathrm{Du, Si}} + p_{\mathrm{Du}} - p_{\mathrm{Si}}),$$

which, by assumption (2.24), is a positive number. Hence the graph G_{1913} is not efficient because savings can be secured by sending empty ships on a route outside it. It should be added that in the reverse case,

(2.26) $$p_j < p_i + s_{ij},$$

no saving can be effected by a negative choice of μ because $x_{ij} = 0$ before the transformation, and any negative value of μ would make $x^*_{ij} < 0$, which is technologically impossible.

To show the sufficiency, assume that (2.13a) holds for the p_i determined from (2.13b). Define a row vector,

(2.27) $$p'_B \equiv [p_1 \quad p_2 \quad \cdots \quad p_n],$$

to contain all p_i. We can then write (2.13a), which was obtained by applying (1.31a) to the second set of columns in the technology matrix A as partitioned in (2.1), in the form

(2.28) $$p'_B B - s' \leq 0.$$

In particular, from (2.13b), i.e., from (1.31b) applied to A, the equality sign in (2.28) applies to all components such that the corresponding component of x is positive. Since the remaining components of x are zero, we have

(2.29) $$(p'_B B - s')x = 0.$$

Now let x^0 be any possible routing plan, i.e., any vector $x^0 \geq 0$ satisfying (2.5) if x^0 is substituted for x, giving

(2.30) $$Bx^0 = -b = Bx.$$

Then, since $x^0 \geq 0$, we have from (2.28)

$$(2.31) \qquad\qquad (p'_B B - s')x^0 \leq 0.$$

Comparison of (2.29) and (2.31), using (2.30) after premultiplication by p'_B, leads to

$$(2.32) \qquad\qquad s'x^0 \geq s'x.$$

Hence there is no possible routing plan x^0 employing less shipping than x, and G is an efficient graph.

We have thus found that, in the case of a connected graph G, the existence of a solution p_i of (2.13) is by itself a necessary and sufficient condition for the efficiency of G.

This does not conflict with the theorem mentioned at the beginning of this section, which includes (2.12) in the condition. For, if p_i satisfies (2.13), the p_{ij} defined by requiring equality in (2.12) for all routes (i, j), whether cargo is moved on them or not, will be positive as a consequence of the inequalities

$$(2.33) \qquad\qquad t_{ij} > s_{ij} \qquad \text{for all } (i, j)$$

similar to (1.13).

A comparison of the p_i-values in Map 2 with the s_{ij} as derived from Table VI establishes that the graph of that map is indeed efficient.

2.5. *The case of a disconnected graph.* The proof that the existence of a solution p_i of (2.13) is sufficient for the efficiency of a graph G does not depend on G being connected. The proof of the necessity of that condition needs to be supplemented for the case of a disconnected graph G. A disconnected graph is possible only if the set of ports can be partitioned into two or more subsets such that the net surpluses b_i add up to zero within each subset. This, again, can only happen by "accident," by "special" choice of the program vector y. Since we have specified that all ports belong to any graph of ballast traffic, the case where a certain port is neither the origin nor the destination of any route of empty ships constitutes, and properly so, a special case of a disconnected graph.

As an illustration of a disconnected graph, add 0.9 million tons to the cargo flow from Durban to Sydney. The graph $G^\dagger_{1913}$ obtained from that of Map 1 by deleting the route (Durban, Sydney) is a possible and disconnected graph for the modified program $y^\dagger$ so obtained. Does the existence of a solution p_i of (2.13) remain a necessary consequence of its efficiency? We shall sketch the reasoning that leads to an affirmative answer.

Let us refer to the two connected subgraphs of $G^\dagger_{1913}$ as the Atlantic and Pacific subgraphs. Values for the p_i in all "Atlantic" ports (with which we include Durban, Bombay, and Singapore) are uniquely determined, by (2.13b), from the value (2.14) arbitrarily assumed for Athens. Similarly, p_j-values for all "Pacific" ports are expressed by

$$(2.34) \qquad p_j = \lambda + q_j, \qquad \lambda \equiv p_{\text{Yokohama}},$$

say, and where the q_j are uniquely determined by (2.13b). Consider all routes leading from an "Atlantic" port i to a "Pacific" port j. For each such route we read from (2.13a) an inequality,

$$(2.35) \qquad \lambda + q_j \leqq p_i + s_{ij}.$$

For each route of the reverse type we have, similarly,

$$(2.36) \qquad \lambda + q_j \geqq p_i - s_{ji}.$$

Hence a value of λ which satisfies (2.13a) can be found if

$$(2.37) \qquad \max_{\substack{i \,\epsilon\, \text{Atl} \\ j \,\epsilon\, \text{Pac}}} (p_i - q_j - s_{ji}) \leqq \min_{\substack{i \,\epsilon\, \text{Atl} \\ j \,\epsilon\, \text{Pac}}} (p_i - q_j + s_{ij}).$$

But if this is not true, there exist "Atlantic" ports i_1, i_2 and "Pacific" ports j_1, j_2 such that

$$(2.38) \qquad p_{i_1} - q_{j_1} - s_{j_1 i_1} > p_{i_2} - q_{j_2} + s_{i_2 j_2},$$

and a circuit can be found which contains the routes (j_1, i_1) and (i_2, j_2) and on which a circular transformation with positive modulus produces a saving in shipping employed. Efficiency of $G^\dagger_{1913}$ thus implies (2.37).

This reasoning can be extended to cover the case of three or more connected subgraphs, not mutually connected, of a possible graph G.

2.6. *Iterative computation of an efficient graph.* The foregoing proof of the necessity of the conditions (2.13) for the efficiency of a graph G suggests a method of iterative improvement of a tentative possible initial graph, G_1. Such a method is described by Dantzig [XXIII]. The difference $p_j - p_i$ is there referred to as the indirect cost of the activity measured by x_{ij} and is denoted by $\bar{c}_{ij}$.

Table VII gives corresponding notations in Dantzig's chapter and the present one. In making the comparisons it should be kept in mind that the program of commodity inflows and outflows, assumed given for the various terminals by Dantzig, corresponds to our net surpluses of shipping at the various ports. His minimum cost transportation program of a homogeneous commodity corresponds to our efficient routing plan of empty ships.

TABLE VII. CORRESPONDING NOTATIONS IN CHAPTERS XXIII AND XIV

XXIII	XIV	XXIII	XIV
c_{ij}	s_{ij}	$a_1, \cdots, a_m, b_1, \cdots, b_n$	$b_1, \cdots, b_n$
x_{ij}	x_{ij}	B_k	a_{ij} such that $x_{ij} > 0$
A_{ij}	a_{ij}	x_k	x_{ij} such that $x_{ij} > 0$
z	$-z$	$\nu_k = \lambda_{lk} + \mu_{mk}$, if $B_k = A_{lm}$	ν_{lm}, if $x_{lm} > 0$
$\bar{c}_{ij}$	$p_j - p_i$	$\nu_k = \lambda_{mk} + \mu_{lk}$, if $B_k = A_{ml}$	ν_{ml}, if $x_{ml} > 0$
u_i	$-p_i$	$c_1, \cdots, c_{m+n-1}$	s_{ij} such that $x_{ij} > 0$
v_j	p_j		

2.7. Routing plans associated with an efficient graph. So far our attention has been directed to the graph G of ballast traffic (i.e., the set of routes for which $x_{ij} > 0$) rather than to the actual values of the x_{ij} and the resulting value z of shipping employed in ballast traffic. We shall now establish the connection between G and x.

Assume first that G contains no circuits and is connected, taking as an example the graph G_{1913} of Map 1 in relation to the unchanged program y_{1913} of Table V. Such a graph, known as a tree, uniquely determines the flows, x_{ij}, of empty ships on all its routes. To show the determination of the flow of 0.9 million of (empty) cargo-carrying capacity on the route (Durban, Sydney), delete that route from G_{1913}. This recreates the graph $G_{1913}^\dagger$ previously considered, but this is not a possible graph in relation to the program y_{1913}. Either of its two trees can be used to determine uniquely the value

$$(2.39) \qquad x_{\mathrm{Du, Sy}} = \sum_{i \,\epsilon\, \mathrm{Atl}} b_i = -\sum_{i \,\epsilon\, \mathrm{Pac}} b_i = 0.9$$

from a summation of the relations (2.6) over all ports of one tree. If G is not connected, the same reasoning can be applied to each of its connected subgraphs.

Each circuit contained in a graph G introduces the possibility of a circular transformation in x, with a modulus limited by a lower and an upper possibility bound depending on the initial routing plan, x_0, say. It can be shown that the set of routing plans x compatible with such a graph G forms a convex polyhedron of a dimensionality equal to the *cyclomatic number* of G (i.e., the maximum number of routes that can be removed from G without disconnecting any pair of ports connected within G) [König, 1936].

If G is efficient, all its circuits are neutral circuits, and all routing plans x associated with G lead to the same value, $-z$, of shipping employed in ballast traffic, which is the minimum value of $-z$ among all possible routing plans.

If G is efficient and connected, then (2.13b) uniquely determines the p_i, and what we shall call the *maximal efficient graph* $\overline{G}$ is obtained by adding to G all routes (i, j) for which the equality sign in (2.13a) holds. (To obtain the maximal efficient graph $\overline{G}$ if G is not connected may require adding two or more routes simultaneously to avoid impossible graphs.) If $\overline{G}$ does not contain a circuit, the efficient routing plan x is unique.

Neutral circuits often occur in practice. Many would be present in the technology of Table VI if all its cells were filled out. Neutral circuits arise whenever all four routes connecting either of two ports i, j with either of two ports k, l go past the same geographical point (cape, narrow passage).

2.8. The marginal cost of variations in the program. We shall now show that the efficiency prices, p_{ij}, on cargo flows, when uniquely determined by (2.12) and (2.13), define marginal rates of substitution of cargo flows against shipping. These substitution rates are applicable to all changes in the program that can be balanced by a change in the efficient routing plan x without causing an essential change in the corresponding graph G of ballast traffic.

As an example, consider the addition of $\mu = 0.1$ million tons of cargo to the monthly flow from New York to San Francisco in the 1913 program of Table V. Since G_{1913} is connected, the route (NY, SF) can be supplemented by routes in G_{1913} to a circuit (NY $\rightarrow$ SF $\rightarrow$ Sy $\leftarrow$ Du $\rightarrow$ LP $\leftarrow$ Ath $\rightarrow$ NY), in which the arrows indicate the direction of ballast traffic on all but the first route. The change in the program can be effected, within the restrictions (2.6), by the circular transformation

$$\bar{x}^*_{\mathrm{NY, SF}} = \bar{x}_{\mathrm{NY, SF}} + \mu, \qquad x^*_{\mathrm{SF, Sy}} = x_{\mathrm{SF, Sy}} + \mu,$$

(2.40) $$x^*_{\mathrm{Du, Sy}} = x_{\mathrm{Du, Sy}} - \mu, \qquad \cdots, \qquad x^*_{\mathrm{Ath, NY}} = x_{\mathrm{Ath, NY}} + \mu,$$

$$\bar{x}^*_{ij} = \bar{x}_{ij} \quad \text{and} \quad x^*_{ij} = x_{ij} \text{ on all other routes.}$$

Because of the moderate amount of its modulus, μ, the graph $G(x^*)$ after this transformation is the same as the original graph, G_{1913}. Since the efficiency of a possible routing plan depends only on the efficiency of its graph, it follows that x^* is again an efficient routing plan for the changed program.

The unit cost of the transformation (2.40) (i.e., the cost divided by the modulus, μ, expressed in terms of additional shipping used) is

(2.41) $t_{\text{NY, SF}} + s_{\text{SF, Sy}} - s_{\text{Du, Sy}} + \cdots + s_{\text{Ath, NY}}.$

By (2.19) and (2.18), this cost equals

(2.42) $t_{\text{NY, SF}} + p_{\text{NY}} - p_{\text{SF}}.$

On the other hand, this expression equals the efficiency price $p_{\text{NY, SF}}$ as determined by (2.12b) whenever $y_{\text{NY, SF}} = \bar{x}_{\text{NY, SF}} > 0$ in the original program, or as permitted by (2.12a) if $y_{\text{NY, SF}} = 0$. This establishes the interpretation of the p_{ij}, when uniquely determined, as marginal cost coefficients,

(2.43) $p_{ij} = t_{ij} + p_i - p_j.$

The term t_{ij} in (2.43) can be called the direct cost of a unit addition to the program on the route (i, j), the term $p_i - p_j$ the indirect cost. The indirect cost arises because, on completion of its loaded movement, the ship is in a different location and hence has a different locational potential. The term allowing for this circumstance is the loss in potential (in the efficiency price of ship appearance) associated with the loaded movement.

Since all relationships involved are linear, the coefficients p_{ij}, if unique, can also be used to express the simultaneous cost of a number of program changes Δy_{ij},

(2.44) $-\Delta \bar{z} = \sum_{i, j} p_{ij} \Delta y_{ij}.$

The validity of this expression is limited to changes in the program which permit the same potential function p_i to apply before and after the change, with the p_{ij} defined by (2.12b) on all routes. This is certainly the case if the same efficient graph applies before and after the change. It remains true in certain boundary cases whenever the efficient graphs G and G^* before and after the change are contained in the same maximal efficient graph $\bar{G}$. It can be shown that all programs y permitting routing plans x whose graphs are contained in the same maximal efficient graph $\bar{G}$ form a closed facet [16] of the efficient point set. The maximum dimensionality of such a facet is $n(n - 1)$, the number of variables y_{ij}, $\bar{z}$, less one. This maximum is reached if $\bar{G}$ is connected, in which case the efficiency price vector p is uniquely determined in every point in the relative interior of the facet in question, and represents the normal to that facet.

[16] For the concept of a facet, see Chapters III, Section 4.5, and XVIII, Section 4.

The cost expression (2.44) for a change in the program y within a facet can be decomposed into direct and indirect cost as follows. If the p_{ij} are to be unique, conditions (2.12b) must apply to all routes (i, j). If we write p_y for the vector with elements p_{ij} ordered as the y_{ij} in Table IV, the normalized efficiency price vector p is given by

$$(2.45) \qquad p' = [p_y' \quad p_B' \quad 1].$$

In this notation, with reference to the technology matrix A as partitioned in (2.1), conditions (2.12b) for all routes can be written as

$$(2.46) \qquad [p_y' \quad p_B' \quad 1] \begin{bmatrix} I \\ B \\ -t' \end{bmatrix} = p_y' + p_B'B - t' = 0,$$

and hence, from (2.44),

$$(2.47) \qquad -\Delta \bar{z} = t'\Delta y - p_B'B\Delta y.$$

In this expression, in view of (2.2) and (2.5),

$$(2.48) \qquad B\Delta y = B\Delta \bar{x} = \Delta b$$

represents the vector of changes in net shipping surpluses b_i in the various ports, resulting from the change Δy in the program. Substituting (2.48) in (2.47), we find that the cost,

$$(2.49) \qquad -\Delta \bar{z} = t'\Delta y - p_B'\Delta b = \sum_{i,j} t_{ij}\Delta y_{ij} - \sum_i p_i \Delta b_i,$$

of a change in the program within an $n(n-1)$-dimensional closed facet of the efficient point set is the sum of a direct cost, $\sum t_{ij}\Delta y_{ij}$, representing the net increase in shipping employed in cargo-transporting activities, and an indirect cost, $-\sum p_i \Delta b_i$, representing the net increase in shipping efficiently employed in empty movements. The latter cost can be obtained, without tracing the changes Δx_{ij} in flows of empty ships on individual routes, as the negative of the sum of the changes Δb_i in the net shipping surpluses, each multiplied by the economic potential, p_i, of a ship in the location of that surplus.[17]

2.9. *Uses of the efficiency prices by a central shipping authority.* In a pool of shipping administered by a central authority, such as existed in the first and second world wars, an efficient routing plan x and a set of efficiency prices p corresponding to a program y can become known to that authority only by explicit computations based on the performance

---

[17] Because of (2.9), the expression (2.49) is not affected by the addition of a constant to the potential function p_i.

times t_{ij}, s_{ij}. Once computed, the prices p_{ij} can be used to assess the opportunity cost of the acceptance of one transportation commitment, in terms of other commitments that have to be rejected, if the total amount of shipping available for active operations [18] is limited. Where two possible commitments are not competitive but substitutes, such as when the same raw material can be obtained from two different sources of supply or when the location of a raw material processing activity is to be selected, calculations based on the prices p_{ij} are needed to arrive at the best solution. It should be emphasized again that these uses are subject to all the limitations of the present analysis. They apply to the comparison of alternative programs, each constant over time and both compatible with the same efficient graph $G(x)$. They therefore do not analyze the cost of transition in time from one constant program to another. These and many other problems in the centralized operations of a pool of shipping can only be approached by dynamic generalizations of the foregoing theory.

2.10. *Efficiency prices as market prices under competition.* The conditions (2.12) and (2.13) would also be fulfilled, with proper interpretation, by freight rates p_{ij} formed in a competitive market in which the composition of demand for transportation services on the various routes is stable and in which shipowners independently bid for and carry out transportation commitments, whenever necessary moving their ships empty to a more advantageous position for the fulfilment of the next commitment. Of course, market freight rates also contain allowances for the cost of other scarce factors besides shipping, represented by such things as port and canal dues, allowance for accumulating repair needs, wages of crews and stevedores, cost of fuel and supplies. To keep matters simple, let us assume that all factors other than the use of shipping can be bought *at constant prices* in any desired quantities. Then we may add one row to the technology matrix, stating for each route the money cost of the amounts of these factors required for the unit of each activity. The commodity flow corresponding to this new row is money input, and the efficiency price can conveniently be taken equal to unity so as to express all other efficiency prices in money terms.

In a model for long-run analysis it would be appropriate to treat the cost of the use of shipping in the same manner by making an overhead charge, including depreciation and interest, based on the money cost of ship construction. However, since adjustment in the size of the world merchant shipping fleet is much slower than the fluctuations in demand-

[18] That is, the total fleet in existence less an allowance for ships in repair or overhauling.

at-constant-price for its services, it is also of interest, in an analysis which is neither too long-run nor too short-run in character, to consider temporarily constant demand schedules on all routes in conjunction with a temporarily constant size of the fleet, which is not necessarily in long-run equilibrium with these demand schedules.

In this case, the row in the technology matrix corresponding to input z of shipping should be retained and the efficiency price p_z on the use of shipping be interpreted as a "rental charge" for the use of one unit of shipping during one unit of time. This charge is expressed by the market as a "time-charter rate," at which the use of a ship is traded.[19] The time-charter rate expresses the "scarcity" of ships in the period in question, in terms of benefits forgone, or cost incurred by alternative methods, because there is not one more ship available. When in a depression ships are laid up idle, the time-charter rate as here understood is zero.[20]

So modified, conditions (2.12) and (2.13) express that the profit on any round voyage that is actually engaged in, or that can be pieced together from legs-of-voyage (with or without cargo) actually engaged in, is zero to the entrepreneur, provided that he calculates the time-charter charge as a cost. The profit is positive on no round voyage, and negative on inefficient round voyages. This is indeed the result of entrepreneurs' decisions in a perfectly competitive market, according to accepted static equilibrium theory. If market demand, y_{ij}, for transportation services on the various routes remains constant for a sufficiently long time, the efficiency prices, p_{ij}, are observable as freight rates per shipload on the various routes. The economic potential function, p_i, is implicit in the calculations of the shipowners in choosing between alternative round voyages. The type of contract that would make the p_i observable as market prices has to our knowledge not been in use in ocean shipping or in any other transportation market.

Where competition is restricted, such as in line shipping, discrepancies between freight rates and efficiency prices may result. This is even more true, empirically, in transportation systems subject to government operation or regulation. This is not an inevitable consequence of governmental activity, but rather of the simple and crude notions of "fairness" which have historically dominated such activity under the watching eyes of highly interested local and functional groups of population and industry. The resulting inefficiency in the geographical dis-

---

[19] The type of time charter approximating most closely the concept of a time-charter rate here applicable is known as the "bareboat charter," by which the use of a ship is handed over for a period without crews or supplies.

[20] This statement is still based on the (unrealistic) assumption, made in Section 1, that all ships are of the same type and quality.

tribution of industry has been briefly commented on elsewhere [Koopmans, 1947].

2.11. *Analogy with Kirchhoff's law on the distribution of current in an electrical network.* There is an interesting analogy, with differences, between the problem of minimizing the amount of shipping in use for a given transportation program and the distribution of (direct) current in a network of electrical conductors to which given electromotive forces are applied at specified points. The latter problem, treated by Kirchhoff [1847], provided the stimulus for the mathematical investigation of linear graphs.[21] The analogy is brought out by the following list of reinterpretations of the symbols used above.

Interpretation in Transportation Model	Symbol	Interpretation in Electrical Network
Ports	$i = 1, \cdots, n$	Connection points of conductors
Routes	(i, j)	Conductors
Empty sailing time	s_{ij}	Resistance
Flow of empty ships	x_{ij}	Electrical current
Net shipping surplus	b_i	Net current made to flow into the network from outside
Locational potential	p_i	Negative of electrical potential

In the electrical application the identity (2.6) expresses that the total inflow of current into a connection point of conductors must equal the total outflow. Kirchhoff's law on the determination of the currents x_{ij} in the various conductors can be derived from the minimization of the total heat,

$$(2.50) \qquad h = \kappa \sum_{\substack{i,j \\ i<j}} s_{ij}x_{ij}^2,$$

generated per unit of time in the network, subject to the restraints (2.6) on the currents. This differs decisively from the transportation problem, in which, instead of the quadratic form (2.50), the linear form

$$(2.51) \qquad -z = \sum_{i,j} s_{ij}x_{ij}$$

is minimized subject to the additional restriction $x_{ij} \geq 0$. The heat minimization problem lends itself naturally to application of calculus

<hr>

[21] The cultural lag of economic thought in the application of mathematical methods is strikingly illustrated by the fact that linear graphs are making their entrance into transportation theory just about a century after they were first studied in relation to electrical networks, although organized transportation systems are much older than the study of electricity.

by the method of Lagrange parameters.   Because the function (2.50) is a sum of squares with positive coefficients, placed under linear restraints, the minimizing solution x_{ij} is unique.   It is found to be such that, instead of (2.13b),

$$(2.52) \qquad\qquad s_{ij}x_{ij} = -p_i + p_j,$$

where $-p_i$ is the electrical potential at the connection point i, obtained as a Lagrange parameter associated with the corresponding restraint (2.6).

It is possible to apply the same method to the minimization of shipping in use, by the substitution

$$(2.53) \qquad\qquad x_{ij} = w_{ij}^2, \qquad w_{ij} \text{ real,}$$

which insures that the condition $x_{ij} \geqq 0$ is met.   The locational potential then plays the same role of a set of Lagrange parameters.   The difference in sign in its definition is motivated by the fact that a ship is more useful at the destination of an empty voyage than at the point of origin, whereas a positively charged particle may be regarded as more usefully located where the electrical potential is high.

Because the degree in the x_{ij} of (2.51) is one less than that of (2.50), the difference in potential between two points i, j in the transportation model is related to the "resistance" or "time cost" only in the case that $x_{ij} > 0$, and is within that case independent of the value of x_{ij}.   Also, the minimizing solution x_{ij} lacks uniqueness if neutral circuits occur in the maximal efficient graph.

Chapter XV

EFFECTS OF TECHNOLOGICAL CHANGE IN A LINEAR MODEL

By Herbert A. Simon

The term "technological change" is employed in many senses in economic literature. In economic history the term is generally applied to any change in the methods of production used in an economy. The change may result from an improvement or a series of improvements in an existing process for making a commodity, which permits the commodity to be produced more cheaply, such as the series of improvements in spinning and weaving processes that revolutionized the textile industry in the eighteenth century. Or the change may involve the partial or total replacement of an old resource by a new, such as the substitution of petroleum for coal as a fuel by use of the internal combustion engine. Or, finally, the change may involve the production of a new consumers' good not previously in existence, such as the radio. These categories are not mutually exclusive but indicate the range of phenomena falling under the general heading of technological change.

In writings on economic theory technological change has been a somewhat narrower concept. There technology is generally represented by production functions that state the maximum quantities of output technologically obtainable from given quantities of inputs. A production function may refer to a whole industry, a firm, a plant, or even a single process within a plant. In such models a technological change is represented by a shift in a production function, so that for some combination of inputs a greater output is obtainable than formerly. For the most part such models have encompassed only technological improvements in the production of existing commodities, and not those that result in the introduction of new commodities. One advantage of the models to be examined in this chapter is that they permit a clarification and separation of the meanings of technological change—both those of economic history and those of theory.

1. We briefly summarize here some of the properties of the models; a more complete discussion has been set forth in Chapter III, Section 1.

The elementary concepts in these models are *commodities* and *activities*. Commodities are produced or used up in the process of production. If we consider a single production period, we will have a stock of commodities at the beginning of the period and a different stock at the end of the period; the changes (commodity flows) being determined by the levels at which the various activities are carried on during the period. Each activity represents a particular method of production (e.g., production of nitrogen by fixation from air with electrolytic hydrogen) and is defined by equations stating the quantities of commodities consumed and produced per unit level of the activity.

Let the vector y represent the commodity flow during a production period. If $y_i < 0$, there is net consumption of the commodity; if $y_i > 0$, there is net production. Let the vector x represent the levels of the several activities during the period. Then

$$(1.1) \qquad\qquad y = \Gamma x,$$

where Γ is the matrix whose elements in the jth column are the quantities of y consumed or produced by the jth activity carried on at unit level. We suppose that y has K elements, x has J elements, so that Γ is a $K \times J$ matrix. We require that [1] $x \geq 0$. Finally, we define as *possible* points those points in the y-space which are transforms of the positive orthant of the x-space, i.e., those y's satisfying (1.1) for some $x \geq 0$.

If we know in advance which commodities are to be produced (final commodities), which are to be used up (primary factors), and which are neither used up nor produced (intermediate commodities), we may partition y and Γ, and write

$$(1.2) \qquad y_{\text{fin}} = \Gamma_{\text{fin}} x \geq 0, \quad \text{for final products;}$$

$$(1.3) \qquad y_{\text{int}} = \Gamma_{\text{int}} x = 0, \quad \text{for intermediate products;}$$

$$(1.4) \qquad y_{\text{pri}} = \Gamma_{\text{pri}} x \leq 0, \quad \text{for primary factors.}$$

We assume that points, $x \geq 0$, exist which satisfy the equations and inequalities (1.2), (1.3), and (1.4). In general, the solutions will not be unique. Hence we impose additional "optimizing" conditions: [2]

(1) We require that the transform, y, of a solution, x, correspond to an *efficient* point in the y-space (i.e., that no possible y^* exists such that $y^* \geq y$). In general, this requirement will reduce by one the dimensionality of the set of solutions.

---

[1] We adopt the notations for vector inequalities introduced in Chapter III, Section 2.4.

[2] See conditions (b), (c), and (d) of Chapter III, Section 1.2.

(2) Certain lower limits to elements of y_{pri}, or upper limits to elements of y_{fin}, or both, may be given.

(3) We may specify certain relations among the elements of y_{fin} (e.g., $y_{\text{fin }1} = k_{12}y_{\text{fin }2}$).

(4) We may limit ourselves to those solutions that maximize some function of y_{fin} (e.g., $\sum_{i=1}^{D} y_{\text{fin }i} = \max$), or those that minimize some function of y_{pri}.

Suppose that we impose sufficient optimizing conditions so that a unique x exists satisfying (1.2), (1.3), and (1.4). We call this an *optimum* solution relative to these particular optimizing conditions.

We may now formulate a definition of technological change that is broad enough to cover virtually all the topics that have at one time or another been discussed under that label. A *technological change* is any change in (a) one or more coefficients in Γ, or (b) the given lower limits of elements of y_{pri}, or (c) the function of y_{pri} to be minimized. We exclude from our definition changes in the other optimizing conditions, as, for example, change in the function of y_{fin} to be maximized; the latter we may refer to as *changes in taste*.

In general, our first category—changes in Γ—corresponds to the economic theorist's definition of technological change. Of course, if the theorist works directly with cost curves instead of production functions, his definition of technological change (i.e., a shift in a cost curve) will encompass the third as well as the first category [Lange, 1944, Chapter XII]. Most economic historians have not distinguished among the three categories of technological change and have been concerned with all of them.

2. In the present chapter we shall consider only special cases of the model (1.2)–(1.4). In particular, we shall impose severe restrictions on the consumption side of the model (optimizing conditions referring to y_{fin}). These restrictions are necessary in order to define unequivocally the *effect of a technological change on total income*. The admissibility of such restrictions is tied up with the question of aggregation and the construction of an income index, but we shall not enter here into a discussion of that question.

One result of our self-imposed restrictions will be to rule out of consideration the very interesting question of the effect of technological change on the pattern of consumption and the introduction of new final products. Since the generalization of the model to encompass such questions would introduce a whole host of mathematical and conceptual problems, it appears wisest at the outset to divide our difficulties by setting a more modest task. We begin with the following simple model:

$$(2.1) \qquad \lambda = x_1,$$

$$(2.2) \qquad \eta_k \leqq y_k = \sum_{j=1}^{J} \gamma_{kj} x_j \qquad (k = 1, \cdots, K).$$

In this model we have one final product, λ, which is produced by a single activity, the first. We have K primary factors and a total of J activities. The η_k (maximum availabilities of primary factors) are given. For an optimum we require that λ be maximized. A technological change will be represented [3] by a change in Γ, the matrix of the γ_{kj}. Furthermore, we assume that the γ_{kj} satisfy postulate C_2 [III, Section 3.6], which guarantees a solution, $x \geq 0$, $x_1 > 0$, for (2.1)–(2.2) with $\eta < 0$. If a solution of (2.1)–(2.2) exists for some $\eta < 0$, say $\eta^* < 0$, then a solution exists for all $\eta < 0$, since Theorem 3.6.2 of Chapter III (equivalent to postulate C_2 [III, Section 3.6] which guarantees a solution) imposes conditions only on Γ irrespective of η.

Suppose that we have found a solution, for given Γ and η, of (2.2). In this solution we shall have, with appropriate ordering of the elements of η,

$$(2.3) \qquad \eta_k = y_k \qquad (k = 1, \cdots, K^\circ),$$

$$(2.4) \qquad \eta_k < y_k \quad (k = K^\circ + 1, \cdots, K; \quad K^\circ \leqq K).$$

We shall also order the x's in such a way that

$$(2.5) \qquad \begin{aligned} x_j > 0 \quad &\text{for} \quad j = 1, \cdots, J^\circ; \\ x_j = 0 \quad &\text{for} \quad j = J^\circ + 1, \cdots, J \qquad (J^\circ \leqq J). \end{aligned}$$

The first K° elements in η then represent the *scarce*, the remaining elements the *free*, primary factors; the first J° elements in x represent *economical* activities, the remainder, *uneconomical* activities.

We shall define as a *reduced system* corresponding to (2.1)–(2.2) the system:

$$(2.6) \qquad \lambda = x_1,$$

$$(2.7) \qquad \eta_k = \sum_{j=1}^{J^\circ} \gamma_{kj} x_j \qquad (k = 1, \cdots, K^\circ).$$

---

[3] Here Γ corresponds to Γ_{pri} in (1.4). We shall continue to omit the subscript in order to simplify our notation. Note also that λ in (2.1) corresponds to y_{fin} in (1.2), and y in (2.2) to y_{pri} in (1.4).

In the reduced system we designate by Γ° the matrix of the γ_{kj} $(k = 1, \cdots, K^\circ; j = 1, \cdots, J^\circ)$; by η° the vector of the η_k $(k = 1, \cdots, K^\circ)$; by x° the vector of the x_j $(j = 1, \cdots, J^\circ)$; and by $_1\Gamma^\circ$ the matrix formed by eliminating the first column of Γ°. We shall restrict ourselves to the case (which is the general case) where the ranks of Γ°, $[\eta^\circ \; \Gamma^\circ]$, and $_1\Gamma^\circ$ are equal to the respective numbers of their rows or columns, whichever is less. In this case we shall say that the reduced system is *regular*. We are confronted with three subcases according to whether $J^\circ < K^\circ$, $J^\circ > K^\circ$, or $J^\circ = K^\circ$.

CASE I: $J^\circ < K^\circ$ (more scarce factors than economical activities). Then equations (2.7) are inconsistent and have no solution, for the rank of $[\eta^\circ \; \Gamma^\circ]$ is $(J^\circ + 1) > J^\circ$, the rank of Γ°.

CASE II: $J^\circ > K^\circ$ (fewer scarce factors than economical activities). Suppose that $x^\circ > 0$ is a solution of (2.7). Then there will exist an ϵ°, with $\overset{\circ}{\epsilon_1} > 0$, which satisfies

$$(2.8) \qquad\qquad 0 = \Gamma^\circ \epsilon^\circ.$$

For sufficiently small $\mu > 0$ we shall have $(x^\circ + \mu\epsilon^\circ) > 0$, and $(x^\circ + \mu\epsilon^\circ)$ will satisfy (2.7) and (2.4). Since we have $(x^\circ + \mu\epsilon^\circ)_1 = (\overset{\circ}{x_1} + \mu\overset{\circ}{\epsilon_1})$ $> \overset{\circ}{x_1}$, it follows that x° is not an optimal solution of (2.7) (i.e., a solution maximizing $\lambda = x_1$).

Hence, for an optimal solution, our reduced system must fall in

CASE III: $J^\circ = K^\circ$ (as many scarce factors as economical activities). We may restate our conclusion in the following

THEOREM: *If the reduced system corresponding to a solution, x, of (2.2) be regular, then a necessary condition that the solution be optimal (i.e., maximize λ for the given η) is that $J^\circ = K^\circ$.*

If the reduced system is regular and $J^\circ = K^\circ$, (2.7) will have a unique solution, x°. Hence, if we know which factors are scarce and which activities economical for the optimal solution, x, of (2.2), this optimal solution can be obtained algebraically from (2.7)—i.e., its nonzero components are the unique solution, x°, of (2.7).

Analogous theorems can be derived for the more general models we shall use in subsequent sections. Hence, so long as we restrict ourselves to a particular regular reduced system, we may find the optimal solution as the unique solution of this reduced system.

3. We now introduce a model that assumes a number of final commodities with perfect substitutability in consumption among them. Alternatively, we may interpret this model as admitting J different

activities for producing a single final product. This model is represented by

(3.1) $$\lambda = \sum_{j=1}^{J} \gamma_{0j} x_j \quad (\gamma_{0j} \geq 0; \quad j = 1, \cdots, J),$$

(3.2) $$\eta_k \leq y_k = \sum_{j=1}^{J} \gamma_{kj} x_j \quad (k = 1, \cdots, K).$$

In the special case where $K = 2$ (two primary factors) but J is unrestricted, this model can be given an instructive graphical representation. In Figure 1, y_1 and y_2 are quantities of the two factors (not necessarily both scarce). The broken line, AA', is an isoquant on the produc-

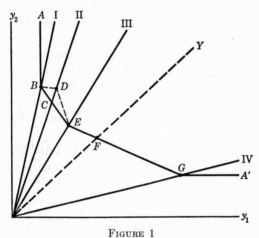

FIGURE 1

tion surface for λ (i.e., λ is constant along this line). The production activities, I, II, III, and IV, employ y_1 and y_2 in varying proportions (e.g., activity I employs γ_{11} units of y_1 to each γ_{21} units of y_2). The dotted portion, BDE, of AA' shows the path of the contour when a combination of activities I and II, or of II and III, is used; the solid portion BCE shows the contour when activities I and III are used. Hence the dotted portion represents noneconomical activity levels. Activities I, III, and IV are economical for particular ranges of factor availabilities, whereas II is uneconomical under any circumstances.

If the ratio of available y_1 to available y_2 (i.e., η_1/η_2) is as shown by line Y, then III and IV will both be economical activities, I will not. It will be shown later that the ratio of factor prices is given by the negative of the slope of EG.

From Figure 1 we can immediately read off a number of conclusions which are easily generalized to the case of one final output and many ($K > 2$) factors.

(a) With the factor supply as shown by Y, a greater product will result from the combined use of activities III and IV in suitable proportions than from either alone.

(b) The points of intersection of AA' with the activity functions I, II, III, and IV (points B, D, E, G) depend on the technical coefficients in these functions. Any change in the coefficients can be represented by the combination of a movement of the line representing the activity through some arc (change in the proportions of the factors) combined with a movement of the point of intersection along the line. Changes in the list of economical activities can come about either through changes in relative factor scarcity (movement of Y) or changes in the technical coefficients (movements of the activity functions and their intersections with AA').

(c) We may call an activity *eligible* if it is economical for some factor ratio. Activities I, III, and IV are eligible, II is not. A sufficient downward movement of point D will make II eligible. A somewhat greater movement will make III ineligible (in which case II and IV would be the economical activities), and a still greater movement will make I ineligible.

(d) If Y were to move sufficiently to the left, I and III would replace III and IV as the economical activities. The same would occur if, instead, III moved sufficiently to the right.

(e) Of the eligible activities, those tend to be economical which employ the factors in ratios closest to the actual ratio of factor availability. This offers a possible explanation for the relative stability of the ratio C/L noted by Douglas in his interindustry studies of the production function.

(f) If Y moves sufficiently to the right, or IV sufficiently to the left, IV will be the only economical process, and y_1 will become a free factor.

(g) If a new process becomes eligible it either (1) has no immediate effect (if it lies to the right of IV or to the left of III), (2) displaces one or both processes previously used (if it lies between III and IV), or (3) makes scarce a factor previously free (if Y lies to the right of IV and the new process to the right of Y).

(h) Suppose that only the process I were known. Then y_1 would be free. Suppose now that the eligible process III were invented. Then III would replace I, and y_1 would remain free. Suppose, however, that IV were invented instead of III. Then I would not be displaced, but both I and IV would be economical and y_1 would become scarce. We have the somewhat paradoxical situation that the less "revolutionary" invention completely displaces the old process, whereas the more "revolutionary" invention only partially displaces it.

These examples will illustrate some of the characteristic properties of our model.

4. Next we may take explicit note of prices. Accounting prices can be introduced into the reduced system corresponding to (3.1)–(3.2) by the following equations:

$$(4.1) \qquad p_j = \gamma_{0j} p_\lambda \qquad\qquad (j = 1, \cdots, J^\circ),$$

$$(4.2) \qquad p_j = - \sum_{k=1}^{K^\circ} \gamma_{kj} P_k \qquad\qquad (j = 1, \cdots, J^\circ),$$

where p_λ is defined as the price of the final product, p_j as the price of a unit level of the jth activity, and P_k as the price of the kth scarce factor. Equations (4.1) state that the price of the jth activity is equal to the value (price times quantity) of the final product produced by the unit level of the jth activity. Equations (4.2) state that the price of the jth activity is equal to the value of the primary factors consumed less the value of the primary factors produced by the unit level of the jth activity. [Compare Chapter III, equations (4.15).]

Since in this reduced system we must have (in analogy to our theorem of Section 2) $K^\circ = J^\circ$, the p_j and P_k will be uniquely determined as homogeneous functions of the first degree in p_λ.

It will be noted that the supplies of the factors affect prices only indirectly (i.e., by determining which factors are scarce and which activities economical). Given the reduced system, prices do not vary with changes in the supply of factors. Changes in factor supply, unless large enough to bring about a shift from one reduced system to another, affect only the levels of the various economical activities.

5. Thus far we have examined the effects of technological change (including changes both in the production coefficients and factor scarcities) on the economy of production activities. An equally important task is to measure the changes in income consequent upon technological changes. In all the models we have introduced, we possess an unambiguous index of income (since utility is derived from consumption of a single final product) in our variable λ. It will be necessary to distinguish two cases:

(1) The technological change may not alter the lists of scarce factors and economical activities. The reduced system would then contain the same set of variables and equations as before. with altered values of η and the γ_{kj} in this reduced system.

(2) The technological change may make some activities economical that were not so before, and vice versa, and may make some factors scarce that were not so before, and vice versa. When the effects of a technological change are of the second type (i.e., when they include changes in the lists of economical activities or scarce factors), we shall call them "trigger effects."

We consider first the income effects of technological changes of the first type, using for this purpose our model, (3.1)–(3.2). Quantities before and after the technological change will be designated by unstarred and starred symbols, respectively, x_j and x_j^*, etc.

If our technological change is confined to the first activity, i.e., $\gamma_{k1}^* \neq \gamma_{k1}, \gamma_{ks}^* = \gamma_{ks}$ ($k = 1, 2, \cdots, K^\circ; s = 2, 3, \cdots, J^\circ$), we shall have the following equations for the reduced system before and after the change:

$$(5.1) \qquad \lambda = \sum_{j=1}^{J^\circ} \gamma_{0j} x_j, \qquad \lambda^* = \sum_{j=1}^{J^\circ} \gamma_{0j} x_j^* \quad (j = 1, \cdots, J^\circ);$$

$$(5.2) \qquad \eta_k^* = \eta_k = \sum_{j=1}^{J^\circ} \gamma_{kj} x_j = \sum_{j=1}^{J^\circ} \gamma_{kj}^* x_j^* \quad (k = 1, \cdots, K^\circ; \quad J^\circ = K^\circ).$$

If we take $p_\lambda = 1$, we have, from (4.1), $\gamma_{0j} = p_j$. Hence

$$(5.3) \qquad \lambda^* - \lambda = \sum_j p_j(x_j^* - x_j).$$

But from (4.1) and (4.2) we also have

$$(5.4) \qquad -\sum_{K=1}^{K^\circ} P_k \gamma_{kj} = p_j^* = p_j = -\sum_{K=1}^{K^\circ} P_k^* \gamma_{kj}^*,$$

whence

$$\lambda^* - \lambda = -\sum_k \sum_j (P_k \gamma_{kj} x_j^* - P_k \gamma_{kj} x_j)$$

$$= -\sum_k \sum_j (P_k \gamma_{kj} x_j^* - P_k \gamma_{kj}^* x_j^*)$$

$$(5.5)$$

$$= -\sum_k [P_k \sum_j (\gamma_{kj} - \gamma_{kj}^*) x_j^*]$$

$$= -\sum_k P_k(\gamma_{k1} - \gamma_{k1}^*) x_1^*.$$

We now define

$$(5.6) \qquad \bar{p}_1 = -\sum_k \gamma_{k1}^* P_k;$$

that is, we take as $\bar{p}_1$ the price of the improved first activity in terms of the original factor prices and obtain

$$(5.7) \qquad\qquad \lambda^* - \lambda = x_1^*(p_1 - \bar{p}_1).$$

The economic significance of (5.7) becomes clearer when we rewrite it

$$(5.8) \qquad \frac{\lambda^* - \lambda}{\lambda} = \frac{x_1 p_1}{\lambda} \frac{p_1 - \bar{p}_1}{p_1} \frac{x_1^*}{x_1} = v_1 \rho_1 E_1,$$

where

$$v_1 \equiv x_1 p_1 / \lambda, \qquad \rho_1 \equiv (p_1 - \bar{p}_1)/p_1, \qquad E_1 \equiv x_1^*/x_1.$$

Since $\sum x_j p_j = \lambda$, the first factor on the right-hand side of (5.8) measures the magnitude of the first activity as a fraction of national income; the second factor measures the relative magnitude of the technological change (the *resource-saving effect*); and the third factor measures the change in level of the first activity resulting from the technological change (the *substitution effect*).

Equation (5.8) lends itself to empirical estimation (in advance of the change) of the income effect of a technological change of known magnitude. The factor v_1 is obtained from production and price data prior to the change, and ρ_1 is obtained from an engineering estimate based on factor prices prior to the change. The estimation of E_1 presents some difficulties, as E_1 is not in general uniquely determined by ρ_1; we can, however, express E_1 as a function of ρ_1 in certain special cases.

CASE A: Suppose that

$$(5.9) \qquad \gamma_{k1}^* = (1 - \sigma)\gamma_{k1} \qquad (k = 1, \cdots, K^\circ; \quad 0 < \sigma < 1).$$

This means that the technological change results in proportionate savings of all factors required in the first activity. In this case we readily find

$$(5.10) \qquad\qquad \rho_1 = \sigma,$$

$$(5.11) \qquad x_1^*/x_1 = 1/(1 - \sigma) = 1/(1 - \rho_1),$$

whence

$$(5.12) \qquad \frac{\lambda^* - \lambda}{\lambda} = v_1 \frac{\rho_1}{1 - \rho_1}.$$

Table I shows the values of $(\lambda^* - \lambda)/\lambda$ for particular values of v_1 and ρ_1, as calculated from (5.12). From this table we read, for example, that, if we had a cost reduction of 25 per cent ($\rho_1 = 0.25$) in an activity producing 10 per cent of national income ($v_1 = 0.1$), the resulting increase in national income would be 3.3 per cent.

TABLE I. $(\lambda^* - \lambda)/\lambda = v_1[\rho_1/(1 - \rho_1)]$

v_1 \ ρ_1	0.01	0.1	0.25	0.5	0.75	0.9	0.95	0.99
0.01	0.0001	0.001	0.003	0.01	0.03	0.09	0.2	1.0
0.10	0.0010	0.011	0.033	0.10	0.30	0.90	1.9	9.9
0.25	0.0025	0.028	0.083	0.25	0.75	2.25	4.8	24.8
0.50	0.0050	0.056	0.167	0.50	1.50	4.50	9.5	49.5
0.75	0.0076	0.083	0.250	0.75	2.25	6.75	14.5	74.3
1.00	0.0101	0.111	0.333	1.00	3.00	9.00	19.0	99.0

CASE B: Suppose that

$$(5.13) \qquad \gamma_{k1}^* = \gamma_{k1} - \tau \eta_k \quad (k = 1, \cdots, K^\circ; \ \ 0 < \tau < \gamma_{k1}/\eta_k).$$

This means that the technological change results in savings in all factors of production in the first activity proportionate to the factor availabilities. In this case we find

$$(5.14) \qquad \rho_1 = \frac{\tau x_1}{v_1},$$

$$(5.15) \qquad \frac{x_1^*}{x_1} = \frac{1}{1 - \tau x_1} = \frac{1}{1 - v_1 \rho_1}$$

whence

$$(5.16) \qquad \frac{\lambda^* - \lambda}{\lambda} = v_1 \frac{\rho_1}{1 - v_1 \rho_1}.$$

TABLE II. $(\lambda^* - \lambda)/\lambda = v_1[\rho_1/(1 - v_1 \rho_1)]$

v_1 \ ρ_1	0.01	0.10	0.25	0.50	0.75	0.90	0.95	0.99
0.01	0.0001	0.001	0.003	0.005	0.008	0.009	0.01	0.01
0 10	0.0010	0.010	0.026	0.053	0.081	0.099	0.11	0.11
0.25	0.0025	0.026	0.067	0.14	0.23	0.29	0.31	0.33
0.50	0.0050	0.053	0.14	0.33	0.60	0.82	0.91	0.98
0.75	0.0076	0.081	0.23	0.60	1.3	2.1	2.5	2.9
0.90	0.0091	0.099	0.29	0.82	2.1	4.3	5.9	8.2
0.95	0.0096	0.11	0.31	0.91	2.5	5.9	9.3	15.7
0.99	0.010	0.11	0.33	0.98	2.9	8.2	15.7	49.0
1.00	0.010	0.11	0.33	1.0	3.0	9.0	19.0	99.0

Since $0 < v_1 \leqq 1$, the income effect for given values of ρ_1 and v_1 is greater in Case A than in Case B. Table II shows values of $(\lambda^* - \lambda)/\lambda$ for particular values of v_1 and ρ_1, as calculated from (5.16). From this table we read that, if we had a cost reduction of 25 per cent ($\rho_1 = 0.25$) in an activity producing 10 per cent of national income ($v_1 = 0.1$), the resulting increase in national income would be 2.6 per cent. (The corresponding value from Table I was 3.3 per cent.)

6. We are now in a position to examine the effects of technological changes of the second type—technological changes that cause the economy to shift from one reduced system to another. We shall restrict ourselves to cases where the list of scarce factors remains the same and only the list of economical activities is altered. The effects of such changes, which we have called trigger effects, are of two kinds:

(1) Through technological improvement of an activity, I' (i.e., changes in the $\gamma_{k\mathrm{I}'}$), this activity becomes economical and replaces a previously economical activity, I, which now becomes uneconomical.[4] That is, if I was the first activity in Γ°, we replace $\gamma_{k2} = \gamma_{k\mathrm{I}}$ by $\gamma_{k2}^* = \gamma_{k\mathrm{I}'}$.

(2) Through changes in the technological coefficients of an economical activity, I, or through changes in the relative availability of the factors, a previously uneconomical activity, II', becomes economical and replaces a previously economical activity, II. That is, if II was the second activity in Γ°, we replace $\gamma_{k2} = \gamma_{k\mathrm{II}}$ by $\gamma_{k2}^* = \gamma_{k\mathrm{II}'}$.

Changes of the first type are indistinguishable, both conceptually and as to their effects, from the changes discussed in the previous section. That is, we really cannot distinguish between (a) a technological change that improves the first activity but does not cause the economy to shift to a new reduced system (i.e., $\gamma_{k1} = \gamma_{k\mathrm{I}}$ becomes $\gamma_{k1}^* = \gamma_{k\mathrm{I}}^*$), and (b) a change that substitutes a "new" activity for the first activity (i.e., $\gamma_{k1} = \gamma_{k\mathrm{I}}$ becomes $\gamma_{k1}^* = \gamma_{k\mathrm{I}'}$). In economic terms, if machine loading methods are so improved that they replace hand loading methods in coal mining, it makes no difference whether we say that there has been an improvement in the activity of coal loading or whether we say that a new activity, machine loading, has replaced an old one, hand loading. From the standpoint of estimation of the effects, too, we proceed exactly as we did in the last section. That is, we replace the coefficients in the first column of Γ° in the reduced system with the new coefficients and proceed to evaluate λ^*.

---

[4] In what follows, we shall use Roman subscripts to denote the coefficients of a particular activity (e.g., $\gamma_{k\mathrm{I}}$), but we shall continue to use Arabic subscripts to denote the columns of Γ (e.g., γ_{k1}). Hence, when activity I becomes the first column of Γ°, we have $\gamma_{k1} = \gamma_{k\mathrm{I}}$ ($k = 1, \cdots, K^\circ$).

"Trigger" changes of the second type are essentially different. Here the initial technological change, consisting of a change in a column of Γ° or a change in η°, brings about a derived change in another column of Γ° in the reduced system. (It may even change the number of rows and columns of Γ° in the reduced system; e.g., a new activity may be added and a previously free factor may become scarce, or vice versa, but we do not discuss this case here.) Such a derived change in Γ°, if induced by an initial change in η°, would not even be considered a technological change in the narrower sense, although it has generally been so considered in economic history. An example of the latter phenomenon would be a (derived) substitution of machine methods for hand methods in coal mining through an increase in the supply of capital relative to labor, and without the introduction of any activities not previously *known* and available.

The procedure for estimating the magnitude of the income effect of a technological change that produces a derived trigger effect of this kind is more complicated than the estimation procedure set forth in Section 5. Our two-dimensional diagram (Figure 2) suggests a method of approach. Let us suppose that, prior to the technological change,

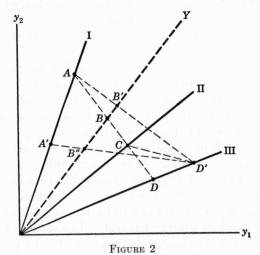

Figure 2

the minimum quantities of the factors required to produce one unit of λ by the use of various activities and combinations of activities are given by the isoquant $ABCD'$. Then activities I and II will be economical and will appear in the reduced system, while activity III will not.

Suppose now that we have a technological improvement in the first activity, giving the new isoquant $A'B''D'$, with III now economical and

II uneconomical.   The movement from the isoquant $ABCD'$ with income λ to the isoquant $A'B''D'$ with income λ^{***} is equivalent to the product of three (hypothetical) movements:

(a) $ABCD'$ to $ABCD$ (λ remains unchanged).   We may interpret this by imagining a technological improvement in activity III which makes it just competitive with activity II; and, in consequence, there is replacement of II by III without decreasing λ.

(b) $ABCD$ to $AB'D'$ (with income $\lambda^{**} < \lambda$).   This is equivalent to returning from the improved to the unimproved form of activity III, but not replacing it with activity II.   Hence we have a decrease in income.

(c) $AB'D'$ to $A'B''D'$ (with income $\lambda^{***} > \lambda$).   This represents a technological improvement in activity I in an economy that is employing activities I and III (the latter in its unimproved form).

The meaning of these three movements may be further clarified by the following comments.   Prior to the technological improvement in activity I, II was economical, III was not; subsequent to the improvement in activity I, III was economical, II was not.   Step (c) gives the increase in income from the technological improvement in activity I on the assumption that activity III was economical *before* the improvement.   From this amount we must subtract a certain portion because III was not economical before the improvement and hence a solution involving a positive level of activity III was not optimal.   This subtraction is accomplished in steps (a) and (b) above.

We now define as a *column transformation of the matrix* Γ° *of the reduced system* the replacement of the γ_{kj} in the jth column by new values, γ_{kj}^{*}.   Column transformations form a group of transformations.   The entire course of our technological change is represented by the product of the following column transformations:

(a') We replace in column 2 of Γ° the γ_{kII} by $\gamma_{kIII} = \gamma_{kIII'}/(1 - \tau)$, where the γ_{kII} correspond to point C, γ_{kIII} to point D, and $\gamma_{kIII'}$ to D' in Figure 2.   Here III' designates the actual coefficients of activity III, and III designates the values of the coefficients required to make this activity just competitive with activity II.   We shall later use the latter condition to find the value of τ.

(b') We replace in column 2 of Γ° the γ_{kIII} by $\gamma_{kIII'}$.

(c') We replace in column 1 of Γ° the γ_{kI} by $\gamma_{kI'} = (1 - \sigma)\gamma_{kI}$ (corresponding to A and A', respectively).   Here I designates the coefficients of activity I before the technological improvement, I' the coefficients after the improvement.   The parameter σ measures the magnitude of the improvement.

Transformations (b') and (c') correspond to Case A of Section 5 and can be evaluated by the method of that section. It remains to find τ, and the effect on the x's of the first transformation. We shall indicate how this can be done in one special case.

We designate by Γ the original reduced matrix [5] of the γ_{kj}; by Γ^*, the matrix after transformation (a′); by Γ^{**}, the matrix after transformation (b′); and by Γ^{***}, the matrix after transformation (c′). Furthermore, we denote by $|\eta, \Gamma_j|$ the determinant of the matrix obtained by substituting η for the jth column in Γ. Since the first transformation leaves λ unchanged, we have

$$(6.1) \qquad \lambda = \sum_{j=1}^{J^\circ} \gamma_{0j} x_j = \sum_{j=1}^{J^\circ} \gamma_{0j} x_j^* = \lambda^*.$$

We take the $\gamma_{k\mathrm{I}}$ as the first column in Γ, and $\gamma_{k\mathrm{II}}$, $\gamma_{k\mathrm{III}}$, and $\gamma_{k\mathrm{III}}'$ as the second column in their respective matrices. Then

$$\gamma_{k1} = \overset{*}{\gamma}_{k1} = \overset{**}{\gamma}_{k1} = \gamma_{k\mathrm{I}};$$

$$\overset{***}{\gamma}_{k1} = \gamma_{k\mathrm{I}}', \qquad \gamma_{k2} = \gamma_{k\mathrm{II}}, \qquad \overset{*}{\gamma}_{k2} = \gamma_{k\mathrm{III}}, \qquad \overset{**}{\gamma}_{k2} = \overset{***}{\gamma}_{k2} = \gamma_{k\mathrm{III}'};$$

$$\gamma_{kj} = \overset{*}{\gamma}_{kj} = \overset{**}{\gamma}_{kj} = \overset{***}{\gamma}_{kj} \qquad (j \neq 1, 2).$$

We also make the special assumption that

$$(6.2) \quad \gamma_{k\mathrm{III}} = \overset{*}{\gamma}_{k2} = \gamma_{k2} + \rho\left(\gamma_{k2} - \frac{\gamma_{02}}{\lambda}\eta_k\right) \quad (\rho > 0; \quad k = 1, \cdots, K^\circ).$$

This corresponds, in Figure 2, to the fact that III is "farther" from Y than is II. It can be shown that (6.2) implies (6.1). We find immediately that

$$(6.3) \qquad |\Gamma^*| = (1 + \rho)|\Gamma| - \frac{\gamma_{02}\rho}{\lambda}|\eta, \Gamma_2|,$$

$$(6.4) \qquad |\eta, \Gamma_j^*| = (1 + \rho)|\eta, \Gamma_j| \qquad (j \neq 2),$$

$$(6.5) \qquad |\eta, \Gamma_2^*| = |\eta, \Gamma_2|,$$

$$(6.6) \qquad x_j^* = \frac{|\eta, \Gamma_j^*|}{|\Gamma^*|} = x_j\left[\frac{\lambda(1 + \rho)}{\lambda(1 + \rho) - \gamma_{02}x_2\rho}\right] \qquad (j \neq 2),$$

$$(6.7) \qquad x_2^* = x_2\left[\frac{\lambda}{\lambda(1 + \rho) - \gamma_{02}x_2\rho}\right].$$

Since ρ is assumed to be known from (6.2), these equations permit us to find the x^*'s in terms of the x's. Next we proceed to evaluate τ.

---

[5] To simplify notation we now omit the superscript $^\circ$ from the matrices and vectors of the reduced system.

Since III is, by definition, just competitive with II, we must have

$$(6.8) \qquad p_2 = \sum_{k=1}^{K^\circ} \gamma_{k2} P_k = \sum_{k=1}^{K^\circ} \gamma_{k2}^* P_k = \sum_{k=1}^{K^\circ} \frac{\gamma_{k2}^{**}}{(1 - \tau)} P_k,$$

and it follows that

$$(6.9) \qquad (1 - \tau) = \frac{\sum_{k=1}^{K^\circ} \gamma_{k2}^{**} P_k}{p_2}.$$

That is, $(1 - \tau)$ is the ratio of the actual cost per unit level of activity III' to the cost per unit level of activity II.

Now we may employ (5.7) to find λ^{**} in terms of λ, and λ^{***} in terms of λ^{**}.

$$(6.10) \qquad \lambda^{**} = \lambda + x_2^{**}(p_2 - \bar{p}_2),$$

$$(6.11) \qquad \begin{aligned} \lambda^{***} &= \lambda^{**} + x_1^{***}(p_1^{**} - \bar{p}_1^{**}) \\ &= \lambda + x_2^{**}(p_2 - \bar{p}_2) + x_1^{***}(p_1^{**} - \bar{p}_1^{**}); \end{aligned}$$

where, in analogy with our previous definitions, $p_1^{**} = \sum_{k=1}^{K^\circ} \gamma_{k1}^{**} P_k^{**}$, $\bar{p}_1^{**} = \sum_{k=1}^{K^\circ} \gamma_{k1}^{***} P_k^{**} = (1 - \sigma)p_1^{**}$, $p_2 = \sum_{k=1}^{K^\circ} \gamma_{k2}^* P_k$, $\bar{p}_2 = \sum_{k=1}^{K^\circ} \gamma_{k2}^{**} P_k$ $= (1 - \tau)p_2$. Hence, from (4.1) and the fact that $p_1^{**} = p_1$,

$$(6.12) \qquad \lambda^{***} = \lambda + x_2^{**} p_2 \tau + x_1^{***} p_1 \sigma.$$

Corresponding to (5.11), we have

$$(6.13) \qquad x_2^{**} = x_2^*/(1 - \tau); \qquad x_1^{***} = x_1^{**}(1 - \sigma).$$

But $\left| \eta, \; \Gamma_1^{**} \right| = (1 - \tau)\left| \eta, \; \Gamma_1^* \right|$; and $\left| \Gamma^{**} \right| = (1 - \tau)\left| \Gamma \right|$; hence $x_1^{**} = x_1^*$. Therefore we get

$$(6.14) \qquad \lambda^{***} = \lambda + x_2^* p_2 \frac{\tau}{1 - \tau} + x_1^* p_1 \frac{\sigma}{1 - \sigma}.$$

The x^*'s in (6.14) can be obtained from (6.6) and (6.7); the parameter σ is known, and τ is obtained from (6.9). Hence (6.14) gives us a procedure for estimating λ^{***} in terms of quantities that are known prior to the technological change in activity I. It should be observed that $(1 - \tau) > 1$, and hence $\tau < 0$. That is, the second term on the right-hand side of (6.14) is negative, as we should expect from the fact that activity III was uneconomical prior to the improvement in I. It should also be observed that the third term on the right-hand side of (6.14) corresponds to the right-hand side of (5.7).

7. The methods of the two preceding sections can be applied without essential alteration to a model where there is an intermediate activity (i.e., one not producing the final good) that undergoes technological change. In this model we take the first activity as an intermediate one (i.e., $\gamma_{01} = 0$, $\eta_1 = 0$, and $\gamma_{11} = 1$) and define $p_1 = P_1 = \sum_{k=2}^{K^\circ} \gamma_{k1} P_k$. We designate by C the submatrix of Γ that omits its first row and first column. We employ η to designate the $(K^\circ - 1)$ vector consisting of all but the first component of η, and γ_1 to designate the vector with components γ_{k1} $(k = 2, \cdots, K^\circ)$.

We now assume that $\gamma_1^* = \alpha\gamma_1$. This corresponds to Case A of Section 5. In this case we find that

$$(7.1) \qquad \lambda^* = \frac{1}{|C|} \begin{bmatrix} \alpha\sum(\gamma_{0j}|\eta, C_j|)\sum(\gamma_{1j}|\gamma_1, C_j|) \\ -\alpha\sum(\gamma_{0j}|\gamma_1, C_j|)\sum(\gamma_{1j}|\eta, C_j|) \\ \underline{\qquad -\sum(\gamma_{0j}|\eta, C_j||C|) \qquad} \\ \alpha\sum(\gamma_{1j}|\gamma_1, C_j|) - |C| \end{bmatrix}.$$

If we further specialize to the case where

$$(7.2) \quad \sum(\gamma_{0j}|\eta, C_j|)\sum(\gamma_{1j}|\gamma_1, C_j|) = \sum(\gamma_{0j}|\gamma_1, C_j|)\sum(\gamma_{1j}|\eta, C_j|),$$

then (7.1) reduces to

$$(7.3) \qquad \lambda^* = \frac{\sum\gamma_{0j}|\eta, C_j|}{|C| - \alpha\sum\gamma_{1j}|\gamma_1, C_j|}.$$

But (7.2) is satisfied under either of the following circumstances:

$$(7.4) \qquad\qquad\qquad \gamma_1 = m\gamma_0,$$

or

$$(7.5) \qquad\qquad\qquad \gamma_1 = n\eta,$$

where m and n are arbitrary constants.

Equation (7.4) corresponds to the case where the requirements of the first factor in the other $(J^\circ - 1)$ activities are proportionate to the prices of these activities. Equation (7.5) corresponds to the case where the requirements of the other factors in the first activity are proportionate to the factor availabilities. The economic meaning of (7.3) is suggested by its limiting value as the first factor becomes free (i e., as $\alpha \to 0$), to wit:

$$(7.6) \qquad\qquad\qquad \lambda^* = \frac{\sum\gamma_{0j}|\eta, C_j|}{|C|}.$$

The value of λ^* in (7.6) is the value it would have in an economy from which the first activity was absent and from which was also absent the commodity represented by the first row of Γ (i.e., the commodity "produced" by the first activity). Equation (7.3) can now be rewritten as

$$(7.7) \quad \lambda^* = \lambda' \, \frac{1}{1 - \alpha \sum \gamma_{1j} \dfrac{|\gamma_1, C_j|}{|C|}} = \lambda' \, \frac{1}{1 + \alpha\beta} = \lambda \, \frac{1 + \beta}{1 + \alpha\beta},$$

where $\beta = -\sum \gamma_{1j}|\gamma_1, C_1|/|C|$, and λ' is the upper limit of λ^* for $\alpha = 0$.

The parameter β may readily be shown to be equal to the value of the scarce factors used up by the first activity as a fraction of the total value of the scarce factors (excluding the commodity in the first row from the scarce factors). Since β can generally be estimated and α is the known magnitude of the technological change in the first activity, (7.7) permits us to estimate λ^*.

8. Although, because of the very special nature of our models, we must not take too seriously the actual numerical calculation of the income effects of technological change by the methods of Sections 5, 6, and 7, still these methods might indicate the order of magnitude of such effects. Their usefulness derives from the fact that they do not require a knowledge of the entire matrix Γ. We need to know only the equilibrium values of prices and quantities prior to the change, the factor availabilities, and the estimated magnitude of the change. In the case where we wish to include trigger effects, we must also predict in advance which derived changes in the set of economical activities are likely to be brought about by the initial technological change. It would be desirable to establish qualitative criteria, based on the general properties of the models, that would assist in such prediction.

COMMENTS

By Ansley Coale

My comments are divided into two parts: first, a proposed terminology to be used in discussing technological change; and, second, a discussion of new products and new materials, which are not, I feel, covered by Simon's model.

I suggest that we distinguish between ways of doing things, which I would call "techniques," and knowledge of techniques, for which I suggest the term "technology." Any adoption of a new manufacturing process, for example, is a technical change. But this change may follow from the spread of technology within or between communities or from a change in relative costs making a known but unused technique advantageous, as well as from the discovery of a new process—and it is for the first and last type of change, especially the last, that I would reserve the term "technological change." Current technique in a community comprises the methods currently in use; the current technique of production corresponds, I believe, to Mr. Simon's reduced matrix. Current technology, on the other hand, includes all known processes, not excepting those at present unexploited. Current technology would determine his full matrix.

The use of a definition of techniques as broad as "ways of doing things" is deliberate. Though the definition is no doubt too inclusive—since we are not directly concerned here with, for example, the techniques of poetry—the broadness of the definition has the virtue of calling attention to the fact that methods other than those defined by coefficients of production are of economic significance. The consumer as well as the producer has techniques; and the introduction of a new consumers' good is often a change in the way the consumer does something (or in what he does).

Only a fraction of the technical change which actually occurs can be described by changes in the technical coefficients of production within a model characterized by a bill of goods of specified composition. The examples of technical changes in the last half century which would occur most readily to a casual observer would surely include air travel, radio and television, and other novelties which have altered the consumers' bill of goods. In fact, I suspect that those changes which at first thought are changes solely in process will on further consideration often prove to entail a change in product as well. For example, when a new process of refining a raw material is discovered, the result is frequently not only a change in the proportions of a fixed list of inputs, but also a change in the nature of the output (a higher octane gasoline or a new useful by-product). To state the point in terms of Simon's matrix: many actual technical changes have the salient feature of introducing new consumers' goods—adding new rows as well as columns to the matrix; even those changes which at first glance seem to be only a change in coefficients are, in fact, inseparable from new items in the bill of goods. For instance, even if women's nylon hose are regarded as the same commodity as silk hose, recognition of the manufacture of nylon as a possible input to the hose industry requires the introduction of a new row for nylon.

. This characteristic of technical change—that it is associated with changes in product and input materials—makes the construction of a realistic model quite difficult. A concept such as "real income," which is sufficiently difficult to define satisfactorily anyway, becomes nearly meaningless when new items are introduced into the bill of consumers' goods. Suppose, for example, that we describe the output of consumers' goods in periods I and II by the following table:

Period \ Good	0	1	$\cdots$	i	j	k	$\cdots$	$n-1$	n
I	q_0^I	q_1^I	$\cdots$	q_i^I	q_j^I	q_k^I	$\cdots$	0	0
II	0	0	$\cdots$	q_i^{II}	q_j^{II}	q_k^{II}	$\cdots$	q_{n-1}^{II}	q_n^{II}

Then the comparison of "real income" by the use of a sum of money value at fixed prices—always an ambiguous and unsatisfactory device—becomes impossible. There are no prices in I for goods $k+1$ to n, and no prices in II for goods 0 to i. Thus, if we attempted to construct a model of technical change wherein product changes were allowed, the meaning of "income effect" would not be clear.

The basic difficulty may be that technical change—by altering the way in which things are done, by changing what consumers do and what they want as well—creates such a basically shifting world that we can put very few restrictions on the matrix we design to describe it.

COMMENTS

By Yale Brozen

The usual definitions of technological change fail to distinguish adequately between change at three different levels. Devising or perfecting a new technique which is economic for some resource combinations adds to the *technological possibilities*. The introduction of a previously unused technique represents a change at the level of the *technological leaders*. The spread of a new, efficient technique by imitation changes the *average technology*. The latter would appear also as a change in the matrix representing the actual input-output relationships of the economy.

Change in technological possibilities can be defined as the addition of a new column to the Koopmans model of production in which some or all of the technical coefficients except one would be larger, in the algebraic sense, than those in an old column. One coefficient would remain the same if a unit of activity were defined in terms of that one. An increase in the negative coefficients would mean a decrease in the amount of factor required per unit of output or required to cooperate with a unit of one factor, the alternative depending on the method of defining a unit of activity. An increase in the positive coefficients means an increase in commodity output per unit of activity.

Whether all coefficients but one in the new column are larger than those in an old will depend on the unit selected for the definition of a unit level of activity. A definition might be selected which would result in the new column having coefficients some of which are larger and some smaller than those in an old column. Since the new technique must be more efficient for some resource combination than the old ones available if it is truly an addition to the technological possibilities, a unit of activity can be chosen for comparison with each of the old techniques that will result in some coefficients appearing larger in the new column and none smaller than in the old column with which it is being compared.

A change in technological possibilities or at the level of technological leaders—assuming that each leader has a relatively small proportion of the resources used in any one activity—would make little or no difference in the input-output coefficients of a Leontief matrix representing aggregate relations in the economy. Only the third form of change defined above would affect that matrix. Under some circumstances, there may be changes in this matrix which are not a reflection of technological change in the sense that a spread of new techniques is the originating factor. Changes may be the result of an adaptive response to changes in the relative scarcities of resources (i.e., there may be shifts from the use of one column in the Koopmans model to another). Typically, some Leontief coefficients will increase and others decrease if this is the case. Increased supplies of capital will cause a shift to more capital-intensive processes with an increase (algebraic) in labor coefficients and a decrease in capital coefficients. However, technological change may produce the same sort of shifts. For this reason, it is often difficult to distinguish between the processes of technological change and the processes of adaptation to changed resource supplies.

Fitting technological change into the linear programming framework. If technological change were solely a function of time, the coefficients could be made a function of time. The rate of change varies, however, according to the amount of resources devoted to developing technological possibilities (research activity), the amount devoted to introducing new discoveries (leadership activity), and the amount devoted to introducing changes into other firms (imitative activity). If we introduce these activities into the matrix as additional columns, the coefficients could be made a function of the previous levels of these activities. This, however, would introduce nonlinearities. If we introduce additional rows as well as columns for these activities and treat the output of these activities as inputs to other activities, linearity can be maintained.

In terms of Simon's graph, changes in technological possibilities of a *cost-saving* type appear either as a movement of the point representing a given level of output toward the origin along a ray, or as an introduction of a new ray with the point representing a given rate of output lying closer to the origin than any point on the old isoquant. *Resource-widening* changes would appear as an increase in the upper limits of the available factors. Where an output using resources recently made available by improved technique is an input to other activities, a resource-widening technique at one level of production may be interpreted as a cost-saving technique at other levels. A new method of drilling that makes accessible oil pools lying beneath hard strata may be regarded as widening the number of oil pools or as reducing the effort required to obtain any given amount of oil. Other cases of resource widening, however, such as the increase in labor of a given skill resulting from the invention of a hearing aid, are not as easily interpreted in cost-saving terms. A third type of technological change, the invention of *new products*, is not easily interpreted in terms of Simon's graph. If we regard the product as giving more services for a given cost, it may be interpreted as a cost-saving invention. This requires some torture of the concept, however, in the case of consumer goods.

Significance of technological change. If we regard change as activities capable of producing certain desired results or as inputs to other activities which produce such results, the problem arises of determining the optimum level of these activities. How much research activity, leadership activity, and imitative activity should we undertake? To make these decisions we need more empirical information about the relationship between inputs to and outputs from research, development, and application. We need measures of the usefulness of research results (inventions) and the cost of applying the results (spreading information to those who can use it, and motivating its use). Simon's graph provides us with a method of measuring the usefulness of cost-saving inventions.

Public policy is being made at every level of technological change. Public funds are being spent on research (e.g., the atomic energy program). Public funds are devoted to change at the level of leadership (e.g., model farms) and to increasing imitation (e.g., county agents). Not only are these levels influenced by direct public activity, but also, indirectly, by public policy embodied in such items as tax and patent law. If linear programming can better formulate the criteria for optimal levels in these various programs, decisions can be more efficiently made.

Chapter XVI

THE ACCURACY OF ECONOMIC OBSERVATIONS [1]

By Oskar Morgenstern

Applications of theories such as those of linear programming use data that are subject to various errors. The significance of the far-reaching computations necessitated by these theories will depend on the knowledge of the errors. It is, therefore, necessary to form as precise ideas as possible about the accuracy of economic observations. So far there have been no tangible results regarding the quantitative estimation of errors in economic statistics, although attempts to improve the statistics in a general sense are made continuously wherever they are collected. But the accuracy actually required depends on the purpose of the statistics. Rough estimates may be all that are needed for one purpose; accuracy down to one-tenth of one per cent may be far too coarse for another. Accuracy of a given statistic can, therefore, not be uniformly good or bad. It can be judged only from the point of view of the theory which interprets the statistics and directs further logical and mathematical operations. Linear programming requires enormously large numbers of operations, and, at least for that reason, a high degree of accuracy is required. As a rule, however, present economic theory is not of a very fine-grain structure—a condition that may gradually be overcome. Furthermore, it is doubtful that there are many fields in economics with a theory powerful enough to make use of more than three or four significant digits. Published statistics, however, often seem to indicate that many more digits would be available. In addition this being frequently questionable, there would hardly be any theory available now to cope with such fine measurements.

It is noteworthy that little is known, except in an over-all way, about the extent of the errors in economic statistics. In the natural sciences a long tradition exists, and the study of errors has occupied a very

---

[1] A memorandum of this title was presented at the Conference on Linear Programming. In view of its length a separate publication has been undertaken [Morgenstern, 1950]. The following abstract serves only to indicate some of the main points that are discussed *in extenso* in that monograph.

This research is part of a project carried out under contract (N6 ONR27009) with the Office of Naval Research (Project NR 042086).

prominent place.   Otherwise their progress would have been unthink-able.   The difficulties of estimating errors of the data for the social sciences, however, cannot possibly be less than for the natural sciences. In fact, the sources of error are more numerous and the statistical prob-lem is far more serious in the social sciences.   Consequently the treat-ment of errors of observation has to be at least as rigorous as in the natural sciences.   A factor not present in the latter field is unfortunately of great importance in social affairs: the deliberate lie, and the hiding and suppression of information.   Statistical theory will have to evolve methods accounting for such possibilities which at present are ignored.

Space precludes a full enumeration of even the main sources of errors. As long as no quantitative measure is available, qualitative description is important.   In economic statistics one of the most troublesome errors arises from the inevitable use of questionnaires.   Furthermore, conflicts with the interests of private business arise when information is demanded. Sales prices and the volume of transactions are often closely guarded secrets, so that statements about these are often worthless.   This is particularly true if the industry is highly cartelized or a monopoly.

Illustrations from various fields, such as foreign trade, employment, prices, indicate that the errors often are very large, even though they can be ascertained only in a rough manner.   Variations in national in-come and especially in its composition are known only with a high degree of uncertainty.   Figures such as these, however, enter significantly into input-output tables.   Thus the uses to which the tables can be put are limited on two accounts: data and extent of numerical operations.   The economic models that can be set up on the basis of information of this type (either with large known errors or with errors only imperfectly described) are naturally limited in scope and value.

Linear programming, or any other similar utilization of great masses of economic data, cannot be expected to make decisive practical progress until there is satisfaction that the data warrant the implied extensive and costly numerical operations.   Therefore current and future collec-tions of data suitable for linear programming, whether for economic or logistic purposes, should give particular attention to the numerical determination of the accuracy of the data.   This work, furthermore, must be guided by the fact that large input-output tables are aimed at, and that their use, whether aggregations take place or not, will require, at any rate, many millions of numerical operations.   These would lose all meaning unless performed with data of a standard of reliability that corresponds to the intricacy of the computations.   Matrix inversions, for example, are performed on matrices in which the entries in each field are subject to errors (as must be the case).   These errors often differ widely from one field to another and in many instances are even unknown. They pose serious problems in addition to those of the inversion of large matrices themselves. Linear programming requires numerical operations of this kind.

In addition to observations made in statistical form there are economic events and phenomena that do not (as yet) lend themselves to statistical, numerical representation. An example is offered by expectations, where whatever information becomes available is also affected by error components. Variations in these data often have a direct bearing on the accuracy of statistical information which also should be taken into account. Another type of difficulty lies with those, possibly highly "accurate," data that lack functional meaning, such as official exchange rates of a country with exchange control. These would falsify, for instance, its foreign trade statistics and make them useless for input-output tables.

Economic measurements are peculiar in that they are most frequently made of *unique* phenomena. Sometimes the same event is observed simultaneously by different observers who are, however, seldom scientific observers. The great sharpening of measurements in the natural sciences is due primarily to the fact that the same event, say the velocity of light, has been measured time and again. But the transactions between two industries in a given year are ascertained only once by a single agency on the basis of questionnaires, with few internal checks that, if they exist at all, rest on the same type of data. It is clear that statistical theory has great tasks to accomplish in order to guide economists to the establishment of information suitable for such vast and important undertakings as linear programming. Applications to military data suffer perhaps less from these sources of errors, but this is probably compensated by the large number of different activities that ought to be recognized [2] for logistic purposes.

In summary, it is clear that the development of theories of linear programming and the establishment of more adequate economic models cannot progress very far without a thorough exploration of the nature of the observations at our disposal.

---

[2] When the number of activities is too large they have to be condensed to manageable proportions. This *aggregation* is itself a source of error and as yet is little understood.

PART THREE

MATHEMATICAL PROPERTIES
OF CONVEX SETS

Chapter XVII

CONVEX POLYHEDRAL CONES AND
LINEAR INEQUALITIES *

By David Gale

A number of problems in econometrics are concerned essentially with solutions of systems of linear inequalities. A typical example is the "linear programming" problem in which it is desired to maximize a linear form subject to linear inequalities. Another is the problem of determining the value and optimal strategies for a zero-sum two-person game. Because of their importance in econometrics, therefore, it seems desirable to summarize the fundamental mathematical facts concerning such systems of inequalities. This chapter represents an attempt to present this material in as simple and unified a form as possible.

As the title suggests, the theory of inequalities is equivalent to what we have called the theory of polyhedral cones. This theory is nothing more than a geometric interpretation of the inequality theory. In fact, the concept of polyhedral cone bears the same relation to systems of inequalities as the notion of linear subspace does to systems of homogeneous equations. Indeed, systems of equations may in an obvious manner be considered a special case of systems of inequalities, so the resemblance between the two theories is not surprising. We shall emphasize the geometric interpretation throughout, since it has been found that it is often helpful to be able to "visualize" results in some geometric form and that certain facts which seem obscure from the purely algebraic point of view become "intuitively obvious" when looked upon geometrically. For this reason we have tried whenever possible to state all results twice, first geometrically, as theorems about polyhedral cones, and second algebraically, as properties of linear inequalities.

We have not attempted to make this chapter self-contained as far as proofs are concerned. In particular, a large portion of the theory to be developed will be derived from a fundamental theorem of H. Weyl, the statement of which is given without proof. In this and similar cases references will be given so that the reader desiring to derive all

* Editor's Note. For the relationship between Chapters XVII and XVIII, see the Introduction.

results from the beginning may refer to the appropriate place in the literature.

Although no attempt has been made at mathematical completeness as far as proofs are concerned, we have tried to list results in a logical order and particularly to arrange the material in a form that will be easy to remember. Section 1 is devoted to definitions needed for the cone theory; in Section 2 the main properties of cones are obtained and interpreted algebraically. The final section involves a few further results of the theory, and some applications are given to indicate how the theory may be used in attacking specific problems.

1. Notations and Definitions

We shall be dealing with an n-dimensional real vector space, V, which may be thought of as Euclidean n-space. The vectors of V will be denoted by small letters, $u, v, x, y, \cdots$, and will be thought of as column vectors, while row vectors will be denoted by primed letters u', v', etc. The inner product of two vectors, u and v, is then denoted by

$$u'v = v'u = \sum_{i=1}^{n} u_i v_i,$$

where u_i and v_i denote the ith components of u and v. Finally, we use inequality signs as follows:

$$u > v \quad \text{means} \quad u_i > v_i \quad \text{for all } i,$$

$$u \geqq v \quad \text{means} \quad u_i \geqq v_i \quad \text{for all } i,$$

$$u \geq v \quad \text{means} \quad u \geqq v \quad \text{but } u \neq v.$$

A. *Convex cones.* A set, C, contained in V is called a *convex cone* (1) if $v_1 + v_2$ is in C whenever v_1 and v_2 are in C, and (2), if whenever v is in C and λ is a nonnegative real number, λv is in C.

Observe that C is convex in the usual sense in that, if a pair of points lies in C, so does the segment connecting them. The cones as defined here are all "homogeneous," i.e., they have their vertices at the origin. Special cases of cones are linear subspaces of V, including the whole space and the origin alone.

B. *Sum, negative, intersection, and polar cone.* If C_1 and C_2 are convex cones, the *sum* $C_1 + C_2$ is defined to be the set of all vectors expressible as the sum of vectors from C_1 and C_2.

The *negative* of a cone, C, is denoted by $-C$ and consists of all vectors whose negatives lie in C.

If C_1 and C_2 are convex cones, the *intersection* $C_1 \cap C_2$ is defined to be the set of all vectors belonging to both C_1 and C_2.

If C is a convex cone, the *polar cone* C^* is defined [1] to be the set of all vectors u such that $u'v \geqq 0$ for all $v \, \epsilon \, C$ (for ϵ read "belongs to"). We may think of C^* as the set of all vectors making a nonobtuse angle with every vector of C.

We may verify at once that sums, negatives, intersections, and polars of convex cones are again convex cones. Also we can easily check the following simple relations:

(1*)   If C_1 is contained in C_2, then C_2^* is contained in C_1^*.

(2*) $$(C_1 + C_2)^* = C_1^* \cap C_2^*.$$

We shall make use of these relations later on.

C. *Rays and halfspaces.* Two special cases of convex cones are of importance. We introduce them now.

A convex cone generated by a single vector v is called a *ray* or *half-line* and is denoted by (v), where (v) is the set of all vectors which are nonnegative multiples of v.

The polar cone of the ray (v) is called a *halfspace* and in our notation is denoted by $(v)^*$. It consists of all vectors u such that $u'v \geqq 0$, or, geometrically, of all vectors making a nonobtuse angle with v.

D. *Polyhedral cones.* We are now prepared to introduce the concept of a polyhedral cone. We shall give two definitions which look quite different but will later be seen to be equivalent.

DEFINITION 1: *C is a polyhedral cone if it is the sum of a finite number of rays,*

$$C = \sum_{i=1}^{k} (v^i).$$

C thus consists of all nonnegative linear combinations of the vectors $v^1, \cdots, v^k$.

DEFINITION 2: *C is a polyhedral cone if it is the intersection of a finite number of halfspaces,*

$$C = \bigcap_{j=1}^{m} (u^j)^*.$$

---

[1] In Chapters III and XVIII the notation C^+ is used to designate the polar cone, along with the notation $C^- = -C^+$ for the negative polar cone.

C is then all vectors making nonobtuse angles with each of the vectors $u^1, \cdots, u^m$. These two definitions may be stated algebraically rather than geometrically, as follows:

DEFINITION 1′: *Let A be an n by k matrix. Then C is a polyhedral cone if it consists of all vectors of the form v = Ax, where x ≧ 0 is a vector of k components.*

We see at once the connection between Definitions 1 and 1′ by taking for the columns of A in Definition 1′ the vectors v^i of Definition 1.

DEFINITION 2′: *Let B be an n by m matrix. Then C is a polyhedral cone if it consists of all vectors v such that B′v ≧ 0.*

Letting the columns of B in Definition 2′ be the vectors u^j of Definition 2, we immediately see the equivalence of Definitions 2 and 2′.

Polyhedral cones are, of course, special cases of convex cones, as we see at once from the definitions.

E. *Linear space, dimension, and lineality of polyhedral cones.* The smallest linear space containing a cone, C, is denoted by $[C]$ and can also be described as the set of all vectors expressible as the difference of vectors in C, i.e., $[C] = C + (-C)$. The *dimension* (rank) of C is the dimension of $[C]$ or, equivalently, the maximum number of linearly independent vectors in C. If C is described by the matrix A of Definition 1′, then the dimension of C is equal to the rank of A.

We may also consider the largest linear space contained in C, denoted by $]C[$. It consists of all vectors v such that both v and $-v$ lie in C, i.e., $]C[= C \cap (-C)$. The dimension of this space is called the *lineality* of C. If C is given by the matrix B of Definition 2′, it can be shown that the lineality of C is n minus the rank of B.

The set of all vectors perpendicular to the polyhedral cone C is denoted by $C^\perp$ and consists of all vectors u such that $u'v = 0$ for all $v \, \epsilon \, C$. Notice that $C^\perp$ is actually a linear subspace of V, rather than simply a polyhedral cone, and is the same as $[C]^*$.

F. *Supporting halfspace and hyperplane, and extreme halfspace.* If C is a polyhedral cone and $u \, \epsilon \, C^*$, then $(u)^*$ is called a *supporting halfspace* for C. Stated informally, $(u)^*$ is simply a halfspace (through the origin) containing C. The linear space $(u)^\perp$ is called a *supporting hyperplane* for C. Now suppose that C is given by Definition 1, that is,

$$C = \sum_{j=1}^{k} (v^i),$$

and let C have dimension n. A supporting halfspace $(u)^*$ is called an *extreme halfspace* if for $n - 1$ linearly independent vectors from among the v^i we have $u'v^i = 0$.   In other terms, $(u)*$ is an extreme halfspace if $(u)^\perp$ contains $n - 1$ linearly independent vectors from among the v^i.

With these definitions in mind we are prepared to discuss the properties of polyhedral cones.

2. Main Properties of Polyhedral Cones

From this point on, since all cones discussed will be polyhedral, we shall omit the adjective and refer to them simply as cones.   Proofs of most of the statements of this section can either be found in Weyl [1935 or 1950], or can be obtained as simple consequences of his theorems.   Most of the results follow readily from the fundamental theorem (Hauptsatz) of Weyl's paper, which we now state in our own terminology.[2]

THEOREM 1 (Weyl's theorem): *If C is an n-dimensional cone in n-space, which is a sum of rays,*

$$C = \sum_{i=1}^{k} (v^i),$$

then it is the intersection of its extreme halfspaces.

We restate this theorem in matrix form as follows:

THEOREM 1a: *Let the cone C be all vectors of the form Ax, where $x \geqq 0$ and A has rank n.   Then there exists a matrix, B, such that C is the set of all v for which $B'v \geqq 0$; and each column of B is orthogonal to $n - 1$ linearly independent columns of A.*

Notice that, if the cone C is the whole space, there are no supporting halfspaces.   On the other hand, if C is not the whole space, then, from the above theorem, it must lie entirely in some halfspace.

If we visualize Weyl's theorem, say in three-space, the result should appear extremely plausible.   Nevertheless, the proof given by Weyl is nontrivial.

Referring to the previous section, we see that Weyl's theorem shows that every n-dimensional cone which satisfies (the sum) Definition 1 also satisfies (the intersection) Definition 2.   The restriction that C be n-dimensional can easily be removed, roughly as follows.   If dimension $C = k < n$, we may apply Weyl's theorem in the linear subspace $[C]$, obtaining a set of extreme halfspaces in $[C]$ whose intersection is C.   It can then be shown that $[C]$ is itself an intersection of halfspaces, and,

---

[2] A new proof of this theorem by M. Gerstenhaber will be found elsewhere in this volume [XVIII, Theorem 11].

by combining these two collections of halfspaces, the desired result is obtained. Thus C is again the intersection of halfspaces (though not, in this case, of extreme halfspaces), and half of the equivalence of Definitions 1 and 2 has been established. In order to prove the other half we need the following important fact.

THEOREM 2: *If C is a cone and C^* is its polar, then C^{**} (the polar of C^*) is identical with C.*

The proof of this theorem is very simple and we give it here.

PROOF: First, C is contained in C^{**}, for if $x \in C$ then for any $y \in C^*$ we have $x'y \geqq 0$; but this means $x \in C^{**}$.

Second, C^{**} is contained in C, for by Weyl's theorem the cone C is an intersection of halfspaces. Therefore, if v is not in C, there exists a halfspace $(y)^*$ such that C lies in $(y)^*$ and v does not. But since C lies in $(y)^*$ we have $x'y \geqq 0$ for all $x \in C$; hence $y \in C^*$, whereas $v'y < 0$, so v is not in C^{**}.

The above may be thought of as a sort of duality theorem, showing that the relation between a cone and its polar is symmetric. It is a direct generalization of the well-known theorem of vector spaces that the orthogonal complement of the orthogonal complement of a linear subspace is the original subspace. At the same time, it has generalizations to cones which are not necessarily polyhedral and which lie in spaces that are not necessarily finite dimensional. The proof given here depends essentially on the fact that, given a cone, C, and a vector not contained in it, there exists a hyperplane separating them. Generally, in any space where this statement is true, we can prove a theorem analogous to $C^{**} = C$. Such extensions will be considered by M. Gerstenhaber in a forthcoming paper.

As an important consequence of Theorem 2, we have

COROLLARY: *Let $v^0, v^1, \cdots, v^m$ be $m + 1$ vectors in n-space with the property that whenever $x'v^i \geqq 0$ for $i = 1, \cdots, m$, then $x'v^0 \geqq 0$. Then v^0 is a nonnegative linear combination of the vectors $v^1, \cdots, v^m$.*

PROOF: Let

$$C = \sum_{i=1}^{m} (v^i).$$

The corollary asserts that, for every $x \in C^*$, $x'v^0 \geqq 0$. This means $v^0 \in C^{**}$ and hence $v^0 \in C$ and is therefore expressible as

$$v^0 = \sum_{i=1}^{m} \lambda_i v^i, \qquad \lambda_i \geqq 0.$$

Using Theorem 1, we easily show that every "intersection" cone is also a "sum" cone as follows: Let $C = (u^1)^* \cap \cdots \cap (u^m)^*$. Then, by property (2*) of the previous section,

$$C = \left[\sum_{j=1}^{m} (u^j) \right]^*.$$

But, by Weyl's theorem, $\sum_j (u^j) = (v^1)^* \cap \cdots \cap (v^k)^*$ for some set of vectors $v^1, \cdots, v^k$. Thus $C = [(v^1)^* \cap \cdots \cap (v^k)^*]^*$ which again, by (2*) and Theorem 2, gives

$$C = \left\{ \left[\sum_{i=1}^{k} (v^i) \right]^* \right\}^* = \sum_{i=1}^{k} (v^i).$$

We have now shown the complete equivalence of Definitions 1 and 2.

We next list the important relations between the operations of sum, intersection, and polar that now follow easily from the preceding results.

(a) *The set of all cones is closed with respect to the operations* $+$, $\cap$, *.

This means that applying any of the operations to cones leads again to a cone.   This follows at once by using the appropriate definition, 1 or 2, of a cone.

(b) $$(C_1 + C_2)^* = C_1^* \cap C_2^*.$$

This is simply the repetition of property (2*), which holds for general convex cones.

(c) $$(C_1 \cap C_2)^* = C_1^* + C_2^*.$$

(d) $$C^{**} = C.$$

Property (d) is simply the statement of Theorem 2.   Property (c) follows from (b) and (d), for

$$(C_1 \cap C_2)^* = (C_1^{**} \cap C_2^{**})^* = (C_1^* + C_2^*)^{**} = C_1^* + C_2^*.$$

The equivalence of the two definitions of a cone together with properties (a)–(d) are the fundamental tools used in proving theorems about cones or linear inequalities.   We can remember the four properties easily if we think of the polar operation as a "mapping" of the set of cones onto itself which interchanges sums and intersections and which, when iterated, takes each cone back onto itself.   Notice that the linear subspaces, as a subclass of the set of cones, are carried onto themselves, and in this special case the operation * becomes the same as the operation $\perp$, and the properties (a)–(d) are classical properties of linear subspaces.

3. Further Properties and Applications

A. *Dimension and lineality.* We shall show the relation between the dimension and lineality of a cone as defined in Section 1E.

THEOREM 3: $\dim C + \operatorname{lin} C^* = n = \operatorname{lin} C + \dim C^*$.

PROOF: Let y belong to the largest linear space in C^*. Then y and $-y$ lie in C^*, so that for any $x \in C$, $y'x \geqq 0$ and $(-y)'x = -(y'x) \geqq 0$; hence $y'x = 0$, so y is in $C^\perp$. On the other hand, if $y \in C^\perp$, then y and $-y$ are in C^*; therefore the largest linear space in C^*, that is, $]C^*[$, is exactly $C^\perp$. Hence, if $\dim C = p$, then $\dim C^\perp = n - p = \dim]C^*[= \operatorname{lin} C^*$, proving the first equality of the theorem. The second equality follows from Theorem 2. (From this we get at once the expression in terms of rank for the lineality of a cone given in Section 1E.)

B. *Nonnegative cones.* In the literature of econometrics and game theory we frequently encounter theorems which, when interpreted geometrically, are concerned with the conditions under which a cone contains a positive vector. We shall show how such results are easily derivable from our cone theory.

DEFINITION: *The set of all vectors* $v \geqq 0$ *is called the* positive orthant *and denoted by* P. *Its negative,* $-P$, *is called the* negative orthant. *The interior of the positive (negative) orthant consists of all vectors* v *such that* $v > 0$ $(v < 0)$.

THEOREM 4: *If the cone* C *contains no vector* $v < 0$, *then* C^* *contains a vector* $w \geq 0$.

PROOF: The cone $C + P$ is not the whole space V and in fact contains no vector interior to $-P$. For, if $v = v_1 + v_2 < 0$ and $v_2 \in P$, then $v_2 \geqq 0$ and hence $v_1 < 0$; therefore v_1 is not in C. By property (2) of cones, $(C + P)^* = C^* \cap P^*$, which contains a vector $w \neq 0$ by property (4) of cones. The proof is complete once we observe that $P^* = P$. This is clear since P can be described as (i) the set of all nonnegative linear combinations of the unit vectors of V or (ii) the set of all vectors whose inner product with the unit vectors is nonnegative, and these two sets are the polars of each other.

We obtain a simple geometric consequence of the above theorem as follows. The hyperplane $(w)^\perp$ is a supporting hyperplane for the cone $C + P$ (see Section 1F). It is also a hyperplane *separating* C from $-P$ in the sense that C is contained in the halfspace $(w)^*$ bounded by $(w)^\perp$ while $-P$ is contained in the other halfspace, $(-w)^*$, bounded by $(-w)^\perp = w^\perp$. Thus we may state

COROLLARY: *If C is a cone which does not intersect the interior of the negative orthant, $-P$, then there exists a hyperplane separating C from $-P$.*

The matrix statement of Theorem 4 is the following:

THEOREM 4a: *If $Ax < 0$ for no $x \geq 0$, then $w'A \geq 0$ for some $w \geq 0$.*

Stated in this form, the above theorem is essentially the same as the "theorem of the alternative for a matrix" of von Neumann and Morgenstern [1947, p. 141] and also Ville's lemma [Ville, 1938].

If we state the contrapositive (negative converse) of Theorem 4 and interchange the roles of C and C^*—permissible because of property (d)—and P and $-P$, we obtain

THEOREM 5: *If the cone C contains no vector $v \leq 0$, then C^* contains a vector $w > 0$.*

This fact is used in some work of Koopmans [III], and a sharpened form is also used by Gale, Kuhn, and Tucker [XIX]. The reader should be able to verify that the geometric interpretation of the theorem is the following:

COROLLARY: *If the cone C does not intersect the negative orthant, $-P$, then there exists a hyperplane which separates C from $-P$ whose normal is interior to P.*

In matrix form Theorem 5 becomes

THEOREM 5a: *If $Ax \leq 0$ for no x, then there exists a $w > 0$ such that $w'A \geq 0$.*

C. *The main theorem of the two-person game.* From the properties of convex cones we may quickly obtain a geometric proof of the existence of a value and optimal strategies for a finite two-person game. In this section we shall describe the geometric proof. The reader should have little difficulty in translating the ideas back into algebra.

Without concerning ourselves with the game theoretic interpretation, we state the main theorem in the following form:

THEOREM 6: *If A is any m by n matrix, there exist a scalar λ_0 and vectors $x = (x_1, \cdots, x_m)$ and $y = (y_1, \cdots, y_n)$ such that*

(1) $$x, y \geq 0,$$

(2) $$\sum_{i=1}^{m} x_i = \sum_{j=1}^{n} y_j = 1,$$

$$x'Av \geqq \lambda_0 \quad \text{for all} \quad v \geq 0 \quad \text{such that} \quad \sum_{j=1}^{n} v_j = 1,$$

(3)

$$u'Ay \leqq \lambda_0 \quad \text{for all} \quad \mu \geq 0 \quad \text{such that} \quad \sum_{i=1}^{m} u_i = 1.$$

To see how this theorem may be proved, let us denote by $a_1, \cdots, a_n$ the column vectors of the matrix A. These vectors can be located as a finite set of points in m-space. Let K denote the smallest convex set containing these points. This set consists of all points of the form $\sum_{j=1}^{n} a_j v_j$, where the v_j are nonnegative scalars whose sum is 1. Now suppose that we denote by $[\lambda]$ the vector in m-space, all of whose components are equal to the scalar λ. The set K_λ then denotes the set obtained from K by subtracting λ from each point in K. Geometrically this corresponds to "sliding" K a distance $-\lambda$ along the line making equal angles with each coordinate line. For λ large we see that K_λ will lie entirely in the negative orthant, $-P$, while for λ small K_λ will lie in P. It follows that we may find a $\lambda = \lambda_0$ such that K_{λ_0} "just touches" $-P$ (i.e., λ_0 is the smallest value of λ for which K_λ intersects $-P$). Since K_{λ_0} does intersect $-P$, there exists a vector

$$v = \sum_{j=1}^{n} a_j y_j - [\lambda_0] \leqq 0,$$

and v can be written as $Ay - [\lambda_0]$, where $y = (y_1, \cdots, y_n)$ satisfies conditions (1) and (2) of Theorem 6. If then we have $u \geq 0$ and $\sum_{i=1}^{m} u_i = 1$, we obtain

$$u'Ay - u'[\lambda] = u'Ay - \lambda_0 \left(\sum_{i=1}^{m} u_i \right) \leqq 0,$$

or

$$u'Ay \leqq \lambda_0,$$

which is the second part of condition (3) of Theorem 6.

Now observe that K_{λ_0} cannot intersect the interior of $-P$, for this would mean that we could decrease λ and still preserve contact between K_λ and $-P$. Likewise, the cone C subtended by K_{λ_0} will not intersect $-P$. Therefore, using the corollary of Theorem 4, we can find a hyperplane which separates C from $-P$. Let x be a normal to this hyperplane directed away from $-P$. We then have $x'(-p) \leqq 0$ for $-p \, \epsilon -P$ or $x'p \geqq 0$ for all $p \, \epsilon \, P$, whence $x \leqq 0$. We also have $x'u \geqq 0$ for all $u \, \epsilon \, K_{\lambda_0}$ or $x'Av - x'[\lambda_0] \leqq 0$ for all v satisfying condition (3) of Theorem 6. We may also assume that

$$\sum_{i=1}^{m} x_i = 1.$$

If this is not the case, we may take a new normal, $x/\sum_i x_i$; thus we obtain $x'Av \geqq \lambda_0$, which completes the proof.

D. *Application to linear programming.* A useful result on cones, which, however, does not seem to follow from our previous results, is the following (essentially Theorem 2 of Weyl [1935, 1950]):

THEOREM 7: *If* $C = \sum_{i=1}^{m}(v_i)$ *is a cone, and* v *lies in* C, *then it is possible to write* v *as a positive linear combination of not more than* n *vectors from among the* v_i.

This theorem has applications to problems in linear programming. In particular, it is used by Dantzig to show that, if "feasible solutions" exist, one can be found depending on not more than n points. The proof is found in Chapter XXI. Stated in matrix form the theorem reads:

THEOREM 7a: *If* $v = x'A$, *where* $x \geq 0$, *and* A *is an* m *by* n *matrix,* $m > n$, *then there exists an* $\bar{x} \geq 0$ *such that* $v = \bar{x}'A$ *and at least* $m - n$ *components of* $\bar{x}$ *are zero.*

Chapter XVIII

THEORY OF CONVEX POLYHEDRAL CONES *

By Murray Gerstenhaber [1]

It is assumed that the reader of this chapter is familiar with certain fundamental topological concepts, such as those of open and closed sets, and with the elementary theory of finite dimensional vector spaces. Only finite dimensional Euclidean spaces will be considered here; points, sets, and subspaces will be points, sets, and subspaces of finite dimensional Euclidean spaces, though the theorems and methods of proof are valid for some more general spaces. The reader who is unfamiliar with topology or vector space theory is referred to Lefschetz [1949, Chapter I] and Halmos [1948].

1. Notations and Definitions

1. E^n represents n-dimensional Euclidean space. Points in E^n will be denoted by lower-case italic letters, sets by capital italic letters, and real numbers (scalar multipliers) by lower-case Greek letters.

2. 0 is both the real number 0 and the zero vector; the origin of E^n.

3. $a \in A$ means a is a member of A.

4. $a \notin A$ means a is not a member of A.

5. $A \subset B$ means A is contained in B.

6. $A < B$ means A is properly contained in B, i.e., $A \subset B$ and $A \neq B$.

7. $A \cap B$ is the *intersection* of A and B, i.e., the set of all points which are members of both A and B.

* Editor's Note. This chapter was originally submitted in a somewhat longer version containing full proofs of the several statements summarized in Theorem 12 below. The condensation in the present version was made to avoid duplication between chapters in this volume. For the relationship of this chapter to Chapter XVII see the Introduction to this volume.

[1] The author wishes to express his indebtedness to T. C. Koopmans for many conjectures which have become theorems in this chapter and for the statement and proof of Theorem 32. The author also wishes to express his indebtedness to M. L. Slater for the statement and proof of Theorem 26, the idea of which has been employed to make the proofs of several theorems considerably shorter than those originally given by the author.

8. $A \cup B$ is the *union* of A and B, i.e., the set of all points which are members of either A or B.

9. (a, b) is the *inner (scalar) product* of a and b.

10. $A^\perp$ is the *orthogonal complement* of A.

11. A^+ is the *positive polar* of A, i.e., the set of all points b such that $(b, a) \geq 0$ for all a in A.

12. A^- is the *negative polar* of A, i.e., the set of all points b such that $(b, a) \leq 0$ for all a in A.

The following statements are obvious: $A^\perp \subset A^+$; $A^\perp \subset A^-$; $A^\perp = A^+ \cap A^-$; $(-A)^+ = -(A^+) = A^-$; $(-A)^- = -(A^-) = A^+$.

13. $\lambda_1 A_1 + \cdots + \lambda_r A_r$ is the set of all points $\lambda_1 a_1 + \cdots + \lambda_r a_r$ with $a_i \in A_i$.

14. $\{a\}$ is the set of all points λa. Such a set will be called a *line*. If a is a point in E^n and $a \neq 0$, then $\{a\}$ is a one-dimensional subspace of E^n.

15. (a) is the set of all points λa with $\lambda \geq 0$. Such a set will be called a *halfline*.

By definitions 14 and 15, the set consisting of 0 alone is both a line and a halfline, and all lines and halflines contain 0.

16. int A is the *interior* of A.

We shall convene that in E^0 (which contains only 0), 0 is open and its boundary is vacuous.

17. a is a $\begin{cases} positive \\ strictly\ positive \end{cases}$ *linear combination* of $a_1, \cdots, a_r$ if $a = $

$\lambda_1 a_1 + \cdots + \lambda_r a_r$ with $\begin{cases} \lambda_i \geq 0 \\ \lambda_i > 0 \text{ and all } a_i \text{ different from 0.} \end{cases}$

18. a is a $\begin{cases} convex \\ strictly\ convex \end{cases}$ *linear combination* of $a_1, \cdots, a_r$ if $a = $

$\lambda_1 a_1 + \cdots + \lambda_r a_r$ with $\begin{cases} \lambda_i \geq 0 \text{ and } \lambda_1 + \cdots + \lambda_r = 1 \\ \lambda_i > 0 \text{ and } \lambda_1 + \cdots + \lambda_r = 1. \end{cases}$

19. a is a *proper positive linear combination* of $a_1, \cdots, a_r$ if a is a strictly positive linear combination of $a_1, \cdots, a_r$ and some a_i is not a positive multiple of a.

20. a is a *proper convex linear combination* of $a_1, \cdots, a_r$ if a is a strictly convex linear combination of $a_1, \cdots, a_r$ and some a_i is not equal to a.

The set of all convex linear combinations of a and b is the line segment joining them. The set of all proper convex linear combinations of a and b is the open line segment joining them.

21. A set is *convex* if with every pair of points a and b it contains the line segment joining them.

It is obvious that the intersection of any number of convex sets is convex and that all sets of the form A^+, A^-, or $A^\perp$ are convex.

22. The *convex hull* of A is the intersection of all convex sets containing A. The convex hull of A is the smallest convex set containing A; any convex set containing A contains the convex hull of A. The convex hull of A will also be called the convex set spanned by A. If B is the convex hull of A we shall say that A spans B.

23. A *convex cone* is the convex hull of a set of halflines.

It is obvious that, if a set A contains with every pair of points a and b the point $a + b$ and all points λa with $\lambda \geq 0$, then A is a convex cone.

24. A *convex polyhedral cone* is the convex hull of a finite set of halflines.

25. A is a *subcone* of B if A and B are convex cones and $A \subset B$.

A subcone of a convex polyhedral cone need not be polyhedral.

26. An *extreme point* of a convex set is one which is not a proper convex linear combination of any two points of the set.

It follows immediately from the definition that an extreme point of a convex set is one which is not in any open line segment contained in the set. Therefore, if an extreme point is removed from a convex set, the set is still convex; an extreme point is not in the convex hull of the remaining points of the set.

27. (a) is an *extreme halfline* of a convex cone if a is not a proper positive linear combination of any two points of the cone.

A convex cone remains convex after removing any extreme halfline; an extreme halfline of a convex cone is not in the convex hull of the remaining halflines of the cone.

The convex hull of a finite set of points is the set of all their convex linear combinations. The convex hull of halflines (a_1), $\cdots$, (a_r) is the set of all positive linear combinations of a_1, $\cdots$, a_r, which is $(a_1) + \cdots + (a_r)$.

If A and B are convex polyhedral cones, it is trivial that $A + B$ (see 13 for definition; $\lambda_1 = \lambda_2 = 1$) is a convex polyhedral cone, but not trivial that $A \cap B$ is a convex polyhedral cone. This is, however, implied in Theorem 12 below.

28. A *frame* of a convex polyhedral cone is a finite set of halflines which span the cone and such that no halfline of the set is in the convex hull of the others.

It is obvious from the definition of a convex polyhedral cone that it always has at least one frame. Generally, however, the frame is not unique, as in the case where the cone is a whole Euclidean space of dimension greater than one. Any frame of a convex polyhedral cone must contain all extreme halflines of the cone if there are any, but the halflines of a frame need not be extreme as the same example shows. It follows that a convex polyhedral cone can have only a finite number of extreme halflines.

29. $D\{A\}$ denotes the intersection of all subspaces containing A. $D\{A\}$ is the smallest subspace containing A; any subspace containing A contains $D\{A\}$. $D\{A\}$ will be called both the *dimensionality space* of A and the subspace spanned by A. We shall say here too that A spans $D\{A\}$. When "span" is used, the sense will be clear from the context.

30. $L\{A\}$ denotes the convex hull of all subspaces contained in A. $L\{A\}$ is a subspace such that any subspace contained in A is contained in $L\{A\}$. If A is convex, $L\{A\}$ is contained in A. $L\{A\}$ will be called the *lineality space* of A.

31. The *relative interior* of A is the interior of A when A is considered as embedded in $D\{A\}$. The relative interior of A will be denoted by "rel int A."

It is obvious that if A is a convex set in E^n, then A has an interior if and only if $D\{A\} = E^n$. But if A is not empty, then rel int A is not empty.

32. The *relative boundary* of A is the boundary of A when A is considered embedded in $D\{A\}$.

33. $d\{A\}$ is the *dimension* of $D\{A\}$. $d\{A\}$ will be called the dimension of A.

34. $l\{A\}$ is the *dimension* of $L\{A\}$.

It is easy to see that $L\{A^+\} = L\{A^-\} = A^\perp$. This may be demonstrated as follows: It is obvious that $L\{A^+\} = -L\{A^-\}$. But $L\{A^+\}$ and $L\{A^-\}$ are linear spaces, hence equal to their negatives. Therefore $L\{A^+\} = L\{A^-\}$. Since A^+ and A^- are convex, $L\{A^+\} \subset A^+$ and $L\{A^-\} \subset A^-$. But $L\{A^+\} = L\{A^-\}$, so $L\{A^+\} \subset A^+ \cap A^- = A^\perp$. On the other hand, $A^\perp$ is a subspace contained in A^+ and therefore $A^\perp \subset L\{A^+\}$. By comparing the inclusions, $A^\perp = L\{A^+\}$.

35. If A is a convex polyhedral cone and $l\{A\} = 0$, A will be said to be *pointed*.

36. If A is a convex polyhedral cone embedded in E^n, and $A = E^n$, then A will be called *solid*.

To determine if a cone is pointed it is not necessary to consider the space in which it is embedded; but to determine if it is solid, this is necessary.

37. A *halfspace* is a set of the form a^+ with $a \neq 0$.

If $a \neq 0$, then the halfspace a^+ is bounded by a hyperplane to which (a) is a normal at the origin. This hyperplane is $a^\perp$; if $a \in E^n$, it is a subspace of E^n of dimension $n - 1$.

2. Interiors and Projections

Let A be a convex set in E^n (with $n > 0$), a be a point of A, and u_1, $\cdots$, u_n be any n linearly independent points in E^n. Then $u_1, \cdots, u_n$ span E^n, and it is trivial to show that a is in the interior of A if and only if there exists a $\lambda > 0$ such that the points $a + \lambda u_1, \cdots, a + \lambda u_n$, $a - \lambda u_1, \cdots, a - \lambda u_n$, are all in A. Since $a = \frac{1}{2}(a + \lambda u_1) + \frac{1}{2}(a - \lambda u_1)$, if a is in the interior of A then a is not extreme. All extreme points of A are on the boundary of A. If $v_1, \cdots, v_s$ is any finite set of points and $a \in \text{int } A$, then there exists a $\lambda > 0$ such that $a + \lambda v_1, \cdots, a + \lambda v_s$, $a - \lambda v_1, \cdots, a - \lambda v_s$, are all in A.

It is easily shown that if A is a convex cone then the following propositions are equivalent:

(a) 0 is in the relative interior of A,

(b) the relative boundary of A is vacuous,

(c) A is a subspace.

THEOREM 1: *If A is a convex polyhedral cone and $(a_1), \cdots, (a_r)$ is a frame of A, then the relative interior of A is the set of all points $\lambda_1 a_1 + \cdots + \lambda_r a_r$ with $\lambda_i > 0$ $(i = 1, \cdots, r)$.*

PROOF: We may assume that A is embedded in $D\{A\}$. Then we must prove that the set of all points $\lambda_1 a_1 + \cdots + \lambda_r a_r$ with $\lambda_i > 0$ $(i = 1, \cdots, r)$ is the interior of A. Let $d\{A\} = n$, and assume that A is embedded in E^n.

It will be shown (1) that the set of all points $\lambda_1 a_1 + \cdots + \lambda_r a_r$ with $\lambda_i > 0$ is contained in int A, and (2) that int A is contained in the set of all points $\lambda_1 a_1 + \cdots + \lambda_r a_r$ with $\lambda_i > 0$.

(1) Since $d\{A\} = n$ there must exist n linearly independent points among the a_i. By reordering the a_i we may assume that $a_1, \cdots, a_n$ are linearly independent. Let $a = \lambda_1 a_1 + \cdots + \lambda_r a_r$ with $\lambda_i > 0$ $(i = 1, \cdots, r)$, and let λ be the smallest of the λ_i. Then the points $a + \lambda a_1$, $\cdots, a + \lambda a_n, a - \lambda a_1, \cdots, a - \lambda a_n$ are all in A. Therefore $a \in \text{int } A$.

(2) Suppose $a \in \text{int } A$. Then there exists a $\lambda > 0$ such that the points $b_i = a - \lambda a_i$ $(i = 1, \cdots, r)$ are all in A. Then $a = (\lambda/r)a_1 + \cdots + (\lambda/r)a_r + (1/r)b_1 + \cdots + (1/r)b_r$. But since $(a_1), \cdots, (a_r)$ is a frame of A, b_i $(i = 1, \cdots, r)$ can be expressed as a positive linear combination of the a_i. Therefore a has been expressed in the form $a = \lambda_1 a_1 + \cdots + \lambda_r a_r$ with $\lambda_i > 0$ $(i = 1, \cdots, r)$.

THEOREM 2 (corollary): *If A is a convex polyhedral cone in E^n and if $n \geq 2$, then any extreme halfline of A is in the boundary of A.*

THEOREM 3 (corollary): *If A is a convex polyhedral cone, a ε rel int A, and b is any point in A, then a + b ε rel int A.*

It is in fact easily shown that if A is a convex cone, a ε rel int A, and b is any point of A, then $a + b$ ε rel int A.

THEOREM 4 (corollary): *If A and B are convex polyhedral cones such that B ⊂ A, then B intersects the relative interior of A if and only if D{B} intersects the relative interior of A.*

PROOF: If B intersects the relative interior of A, then certainly so does $D\{B\}$. Conversely, suppose that $D\{B\}$ intersects the relative interior of A. Let $(b_1), \cdots, (b_r)$ be a frame of B, and $(a_1), \cdots, (a_s)$ be a frame of A. Then $\lambda_1 b_1 + \cdots + \lambda_r b_r = \mu_1 a_1 + \cdots + \mu_s a_s$ for some set of λ_i and μ_j, with $\mu_j > 0$ $(j = 1, \cdots, s)$. If all the λ_i are negative, then $0 = -\lambda_1 b_1 - \cdots - \lambda_r b_r + \mu_1 a_1 + \cdots + \mu_s a_s$, and 0 is in the relative interior of A. B contains 0, so B intersects the relative interior of A. If some of the λ_i are positive, we may suppose $\lambda_1, \cdots, \lambda_p > 0$. Then $\lambda_1 b_1 + \cdots + \lambda_p b_p = \mu_1 a_1 + \cdots + \mu_s a_s - \lambda_{p+1} b_{p+1} - \cdots - \lambda_r b_r$, and $\lambda_1 b_1 + \cdots + \lambda_p b_p$ is in the relative interior of A, so B intersects the relative interior of A.

If E^n is an n-dimensional Euclidean space and S an r-dimensional subspace, there exists a natural mapping from E^n onto an $(n - r)$-dimensional Euclidean space which maps S into 0, is continuous, linear, and sends open sets into open sets. This $(n - r)$-dimensional space may be taken to be $S^\perp$ and the mapping to be the projection on $S^\perp$. If A is any subset of E^n, the image of A under this mapping will be denoted by A mod S. That the image of A has the property P and a relation R exists between the images of subsets A and B of E^n will be denoted; A has property P mod S, and the relation R exists between A and B mod S.

If T' is a linear subspace of E^n mod S, and if T is the set of all points of E^n that map into T', then T is a linear subspace of E^n, T contains S, and the mapping which sends E^n onto E^n mod S mod T' is the same as that which sends E^n onto E^n mod T. If, in particular, T' is a hyperplane of E^n mod S, then T is a hyperplane of E^n.

If H' is a halfspace of E^n mod S and H the set of all points of E^n mapping into H', then H is a halfspace of E^n.

If $a_1, \cdots, a_r$ are points of E^n, both the set of all their convex linear combinations and the set of all their positive linear combinations are closed. Therefore a convex polyhedral cone is closed. Its boundary is vacuous if and only if the cone is the entire space. If A is a convex polyhedral cone in E^n, then A mod S is a convex polyhedral cone spanned by the images of the halflines which span A. These images are halflines in E^n mod S. Therefore A mod S is closed. If A is not polyhedral, A mod S may not be closed. If (a') is any halfline of A mod S, there is a halfline (a) in A which maps into it. For, since A mod S contains (a'), it contains the point a'. Therefore a' is the image of some point a in A, and (a) mod $S = (a')$.

3. Relations between Convex Polyhedral Cones and Subspaces

Theorem 5: *If A is a convex polyhedral cone, then A mod $L\{A\}$ is pointed.*

Proof: If A mod $L\{A\}$ were not pointed, it would contain a linear subspace of dimension at least one. Therefore it would contain a pair of halflines, (a') and $-(a')$, with $a' \neq 0$. Let a_1 and a_2 be points of A whose images are a' and $-a'$. Then $a_1 + a_2 = 0$ mod $L\{A\}$, whence $a_1 + a_2 \, \epsilon \, L\{A\}$. Since $L\{A\}$ is a subspace contained in A, $-a_1 - a_2 \, \epsilon \, A$. But then $-a_1 \, \epsilon \, A$. Since both a_1 and $-a_1$ are in A, $a_1 \, \epsilon \, L\{A\}$, whence a_1 mod $L\{A\} = 0$. But a_1 mod $L\{A\} = a' \neq 0$, contrary to assumption.

Theorem 6 (corollary): *Let A be a convex polyhedral cone and a and b be points of A. Then $a + b \, \epsilon \, L\{A\}$ implies $a \, \epsilon \, L\{A\}$ and $b \, \epsilon \, L\{A\}$.*

Proof: Since $a = -b$ mod $L\{A\}$, and A mod $L\{A\}$ is pointed and contains both a mod $L\{A\}$ and b mod $L\{A\}$, it must be that $a = 0$ mod $L\{A\}$. Therefore $a \, \epsilon \, L\{A\}$. Likewise, $b \, \epsilon \, L\{A\}$.

It follows immediately that, if a strictly positive linear combination of $a_1, \cdots, a_r$ is in $L\{A\}$, then $a_i \, \epsilon \, L\{A\}$ $(i = 1, \cdots, r)$.

Theorem 7 (corollary): *If A is a convex polyhedral cone and $(a_1), \cdots, (a_r)$ is a frame of A, then $L\{A\}$ is the convex hull of those (a_i) which are in $L\{A\}$.*

Theorem 8: *Let A be a convex polyhedral cone, $(a_1), \cdots, (a_r)$ be a frame of A, and suppose $(a_1), \cdots, (a_s) \, \xi \, L\{A\}$, $(a_{s+1}), \cdots, (a_r) \, \epsilon \, L\{A\}$. Then (a_1) mod $L\{A\}, \cdots, (a_s)$ mod $L\{A\}$ are all distinct and are extreme halflines of A mod $L\{A\}$.*

Proof: Set a_i mod $L\{A\} = b_i$ $(i = 1, \cdots, s)$. Suppose (b_1) not extreme or not distinct from the other (b_i). Then $b_1 = \lambda_1 b_1 + \cdots + \lambda_s b_s$, with $\lambda_i \geq 0$ and at least one of the λ_i greater than zero. There are three cases to consider:

Case 1: $\lambda_1 < 1$. Then $(1 - \lambda_1)b_1 = \lambda_2 b_2 + \cdots + \lambda_s b_s$, whence $(1 - \lambda_1)a_1 = \lambda_2 a_2 + \cdots + \lambda_s a_s + c$, where c is in $L\{A\}$. By Theorem 7, c is a positive linear combination of $a_{s+1}, \cdots, a_r$. Therefore a_1 is a positive linear combination of the other a_i, which contradicts the assumption that $(a_1), \cdots, (a_r)$ is a frame.

CASE 2: $\lambda_1 = 1$. Then $\lambda_2 b_2 + \cdots + \lambda_s b_s = 0$. Of the $\lambda_2, \cdots, \lambda_s$, at least one is not zero. We may assume that it is λ_2. Then A mod $L\{A\}$ contains both (b_2) and $-(b_2)$ and is not pointed, which contradicts Theorem 5.

CASE 3: $\lambda_1 > 1$. Then A mod $L\{A\}$ contains both (b_1) and $-(b_1)$ and is not pointed, which again is a contradiction of Theorem 5.

THEOREM 9 (corollary): *A pointed convex polyhedral cone is spanned by its extreme halflines. Its frame is therefore unique and consists of the extreme halflines of the cone.*

If A is a convex polyhedral cone which is not pointed, the halflines of a frame of A, though not uniquely determined, are determined up to an element of $L\{A\}$.

THEOREM 10: *Let A be a pointed convex polyhedral cone and (a) be an extreme halfline of A. Then $1\{A - (a)\} = 1$, $L\{A - (a)\} = \{a\}$, and A mod $\{a\}$ is pointed.*

PROOF: Since $A - (a)$ contains $\{a\}$, $1\{A - (a)\} \geq 1$. Suppose $1\{A - (a)\} \geq 2$. Then $A - (a)$ contains a line $\{b\}$ distinct from $\{a\}$ and with $b \neq 0$. Therefore there exist points $a_1, a_2 \in A$, and real numbers λ_1, λ_2 such that $a_1 - \lambda_1 a = b$, $a_2 - \lambda_2 a = -b$. Neither a_1 nor a_2 may be zero or a scalar multiple of a, for then b would be a multiple of a and we would have $\{a\} = \{b\}$, contrary to assumption. Adding the equations, we have $a_1 + a_2 - (\lambda_1 + \lambda_2)a = 0$, or $a_1 + a_2 = (\lambda_1 + \lambda_2)a$. It must be the case that $\lambda_1 + \lambda_2$ is positive, for $a_1 + a_2$ is in A. Therefore, if $\lambda_1 + \lambda_2$ were negative, $-a$ would be in A, and A would not be pointed; and if $\lambda_1 + \lambda_2$ were zero, A would contain both a_1 and $-a_1$ and would not be pointed. But, if $\lambda_1 + \lambda_2$ is positive, a can be expressed as a proper positive linear combination of a_1 and a_2, contrary to the assumption that a is extreme. Therefore $1\{A - (a)\} = 1$.

Since $1\{A - (a)\} = 1$, and $A - (a)$ contains $\{a\}$, $L\{A - (a)\} = \{a\}$. Since (a) mod $\{a\} = 0$, A mod $\{a\} = (A - (a))$ mod $\{a\} = (A - (a))$ mod $L\{A - (a)\}$. Therefore, by Theorem 5, A mod $\{a\}$ is pointed.

It is easy to show in a similar manner that, if A is a pointed convex polyhedral cone and $a \notin A$, then $A - (a)$ is still pointed, and, if $a \in A$ but (a) is not an extreme halfline of A, then $1\{A - (a)\} > 1$.

THEOREM 11 (Minkowski, Weyl): *Let A be a convex polyhedral cone in E^n with $d\{A\} = n$. Then A is the intersection of a finite number of half-*

*spaces such that the hyperplanes bounding them each contain at least $n - 1$
linearly independent points of A and are spanned by halflines of any frame
of A.*

PROOF: It will be shown first that, if the theorem is true for pointed
convex polyhedral cones, it is true for all convex polyhedral cones, and
then it will be shown that the theorem is true for pointed convex polyhedral cones.

Suppose that the theorem is true for pointed convex polyhedral cones,
and let A be an arbitrary convex polyhedral cone in E^n with $d\{A\} = n$.
Then the theorem is true for $A \bmod L\{A\}$, which is pointed. Suppose
$l\{A\} = s$. Then there exist halfspaces, $H'_1, \cdots, H'_r$, in $E^n \bmod L\{A\}$
such that $H'_1 \cap \cdots \cap H'_r = A \bmod L\{A\}$, and such that the hyperplanes
bounding the H'_i each contain $n - s - 1$ linearly independent points of
$A \bmod L\{A\}$ and are spanned by halflines of the frame of $A \bmod L\{A\}$.
Let $H_1, \cdots, H_r$ be the sets of all points mapping into $H'_1, \cdots, H'_r$, respectively, let S'_i be the hyperplane bounding H'_i, and let S_i be the hyperplane bounding H_i $(i = 1, \cdots, r)$. Then the H_i are halfspaces in E^n,
each S_i contains $L\{A\}$, and $S_i \bmod L\{A\} = S'_i$ $(i = 1, \cdots, r)$.

By assumption, S'_i contains $n - s - 1$ linearly independent points of
$A \bmod L\{A\}$; call them $a'_{i, 1}, \cdots, a'_{i, n-s-1}$. Let $a_{i, 1}, \cdots, a_{i, n-s-1}$
be points of S_i whose images are $a'_{i, 1}, \cdots, a'_{i, n-s-1}$. Since $l\{A\} = s$,
$L\{A\}$ contains s linearly independent points; call them $a_{n-s}, \cdots, a_{n-1}$.
But $L\{A\} \subset S_i$. Therefore S_i contains all the points $a_{i, 1}, \cdots,$
$a_{i, n-s-1}, a_{n-s}, \cdots, a_{n-1}$. This set of $n - 1$ points must be linearly
independent. For suppose $\lambda_1 a_{i, 1} + \cdots + \lambda_{n-s-1} a_{i, n-s-1} + \lambda_{n-s} a_{n-s}$
$+ \cdots + \lambda_{n-1} a_{n-1} = 0$ for some set of λ_j not all zero. It cannot be
the case that $\lambda_1 = \lambda_2 = \cdots = \lambda_{n-s-1} = 0$, for then $a_{n-s}, \cdots, a_{n-1}$
would be linearly dependent, contrary to assumption. Since $a_j = 0$
$\bmod L\{A\}, j = n - s, \cdots, n - 1$, and $a'_{i, k} = a_{i, k} \bmod L\{A\}$, we must
then have $\lambda_1 a'_{i, 1} + \cdots + \lambda_{n-s-1} a'_{i, n-s-1} = 0$, whence $a'_{i, 1}, \cdots, a'_{i, n-s-1}$
are not linearly independent, contrary to assumption.

Let $(b_1), \cdots, (b_p)$ be any frame of A. By Theorem 7 we may assume
that $(b_1), \cdots, (b_q)$ span $L\{A\}$, and by Theorem 8 $(b_{q+1}) \bmod L\{A\}, \cdots,$
$(b_p) \bmod L\{A\}$ are all distinct, extreme, and span $A \bmod L\{A\}$. $A \bmod$
$L\{A\}$ is pointed by Theorem 5 and therefore has a unique frame by
Theorem 9; therefore $(b_{q+1}) \bmod L\{A\}, \cdots, (b_p) \bmod L\{A\}$ is the
unique frame of $A \bmod L\{A\}$. Set $(b_j) \bmod L\{A\} = (b'_j)$ $(j = p + 1,$
$\cdots, q)$. Since the theorem is assumed true for pointed cones, S'_i is
spanned by a set of halflines from the frame of $A \bmod L\{A\}$, say $(b'_{i_1}),$
$\cdots, (b'_{i_m})$, i.e., $S'_i = (b'_{i_1}) + \cdots + (b'_{i_m})$. But then it is clear that

$S_i = (b_{i_1}) + \cdots + (b_{i_m}) + (b_1) + \cdots + (b_p)$, whence S_i is spanned by a set of halflines from the given frame of A.

Now suppose $a \epsilon H_1 \cap \cdots \cap H_r$. Then $a \bmod L\{A\} \epsilon H_1 \bmod L\{A\} \cap \cdots \cap H_r \bmod L\{A\} = H_1' \cap \cdots \cap H_r' = A \bmod L\{A\}$. Therefore there exists a point b in A such that $a = b \bmod L\{A\}$, or $a - b = c \epsilon L\{A\}$. But then $a = b + c \epsilon A$. Therefore $H_1 \cap \cdots \cap H_r \subset A$. But $A \bmod L\{A\} \subset H_i'$ $(i = 1, \cdots, r)$. Since H_i is the set of all points mapping into H_i', $A \subset H_i$ $(i = 1, \cdots, r)$. Therefore $A \subset H_1 \cap \cdots \cap H_r$, whence $A = H_1 \cap \cdots \cap H_r$.

It has therefore been demonstrated that, if the theorem holds for pointed convex polyhedral cones, it holds for all convex polyhedral cones. In the remainder of this proof it will be assumed that A is pointed.

The theorem will be proved by constructing a set of halfspaces such that the hyperplanes bounding them each contain $n - 1$ linearly independent points of A and are spanned by halflines of the frame of A, and such that the halfspaces themselves each contain A; but if p is a point not in A, at least one of the halfspaces does not contain p. Since there are only a finite number of halflines in the frame of A, the set of halfspaces so constructed must be finite. It is clear that their intersection is A.

If A is embedded in E^1, and $d\{A\} = 1$, the theorem is trivial. Assume that the theorem is true if A is embedded in E^{n-1}, and $d\{A\} = n - 1$. It will then be proved true when A is embedded in E^n and $d\{A\} = n$. We may assume $n \geq 2$.

Let p be a point not in A. Then it will be shown first that there exists a halfline (a) in the frame of A such that $p \not\epsilon A \bmod \{a\}$. Since $p \not\epsilon A$, $A - (p)$ is still pointed. Let (a) be an extreme halfline of $A - (p)$, and let (a) be different from $-(p)$. Then (a) must in fact be in A and therefore in the frame of A. For $a = c - \mu p$ for some c in A and different from zero, and some $\mu \geq 0$. If $\mu \neq 0$ then (a) is not extreme. Therefore $a = c \epsilon A$. But then $p \not\epsilon A \bmod \{a\}$. For $p \epsilon A \bmod \{a\}$ implies that for some λ, $p + \lambda a = b \epsilon A$. If $\lambda \leq 0$, then $p \epsilon A$, which is a contradiction; and if $\lambda > 0$, then (a) is not extreme in $A - (p)$, which again is a contradiction.

$A \bmod \{a\}$ is of dimension $n - 1$, and is embedded in $E^n \bmod \{a\}$, an $(n - 1)$-dimensional Euclidean space. By the inductive assumption, the theorem is true for $A \bmod \{a\}$. Since $p \not\epsilon A \bmod \{a\}$, there exists a halfspace H' of $E^n \bmod \{a\}$ such that $A \bmod \{a\} \subset H'$, $p \bmod \{a\} \not\epsilon H'$, and such that the hyperplane bounding H' is spanned by halflines of the frame of $A \bmod \{a\}$ and contains $n - 2$ linearly independent points of $A \bmod \{a\}$. By Theorem 10, $A \bmod \{a\}$ is pointed and there-

fore has a unique frame. Let (a), (a_2), $\cdots$, (a_t) be the frame of A.
Then (a_2) mod $\{a\}$, $\cdots$, (a_t) mod $\{a\}$ must be the frame of A mod $\{a\}$.
We may suppose that the halflines are so ordered that the hyperplane
bounding H' is spanned by (a_2) mod $\{a\}$, $\cdots$, (a_{n-1}) mod $\{a\}$.

Let H be the halfspace of E^n whose image is H'; H mod $\{a\} = H'$.
Then the hyperplane bounding H is spanned by (a), (a_2), $\cdots$, (a_{n-1}).
Since the hyperplane bounding H' contained $n - 2$ linearly independent
points of A mod $\{a\}$, the hyperplane bounding H must contain $n - 1$
linearly independent points of A, for it contains a. Obviously $A \subset H$,
and since $p \notin H$ mod $\{a\}$, certainly $p \notin H$. Since for every $p \notin A$ such a
halfspace H may be found, the theorem is proved.

If A is solid, the arguments of the above proof do not hold. It is
natural to make the convention that an intersection containing no factors
shall be the whole space. Accordingly, if A is solid, A is the intersection
of zero halfspaces.

If A is a convex polyhedral cone in E^n, and $\mathrm{d}\{A\} < n$, it is obvious
from Theorem 11 that A is the intersection of a finite number of halfspaces of E^n such that the hyperplanes bounding them each contain at
least $\mathrm{d}\{A\} - 1$ linearly independent points of A, but it will no longer
be the case that the hyperplanes are spanned by halflines of a frame of A.

Theorem 11 has numerous important corollaries due to Minkowski
and Weyl. These are given in Theorem 12 in forms due mainly to
Gale. Most of their proofs may be found in Chapter XVII, the remainder supplied by the reader.

THEOREM 12: (1) *If A and B are convex polyhedral cones, then*

    (a) $A \subset B$ *implies* $B^+ \subset A^+$;

    (b) $A < B$ *implies* $B^+ < A^+$;

    (c) $A^{++} = A$;

    (d) $(A + B)^+ = A^+ \cap B^+$;

    (e) $(A \cap B)^+ = A^+ + B^+$;

    (f) *statements* (a) *to* (c) *hold when negative polars are substituted for
positive polars;*

    (g) $A \cap A^- = 0$. (*In general* $A \cap A^+ = 0$ *is false.*)

(2) *If A is a convex polyhedral cone, then* $\mathrm{D}\{A^+\} + \mathrm{L}\{A\} = E^n$, *whence*
$\mathrm{d}\{A^+\} + \mathrm{l}\{A\} = n$.

(3) (a) *A is a convex polyhedral cone if and only if A^+ is a convex
polyhedral cone.*

    (b) *A is a convex polyhedral cone if and only if A is an intersection
of a finite number of halfspaces.*

    (c) *The intersection of two convex polyhedral cones is a convex poly-
hedral cone.*

THEOREM 13: *Let A and B be convex polyhedral cones. Then $A - B$ = $D\{A + B\}$ ($= D\{A\} + D\{B\}$) if and only if the relative interior of A intersects the relative interior of B.*

PROOF: Suppose $A - B = D\{A + B\}$. Let a_1 be in the relative interior of A and b_1 be in the relative interior of B. Then, since $-a_1 + b_1 \, \epsilon$ $D\{A + B\}$, there exist points $a_2 \, \epsilon \, A$ and $b_2 \, \epsilon \, B$ such that $a_2 - b_2 =$ $-a_1 + b_1$. But then $a_1 + a_2 = b_1 + b_2$. Since $a_1 + a_2$ is in the relative interior of A, and $b_1 + b_2$ is in the relative interior of B, the relative interior of A intersects the relative interior of B.

Suppose that the relative interior of A intersects the relative interior of B. Let $(a_1), \cdots, (a_r)$ be a frame of A. Then, for some set of $\lambda_i > 0$, $\lambda_1 a_1 + \cdots + \lambda_r a_r \, \epsilon \, B$. Therefore $-\lambda_1 a_1 - \cdots - \lambda_r a_r \, \epsilon \, A - B$. But then $-\lambda_1 a_1, \cdots, -\lambda_r a_r$ are all in $A - B$, whence $-a_1, \cdots, -a_r$ are all in $A - B$. Therefore $D\{A\} \subset A - B$. Likewise, $D\{B\} \subset A - B$, whence $D\{A\} + D\{B\} \subset A - B$. Therefore, since $D\{A + B\}$ = $D\{A\} + D\{B\}$, $D\{A + B\} \subset A - B$. But $A - B \subset D\{A + B\}$. Therefore, $A - B = D\{A + B\}$.

It follows, as a special case of Theorem 13, that, if A and B are convex polyhedral cones, and B intersects the interior of A, then $A - B$ is solid.

THEOREM 14 (corollary): *If A and B are convex polyhedral cones, and if $B \subset A$, then a necessary and sufficient condition that B be in the relative boundary of A is that $l\{A - B\} < d\{A\}$, i.e., that $A - B \neq D\{A\}$, and a necessary and sufficient condition that B intersect the relative interior of A is that $l\{A - B\} = d\{A\}$, i.e., that $A - B = D\{A\}$.*

THEOREM 15: *If A is a convex polyhedral cone in E^n, then the mapping which sends E^n onto E^n mod $L\{A\}$ maps the relative interior of A onto the relative interior of A mod $L\{A\}$ and maps the relative boundary of A onto the relative boundary of A mod $L\{A\}$.*

PROOF: It is sufficient to assume that A is embedded in $D\{A\}$, i.e., that $D\{A\} = E^n$. Then the relative interior of A is the interior of A, and we shall prove that the interior of A is mapped on the interior of A mod $L\{A\}$ and the boundary of A is mapped on the boundary of A mod $L\{A\}$.

Since the image of an open set under the mapping which sends E^n onto E^n mod $L\{A\}$ is an open set, the interior of A is mapped on the interior of A mod $L\{A\}$. Therefore it is only necessary to show that no point in the boundary of A is mapped into the interior of A mod $L\{A\}$.

Suppose that a were a point on the boundary of A which is mapped into the interior of A mod $L\{A\}$. Set a mod $L\{A\} = b$, A mod $L\{A\} =$

B. Then, since b is in the interior of B, $B - (b)$ is solid, or $A - (a)$ mod $L\{A\} = E^n$ mod $L\{A\}$. But then $A - (a) + L\{A\} = E^n$. Since $L\{A\} \subset A$, $A - (a) = E^n$. Hence a is in the interior of A, contrary to assumption.

THEOREM 16: *Let A be a convex polyhedral cone in E^n. Then*

(1) *if A is not solid, i.e., if $A \neq E^n$, then $L\{A\}$ is on the boundary of A;*

(2) *if $d\{A\} = n$ and $l\{A\} = n - 1$, i.e., if A is a halfspace, then any frame of A contains exactly one halfline which is not in $L\{A\}$. This halfline is in the interior of A;*

(3) *if $d\{A\} < n$, or $l\{A\} < n - 1$, then all the halflines in any frame of A lie in the boundary of A.*

PROOF: (1) If $A \neq E^n$, then the dimension of E^n mod $L\{A\}$ is at least one. Since A mod $L\{A\}$ is pointed, 0 is in the boundary of A mod $L\{A\}$. Therefore, by Theorem 14, $L\{A\}$ is in the boundary of A.

(2) If $d\{A\} = n$, and $l\{A\} = n - 1$, then A mod $L\{A\}$ is a halfline in a one-dimensional space and has therefore a unique frame consisting of one halfline which is in the interior. Therefore, by Theorems 8 and 15, any frame of A contains exactly one halfline which is not in $L\{A\}$, and it is in the interior of A.

(3) If $d\{A\} < n$, then A has no interior. If $l\{A\} < n - 1$, then E^n mod $L\{A\}$ is at least two-dimensional. The frame halflines of A which are not in $L\{A\}$ are mapped onto the extreme halflines of A mod $L\{A\}$ by Theorem 8, and, in a space of dimension at least two, these are all on the boundary. Therefore those frame halflines of A which are not in $L\{A\}$ are in the boundary of A. Since it was shown in (1) that $L\{A\}$ is in the boundary of A, all the halflines in any frame of A are in the boundary of A.

THEOREM 17: *Let A be a convex polyhedral cone in E^n. Then A is pointed if and only if there exists a halfspace H of E^n such that, except for the origin, A is contained in the interior of H.*

PROOF: Suppose that, except for the origin, A is contained in the interior of a halfspace H. H is a convex polyhedral cone. Therefore, by Theorem 16 (1), $L\{H\}$ is contained in the boundary of H, whence the interior of H can contain no subspace of E^n of positive dimension. Therefore, $l\{A\} = 0$.

Conversely, suppose $l\{A\} = 0$, then by Theorem 12(2), $d\{A^+\} = n$ and A^+ has an interior. Suppose $b \in$ int A^+. If $n = 0$, the theorem is vacuous, and, if $n > 0$, then $b \neq 0$ and b^+ is a halfspace such that except for the origin A is contained in the interior of b^+. For suppose

$a \, \epsilon \, A$ and a is on the boundary of b^+. Since the boundary of b^+ is $b^\perp$, $a \, \epsilon \, b^\perp$. Therefore $(a, \, b) = 0$. Since $b \, \epsilon$ int A^+, there exists a $\lambda > 0$ such that $b - \lambda a \, \epsilon$ int A^+. Then, by the definition of A^+, $(a, \, b - \lambda a) \geqq 0$. But $(a, \, b - \lambda a) = (a, \, b) - \lambda(a, \, a)$, and $(a, \, b) = 0$ by assumption. Therefore $-\lambda(a, \, a) \geqq 0$, or $(a, \, a) \leqq 0$. But $(a, \, a) \geqq 0$ for any a, hence $(a, \, a) = 0$. Since $(a, \, a) = 0$ if and only if $a = 0$, it follows that $a = 0$. Therefore, except for the origin, A is contained in the interior of b^+.

THEOREM 18 (corollary to Theorem 13): *Let A be a convex polyhedral cone in E^n, and let S be a subspace of E^n. Then A mod S = $D\{A\}$ mod S if and only if S intersects the relative interior of A.*

PROOF: Since S is a subspace, $S = -S = D\{S\}$, and S mod $S = 0$. Suppose that S intersects the relative interior of A. Then $A - S = D\{A\} + S$, whence A mod $S = D\{A\}$ mod S. Conversely, if A mod $S = D\{A\}$ mod S, then $A - S = D\{A\} + S$, and S intersects the relative interior of A.

As a special case of Theorem 18 it follows that if A is a convex polyhedral cone in E^n, $d\{A\} = n$, and S is a subspace of E^n, then A mod S is solid if and only if S intersects the interior of A.

THEOREM 19: *Let A be a convex polyhedral cone in E^n and S an $(n - 1)$-dimensional subspace of E^n which does not intersect the relative interior of A. Then $a, \, b \, \epsilon \, A$, and $a + b \, \epsilon \, S$ imply $a, \, b \, \epsilon \, S$.*

PROOF: Suppose $a, \, b \, \epsilon \, A$, $a + b \, \epsilon \, S$, and $a \notin S$. Then, since a mod S $\neq 0$, and $a = -b$ mod S, A mod S would not be pointed. But E^n mod S is one-dimensional; hence if A mod S is not pointed it is solid. By Theorem 18 this implies that S intersects the relative interior of A, which is a contradiction.

THEOREM 20 (corollary): *Let A be a convex polyhedral cone in E^n, and S be an $(n - 1)$-dimensional subspace of E^n which does not intersect the relative interior of A. Then (1) $L\{A\} \subset S$, and (2) any frame of A contains a set of halflines spanning $A \cap S$.*

PROOF: (1) Suppose $a \, \epsilon \, L\{A\}$. Then $a, \, -a \, \epsilon \, A$, and $a - a = 0 \, \epsilon \, S$, whence $a \, \epsilon \, S$. (2) Suppose $\lambda_1 a_1 + \cdots + \lambda_r a_r \, \epsilon \, S$, where $(a_1), \, \cdots , \, (a_r)$ are halflines in some frame of A, and $\lambda_i > 0$, $i = 1, \, \cdots , \, r$. Then a_1, $\cdots , \, a_r \, \epsilon \, S$, whence $(a_1), \, \cdots , \, (a_r) \, \epsilon \, S$. Therefore, given any frame of A and an arbitrary point of $A \cap S$, the frame contains a set of halflines whose convex hull contains the point.

4. FACETS

DEFINITION: *Let A be a convex polyhedral cone of dimension n. Then A shall have one n-facet, itself, and no r-facets for $r > n$. If $r < n$, then F shall be an r-facet of A if F is a subcone of an $(r + 1)$-facet G and (1) F is contained in the relative boundary of G, (2) no subcone of G contained in the relative boundary of G properly contains F, and (3) F is not empty.*

Conditions (1) and (2) state that F is maximal with respect to being a subcone in the relative boundary of G.

THEOREM 21: *Let A be a convex polyhedral cone, and suppose that $d\{A\} = n$, and that A is not solid. If B is a subcone on the relative boundary of A, then A has an $(n - 1)$-facet containing B, and this facet is of dimension $n - 1$.*

PROOF: Since $d\{A\} = n$, we may suppose that A is embedded in E^n. Then the relative boundary of A is the boundary of A. If B is in the boundary of A, then, by Theorem 18, $A \bmod D\{B\}$ is not solid. Suppose $d\{B\} = r$. Then $E^n \bmod D\{B\}$ is of dimension $n - r$. $A \bmod D\{B\}$ is an intersection of a finite number of halfspaces of $E^n \bmod D\{B\}$, each of which is bounded by a hyperplane of $E^n \bmod D\{B\}$ containing $n - r - 1$ linearly independent points of $A \bmod D\{B\}$. Let S' be one of these hyperplanes and S the set of all points of E^n mapping into S'. Then S is an $(n - 1)$-dimensional subspace of E^n containing B and not intersecting the interior of A.

We shall prove that $A \cap S$ is an $(n - 1)$-facet of A containing B, and that $d\{A \cap S\} = n - 1$. $A \cap S$ is certainly a subcone of A contained in the boundary of A. Also, $d\{A \cap S\} = n - 1$, since S' contains $n - r - 1$ linearly independent points of $A \bmod D\{B\}$, and $d\{B\} = r$. If C were a subcone of A properly containing $A \cap S$, then C would contain some point of A which was not in S. But then C would contain $n - 1$ linearly independent points of S and at least one point not in S, whence $d\{C\} = n$. C would then intersect the interior of A. Therefore $A \cap S$ is a facet.

THEOREM 22 (corollary): *If A is a convex polyhedral cone of dimension n and F is an $(n - 1)$-facet of A, then $d\{F\} = n - 1$, and $F = A \cap D\{F\}$.*

PROOF: By the preceding theorem, there is an $(n - 1)$-facet G of A which contains F, and which is of dimension $n - 1$. G cannot contain F properly, by definition. Therefore $G = F$, and $d\{F\} = n - 1$.

Since F does not intersect the relative interior of A, by Theorem 4, $D\{F\}$ does not intersect the relative interior of A. Therefore $A \cap D\{F\}$ is in the relative boundary of A. Since $F \subset (A \cap D\{F\})$ and the inclusion cannot be proper by the definition of a facet, $F = A \cap D\{F\}$.

THEOREM 23: *Let A be a convex polyhedral cone and F be an r-facet of A. Then*

(1) $d\{F\} = r$,
(2) $F = A \cap D\{F\}$,
(3) *F is a convex polyhedral cone,*
(4) *in any frame of A there is a set of halflines spanning F,*
(5) $L\{A\} \subset F$.

PROOF: (1) By Theorem 22, if $d\{A\} = n$, then an $(n-1)$-facet of A is of dimension $n-1$. It follows by induction that an r-facet is of dimension r.

(2) By Theorem 22, if $d\{A\} = n$, and G is an $(n-1)$-facet of A, then $G = A \cap D\{G\}$. We may make the inductive assumption that, if G is an $(r+1)$-facet of A, then $G = A \cap D\{G\}$. By definition, A has an $(r+1)$-facet, F', of which F is an r-facet. Then $F' = A \cap D\{F\}$ by the inductive assumption, and $F = F' \cap D\{F'\}$ by Theorem 22. Therefore $F = A \cap D\{F'\} \cap D\{F\}$. But $D\{F\} \subset D\{F'\}$, whence $F = A \cap D\{F\}$.

(3) By (2) F is the intersection of two convex polyhedral cones and is therefore a convex polyhedral cone.

(4) and (5) If $d\{A\} = n$, we may assume that A is embedded in E^n. Then, if F is an $(n-1)$-facet, (4) and (5) follow immediately from (2) and Theorem 20. But then (4) and (5) hold for all facets of A by a trivial induction.

THEOREM 24 (corollary): *If A is a convex polyhedral cone and F_1 and F_2 are facets of A, then $F_1 = F_2$ if and only if $D\{F_1\} = D\{F_2\}$.*

THEOREM 25: *If A is a convex polyhedral cone and F a facet of A, then A mod $D\{F\}$ is pointed.*

PROOF: If $d\{A\} = n$, then the theorem is true for n-facets because there is only one, A itself. Suppose that the theorem for r-facets of A is true. It will then be proved true for $(r-1)$-facets of A, from which the theorem follows for all facets of A by induction.

Suppose that F is an $(r-1)$-facet of A. By definition there exists an r-facet, G, of A, such that F is a facet of G. (It has not yet been proved that, if G is any r-facet of A containing F, then F is a facet of G.) If A mod $D\{F\}$ were not pointed, there would exist halflines (a)

and (b) in A such that $(a) = -(b) \bmod D\{F\}$, and (a), $(b) \neq 0$. If (a) and (b) were both in G, then $G \bmod D\{F\}$ would not be pointed. Consider G as embedded in $D\{G\}$. Then $G \bmod D\{F\}$ is a one-dimensional cone in a one-dimensional space and is therefore either pointed or solid. Since it is not pointed, it is solid. Then, by Theorem 18, $D\{F\}$ intersects the relative interior of G. But then, by Theorem 4, F intersects the relative interior of G, contrary to the definition of a facet.

But, if (a) is not in G, then a is not in $D\{G\}$, $(a) \bmod D\{G\} \neq 0$, and, since $D\{F\} \subset D\{G\}$, $(a) = -(b) \bmod D\{G\}$. But then $A \bmod D\{G\}$ is not pointed, contrary to the inductive assumption.

THEOREM 26 (Slater): *Let A be a convex polyhedral cone and F a subcone of A. Then F is a facet of A if and only if a, $b \in A$ and $a + b \in F$ imply $a \in F$ and $b \in F$.*

PROOF: If F is a facet, a, $b \in A$ and $a + b \in F$, then $a = -b \bmod D\{F\}$. If $a \neq 0 \bmod D\{F\}$, $A \bmod D\{F\}$ is not pointed, contradicting Theorem 25. Therefore $a = 0 \bmod D\{F\}$, whence $a \in D\{F\}$. Likewise, $b \in D\{F\}$. But $F = A \cap D\{F\}$. Therefore a, $b \in F$.

Let F be a subcone of A such that a, $b \in A$ and $a + b \in F$ imply $a \in F$ and $b \in F$. Then, as in the proof of Theorem 20, any frame of A contains a set of halflines spanning F. F is therefore a convex polyhedral cone. Let G be a facet of A of lowest possible dimension which contains F. Then F must intersect the relative interior of G. For, if F is on the relative boundary of G, then, by Theorem 19, there exists a facet H of G which is of dimension one less than that of G and which contains F. Since F intersects the relative interior of G, by Theorem 13, $G - F = D\{G\}$. Let g be any point in G. Then there exist points $g_1 \in G$ and $f \in F$ such that $g_1 - f = -g$, or $g_1 + g = f$. But then, by hypothesis, $g \in F$. Therefore $G = F$ and F is a facet.

THEOREM 27 (corollary): *If A is a convex polyhedral cone and G and F are facets of A such that $F \subset G$, then F is a facet of G.*

PROOF: F is a subcone of A such that a, $b \in A$, and $a + b \in F$ imply a, $b \in F$. Then, in particular, a, $b \in G$ and $a + b \in F$ imply a, $b \in F$, whence F is a facet of G.

THEOREM 28 (corollary): *Let A be a convex polyhedral cone and let F and G be facets of A. Then $F \cap G$ is a facet of A.*

PROOF: Suppose a, $b \in A$ and $a + b \in F \cap G$. Then $A + b \in F$ and $a + b \in G$, whence a, $b \in F$ and a, $b \in G$. Therefore a, $b \in F \cap G$ and $F \cap G$ is a facet.

THEOREM 29 (corollary): *Let A be a convex polyhedral cone and let F and G be facets of A. Then F intersects the relative interior of G if and only if F contains G.*

PROOF: If F contains G, then F certainly intersects the relative interior of G.

Suppose that F intersects the relative interior of G. Then $F \cap G$ intersects the relative interior of G. By Theorem 26, $F \cap G$ is a facet, and by Theorem 25 it is a facet of G. This is possible only if $F \cap G = G$. But then F must contain G.

THEOREM 30: *Let A be a convex polyhedral cone and F be a subcone of A. Then F is a facet of A if and only if A mod $D\{F\}$ is pointed and $F = A \cap D\{F\}$.*

PROOF: If F is a facet, it has already been shown that A mod $D\{F\}$ is pointed and $F = A \cap D\{F\}$.

Suppose that F is a subcone of A such that A mod $D\{F\}$ is pointed and $F = A \cap D\{F\}$. If a, $b \in A$ and $a + b \in F$, then $a + b = 0$ mod $D\{F\}$. Therefore, since A mod $D\{F\}$ is pointed, $a = b = 0$ mod $D\{F\}$. But then a, $b \in D\{F\}$. Since $F = A \cap D\{F\}$, a, $b \in F$ and F is a facet.

THEOREM 31: *If A is a convex polyhedral cone and F a facet of A, then $L\{A - F\} = D\{F\}$.*

PROOF: Since $A - F$ contains $F - F = D\{F\}$, $D\{F\} \subset L\{A - F\}$. If the inclusion were proper, $A - F$ mod $D\{F\}$ would not be pointed. But $A - F$ mod $D\{F\} = A$ mod $D\{F\}$, whence A mod $D\{F\}$ would not be pointed, contradicting Theorem 25.

ALTERNATE PROOF: Suppose $c \in L\{A - F\}$. Then $-c \in L\{A - F\}$, and there exist points a_1, $a_2 \in A$, f_1, $f_2 \in F$ such that $c = a_1 - f_1$, $-c = a_2 - f_2$. Then $0 = a_1 + a_2 - f_1 - f_2$, or $a_1 + a_2 = f_1 + f_2$. Therefore $a_1 + a_2 \in F$, whence a_1, $a_2 \in F$. Therefore $c \in D\{F\}$. Therefore $L\{A - F\} \subset D\{F\}$. Since $D\{F\} \subset L\{A - F\}$, $L\{A - F\} = D\{F\}$.

THEOREM 32 (Koopmans): *Let A be a convex polyhedral cone and F a subcone of A. Then F is a facet of A if and only if $F = A \cap L\{A - F\}$.*

PROOF: Let F be a subcone of A, and G the lowest-dimensional facet of A containing F. Then F intersects the relative interior of G, because, if F were in the relative boundary of G, there would exist, by Theorem 21 applied to the cone G, a facet of G of lower dimensionality than G and containing F, contrary to assumption. Let $f \in F \cap$ rel int G, and $f \neq 0$. Then $L\{A - F\} \supset L\{G - f\} = D\{G\} = L\{A - G\}$, by Theorems 14 and 31. Since also $L\{A - F\} \subset L\{A - G\}$, we have

$L\{A - F\} = L\{A - G\}$. Hence $A \cap L\{A - F\} = A \cap L\{A - G\}$ $= A \cap D\{G\} = G$, by Theorems 31 and 30. Therefore, if $F = A \cap L\{A - F\}$, we conclude that $F = G$.

Conversely, let F be a facet of A. Then, by Theorems 30 and 31, $F = A \cap D\{F\} = A \cap L\{A - F\}$.

THEOREM 33: *Let A be a convex polyhedral cone in E^n. Then* (1) *if S is an $(n - 1)$-dimensional subspace not intersecting the relative interior of A, then $A \cap S$ is a facet of A, and* (2) *if F is an r-facet of A with $r < n$, then there exists an $(n - 1)$-dimensional subspace S of E^n such that $F = A \cap S$.*

PROOF: (1) If S is an $(n - 1)$-dimensional subspace of E^n, then $A \cap S$ is a facet of A by Theorems 19 and 26. (2) Let F be an r-facet of A with $r < n$. Then $d\{F\} = r$ by Theorem 23 (1), and the dimension of E^n mod $D\{F\} = n - r \geq 1$. By Theorem 17, A mod $D\{F\}$ is contained, except for the origin, in an open halfspace of E^n mod $D\{F\}$. Let S' be the boundary of this open halfspace. Then S' is an $(n - d\{F\} - 1)$-dimensional subspace of E^n mod $D\{F\}$, and $(A$ mod $D\{F\}) \cap S' = 0$. Let S be the set of all points of E^n which map into S'. Then S is an $(n - 1)$-dimensional subspace of E^n, S contains $D\{F\}$ and $A \cap S \subseteq D\{F\}$. Therefore $A \cap S = A \cap S \cap D\{F\} = A \cap D\{F\} = F$, the last equality by Theorem 23 (2). Therefore $A \cap S = F$, and (2) is proved.

THEOREM 34: *If A is a pointed convex polyhedral cone and (a) a halfline in the frame of A, then (a) is a facet of A.*

PROOF: By Theorem 10, (a) satisfies the criterion of Theorem 30.

THEOREM 35: *Let A be a convex polyhedral cone. Then every point of A is contained in the relative interior of one and only one facet of A.*

PROOF: Let a be a point of A and F the facet of least dimension containing a. Since A itself is a facet of A, such an F exists. Then a is in the relative interior of F. For if a were in the relative boundary of F, (a) would also be in the relative boundary of F. Applying Theorem 21 to the convex polyhedral cone F, F has a facet G of dimension $d\{F\} - 1$ which contains (a) and hence a. Since G is a facet of A, this is a contradiction.

Suppose that a is in the relative interior of facets F_1 and F_2. Then F_1 intersects the relative interior of F_2, and F_2 intersects the relative interior of F_1. By Theorem 29 it follows that $F_1 \subset F_2$ and $F_2 \subset F_1$. Therefore $F_1 = F_2$, and a is contained in the relative interior of exactly one facet.

CHAPTER XIX

LINEAR PROGRAMMING AND THE THEORY OF GAMES [1]

By DAVID GALE, HAROLD W. KUHN, AND ALBERT W. TUCKER [2]

The basic "scalar" problem of *linear programming* is to maximize (or minimize) a linear function of several variables constrained by a system of linear inequalities [Dantzig, II]. A more general "vector" problem calls for maximizing (in a sense of partial order) a system of linear functions of several variables subject to a system of linear inequalities and, perhaps, linear equations [Koopmans, III]. The purpose of this chapter is to establish theorems of duality and existence for general "matrix" problems of linear programming which contain the "scalar" and "vector" problems as special cases, and to relate these general problems to the theory of zero-sum two-person games.

1. NOTATION AND INTRODUCTORY LEMMAS

Capital letters, A, B, C, etc., denote rectangular matrices; lower-case letters, b, c, u, x, etc., denote vectors, regarded as one-column matrices; and Greek letters (lower case) δ, λ denote scalars—all quantities being real. A prime is used to denote transposition: thus A' denotes A transposed, and b' denotes a one-row matrix obtained by transposing the vector b. The number of components of a vector or the numbers of rows and columns of a matrix are not specified, but of course there are some implicit relations: thus the product Ax implies that the number of columns of A is the same as the number of components of x. Vector equations and inequalities are based on the following notation:

$u = 0$ means that all components of u are zero;

$u \geqq 0$ means that no components of u are negative;

$u \geq 0$ means $u \geqq 0$ with $u = 0$ excluded;

$u > 0$ means that all components of u are positive.

Other usages follow naturally: thus $u < 0$ means $-u > 0$, $u_1 \geqq u_2$ means $u_1 - u_2 \geqq 0$, etc. It should be noted that the inner product

[1] This chapter was presented in a preliminary form by A. W. Tucker at a meeting of the Econometric Society at Boulder, Colorado, September 2, 1949.

[2] Under contracts with the Office of Naval Research.

$b'u > 0$ if $b \geq 0$, $u > 0$; of course, $b'u \geq 0$ if $b \geq 0$, $u \geq 0$. Matrix equations and inequalities use the same rules: thus $\Delta \geq D$ means $\Delta - D \geq 0$ (i.e., each element of $\Delta - D$ is nonnegative, and at least one element is positive).

The following lemmas provide the basis for the theorems in this chapter. Lemma 1 expresses a fundamental property of homogeneous linear inequalities observed by H. Minkowski [1896, p. 45]. Lemma 2 is an immediate consequence of Lemma 1, and Lemma 3 is a generalization of Lemma 2.

LEMMA 1: *In order that a homogeneous linear inequality $b'u \geq 0$ hold for all u satisfying a system of homogeneous linear inequalities $A'u \geq 0$, it is necessary and sufficient that $b = Ax$ for some $x \geq 0$.*

For proofs the reader is referred to J. Farkas [1901, pp. 5–7], H. Weyl [1935 or 1950, Theorem 3], and in this volume David Gale [XVII, corollary to Theorem 2] and M. Gerstenhaber [XVIII, Theorem 11].

LEMMA 2: *In order that $b'u < 0$ for no $u \geq 0$ such that $A'u \geq 0$, it is necessary and sufficient that $Ax \leq b$ for some $x \geq 0$.*

PROOF: In Lemma 1 replace A by $[A \quad I]$ and x by $\begin{bmatrix} x \\ t \end{bmatrix}$, where I denotes an identity matrix. Then, in order that $b'u \geq 0$ hold for all u satisfying $A'u \geq 0$, $u \geq 0$, it is necessary and sufficient that $b = Ax + t$ for some $x \geq 0$, $t \geq 0$. That is, in order that $b'u < 0$ for no $u \geq 0$ such that $A'u \geq 0$, it is necessary and sufficient that $Ax \leq b$ for some $x \geq 0$.

LEMMA 3: *In order that $B'u \leq 0$ for no $u \geq 0$ such that $A'u \geq 0$, it is necessary and sufficient that $Ax \leq By$ for some $x \geq 0$, $y > 0$.*

PROOF: To show that the x, y-condition is implied by the u-condition, we proceed as follows. Let b_k denote the kth column of the matrix B. Then the u-condition implies that $b'_k u < 0$ for no $u \geq 0$ such that $A'u \geq 0$, $-B'u \geq 0$. Hence, substituting $[A \quad -B]$ for A and $\begin{bmatrix} x_k \\ y_k \end{bmatrix}$ for x in Lemma 2, we have $Ax_k - By_k \leq b_k$ for some $x_k \geq 0$, $y_k \geq 0$. Then, summing for all columns of B, $A(\sum x_k) - B(\sum y_k) \leq \sum b_k$. But $\sum b_k = Bj$, where j denotes a vector whose components are all 1's. So $A(\sum x_k) \leq B(j + \sum y_k)$. That is, since $\sum x_k \geq 0$ and $j + \sum y_k \geq j > 0$, we have

$$Ax \leq By \quad \text{for some} \quad x \geq 0, y > 0.$$

This shows that the x, y-condition is implied by the u-condition.

To show that the x, y-condition implies the u-condition we assume, if possible, that

$$B'u_0 \leq 0 \quad \text{for some} \quad u_0 \geq 0 \quad \text{such that} \quad A'u_0 \geq 0.$$

Then

$$u_0'Ax \geq 0 > u_0'By \quad \text{for all} \quad x \geq 0, y > 0.$$

But, by the x, y-condition,

$$u_0'Ax \leq u_0'By \quad \text{for some} \quad x \geq 0, y > 0.$$

This contradiction shows that the denial of the u-condition implies the denial of the x, y-condition. Therefore the x, y-condition implies the u-condition. This completes the proof of Lemma 3.

2. Linear Programming Problems

Two general *dual* problems of linear programming are stated below. Each is based on the same given information—three matrices, A, B, C—and in each a matrix D is to be determined. A matrix D having a certain property is said to be *maximal* or *minimal* (under partial ordering by the rules of matrix inequalities explained in Section 1) if no other matrix Δ possessing the property is such that $\Delta \geq D$ or $\Delta \leq D$, respectively.

Problem 1: *To find a* maximal *matrix D having the property that*

(1) $Cx \geq Dy$ for some $x \geq 0, y > 0$ such that $Ax \leq By.$

Problem 2: *To find a* minimal *matrix D having the property that*

(2) $B'u \leq D'v$ for some $u \geq 0, v > 0$ such that $A'u \geq C'v.$

It will be shown (in Theorem 4) that there exists a matrix D providing solutions for both problems if the following existence conditions both hold:

(3) $Ax \leq By$ for some $x \geq 0, y > 0,$

(4) $A'u \geq C'v$ for some $u \geq 0, v > 0.$

It will also be shown (in Theorem 2) that Problem 1 admits a particular matrix D as solution if, and only if, Problem 2 also admits this D as a solution.

If the matrix B consists of a single column, b, and the matrix C consists of a single row, c', then D becomes a scalar, δ, and y and v become positive scalars that may be eliminated by dividing through by them. In this case the two general matrix problems reduce to the following two simple scalar problems: (a) to find the ordinary maximum, δ, of the linear function $c'x$ constrained by $Ax \leq b$, $x \geq 0$, and (b) to find the ordinary minimum, δ, of the linear function $b'u$ constrained by $A'u \geq c$, $u \geq 0$.

PROBLEM 1δ: *To find a* maximal *scalar δ having the property that*

$$c'x \geq \delta \quad \text{for some} \quad x \geq 0 \quad \text{such that} \quad Ax \leq b.$$

PROBLEM 2δ: *To find a* minimal *scalar δ having the property that*

$$b'u \leq \delta \quad \text{for some} \quad u \geq 0 \quad \text{such that} \quad A'u \geq c.$$

The "diet problem" of Cornfield and Stigler [1945] furnishes a typical example of Problem 2δ; another, more specialized, example occurs in the "transportation problem" of Hitchcock [1941] and Koopmans [XIV]. Fundamental methods for attacking such scalar problems have been developed by Dantzig [II, XXI, and XXIII]. The duality and existence theorems for Problems 1δ and 2δ are contained in the corollary to Theorem 2 (at the end of Section 3 of this chapter) and in the remark following the proof of Theorem 4 (in Section 4 of this chapter).

If the matrix B consists of a single column, b, but C consists of more than one row, then D becomes a vector, d, and y becomes a positive scalar that may be eliminated by division. In this case the two general matrix problems reduce to the following vector problems.

PROBLEM 1d: *To find a* maximal *vector d having the property that*

$$Cx \geq d \quad \text{for some} \quad x \geq 0 \quad \text{such that} \quad Ax \leq b.$$

PROBLEM 2d: *To find a* minimal *vector d having the property that*

$$b'u \leq d'v \quad \text{for some} \quad u \geq 0, v > 0 \quad \text{such that} \quad A'u \geq C'v.$$

A representative vector problem is the "efficient point" problem of Koopmans [III] from which the general matrix problems in this chapter have evolved. The following equations relate our notation to Koopmans' partitioning of his *technology* matrix A, *commodity* vector y, and *price* vector p, as regards *primary* and *final* commodities:

$$A = -A_{\text{pri}}, \qquad b = -\eta_{\text{pri}}, \qquad u = p_{\text{pri}},$$

$$C = A_{\text{fin}}, \qquad d = y_{\text{fin}}, \qquad v = p_{\text{fin}}.$$

The extension to include *intermediate* commodities is indicated at the end of Section 6 of this chapter.

Of course, there are also vector problems, 1d' and 2d', that occur when the matrix C consists of a single row c' and v becomes a positive scalar that may be eliminated by division.

3. DUALITY

In preparation for the duality theorem (Theorem 2), we will now prove that the following new forms of Problems 1 and 2 are equivalent to the original forms.

PROBLEM 1 (new form): *To find a matrix D having both of the following properties:*

(1) $Cx \geqq Dy$ for some $x \geqq 0, y > 0$ such that $Ax \leqq By,$

(2*) $Cx \geq Dy$ for no $x \geqq 0, y \geqq 0$ such that $Ax \leqq By.$

PROBLEM 2 (new form): *To find a matrix D having both of the following properties:*

(2) $B'u \leqq D'v$ for some $u \geqq 0, v > 0$ such that $A'u \geqq C'v,$

(1*) $B'u \leq D'v$ for no $u \geqq 0, v \geqq 0$ such that $A'u \geqq C'v.$

Properties (1) and (2) occur also in the original statements of Problems 1 and 2. The new properties (2*) and (1*) are so denoted because they are equivalent to (2) and (1), respectively, as will be shown in the course of the proof of Theorem 2. It is to be remarked that a matrix D having both properties (1) and (2*) must produce equality, $Cx = Dy$, in property (1), and similarly that a matrix D having both properties (2) and (1*) must produce equality, $B'u = D'v$, in property (2).

THEOREM 1: *The new forms of Problems 1 and 2 are equivalent to the original forms.*

PROOF: To show that a solution D for the new Problem 1 is maximal as regards matrices having property (1), let us assume, if possible, that there is a matrix $\Delta \geq D$ having property (1). That is,

$Cx \geqq \Delta y$ for some $x \geqq 0, y > 0$ such that $Ax \leqq By.$

Then $Cx \geqq \Delta y \geq Dy$ for the same x and y—thereby contradicting property (2*) possessed by D as a solution for the new Problem 1. Consequently, D is maximal as regards matrices having property (1). A similar argument shows that a solution D for the new Problem 2 is minimal as regards matrices having property (2).

To show that a solution D for the original Problem 1 possesses property (2*), let us assume, if possible, that

$Cx_0 \geq Dy_0$ for some $x_0 \geqq 0, y_0 \geqq 0$ such that $Ax_0 \leqq By_0.$

Adding this to (1), we get

$$C(x + x_0) \geq D(y + y_0) \quad \text{for some} \quad x + x_0 \geqq 0, \, y + y_0 > 0$$
$$\text{such that} \quad A(x + x_0) \leqq B(y + y_0).$$

In the system of inequalities $C(x + x_0) \geq D(y + y_0)$ there must be at least one individual inequality containing $>$, and so any element in the corresponding row of D may be increased slightly without disturbing the inequality. Then D is not maximal as regards matrices having property (1)—thereby contradicting the hypothesis that D is a solution for the original Problem 1. Hence D must possess property (2*). A similar argument shows that a solution, D, for the original Problem 1 possesses property (1*). This completes the proof of Theorem 1.

THEOREM 2 (duality theorem): *A matrix D is a solution for Problem 1 if, and only if, it is a solution for Problem 2.*

PROOF: It follows directly from Lemma 3, by substituting $\begin{bmatrix} A \\ -C \end{bmatrix}$ for A, $\begin{bmatrix} B \\ -D \end{bmatrix}$ for B, and $\begin{bmatrix} u \\ v \end{bmatrix}$ for u, that a matrix D has property (1) if, and only if, it has property (1*). Then, replacing A, B, C, D, x, y, u, v in (1) and (1*) by $-A', -C', -B', -D', u, v, x, y$, respectively, it follows that a matrix D has property (2) if, and only if, it has property (2*). In face of Theorem 1, this completes the proof of Theorem 2.

COROLLARY: *Problems 1δ and 2δ have a unique common solution, δ, or else no solution at all.*

PROOF: From Theorem 2 it follows that both problems have a common solution δ if either admits δ as a solution. Suppose that δ_1 provides another solution for either problem. Then, by Theorem 2, δ_1 provides also a solution for the dual problem. Clearly, δ_1 cannot exceed δ due to the maximal property of δ, nor can δ exceed δ_1 due to the maximal property of δ_1. So $\delta_1 = \delta$, which completes the corollary.

4. EXISTENCE

In preparation for the existence theorems (Theorems 4 and 5) we introduce a third problem based on the same data as Problems 1 and 2 and employing jointly the two properties involved in the original forms of Problems 1 and 2.

PROBLEM 3: *To find a matrix D that has both the following properties:*

(1) $Cx \geqq Dy$ for some $x \geqq 0, y > 0$ such that $Ax \leqq By;$

(2) $B'u \leqq D'v$ for some $u \geqq 0, v > 0$ such that $A'u \geqq C'v.$

A problem of this symmetric sort was formulated by von Neumann [1947] for the case in which D reduces to a scalar δ, corresponding to Problems 1δ and 2δ.

THEOREM 3: *A matrix D is a solution for Problem 1 or 2 if, and only if, it is a solution for Problem 3.*

PROOF: It is an immediate consequence of the equivalence of properties (1) and (1*), and of properties (2) and (2*), established in the proof of Theorem 2, that a matrix D has properties (1) and (2*) or (1*) and (2) if, and only if, it has properties (1) and (2); and of course, by Theorem 1, a matrix D has properties (1) and (2*) or (1*) and (2) if, and only if, it is a solution for the original Problem 1 or 2. This completes the obvious proof.

Remark: Problem 3 is not changed if the leading inequalities in properties (1) and (2) are made equalities: $Cx = Dy$ and $B'u = D'v$. This follows from the obvious facts (pointed out in sentences just preceding Theorem 1) that a matrix D having properties (1) and (2*) must give $Cx = Dy$ and that a matrix D having properties (2) and (1*) must give $B'u = D'v$.

THEOREM 4 (existence theorem): *There exists a solution, D, for Problem 3, and so for Problems 1 and 2 also, if, and only if, the following existence conditions are both satisfied:*

(3) $Ax \leqq By$ for some $x \geqq 0, y > 0,$

(4) $A'u \geqq C'v$ for some $u \geqq 0, v > 0.$

PROOF: Let $b = By_0$, and $c = C'v_0$, where y_0 and v_0 are the values of y and v in any particular set of x, y and u, v that satisfy the existence conditions (3) and (4). Then (3) and (4) imply that

(3δ) $Ax \leqq b$ for some $x \geqq 0,$

(4δ) $A'u \geqq c$ for some $u \geqq 0.$

[These two conditions are denoted by (3δ) and (4δ) because they are the counterparts of (3) and (4) for the scalar problems, 1δ and 2δ.]

By Lemma 2, (3δ) and (4δ) are equivalent to

(3δ*) $b'u < 0$ for no $u \geqq 0$ such that $A'u \geqq 0,$

(4δ*) $c'x > 0$ for no $x \geqq 0$ such that $Ax \leqq 0,$

where in the case of (4δ) and (4δ*) we must replace A, b, u, x in Lemma 2 by $-A', -c, x, u$, respectively.

The inequality $b'u \geqq c'x$ holds for all $\lambda \geqq 0$, $u \geqq 0$, $x \geqq 0$ such that $Ax \leqq \lambda b$, $A'u \geqq \lambda c$. For, if $\lambda > 0$, we have

$$b'u \geqq \lambda^{-1}u'Ax \geqq c'x,$$

and, if $\lambda = 0$, we have

$$b'u \geqq 0 \geqq c'x,$$

by $(3\delta^*)$ and $(4\delta^*)$. Consequently,

$$\begin{bmatrix} 0 \\ b \\ -c \end{bmatrix}' \begin{bmatrix} \lambda \\ u \\ x \end{bmatrix} < 0 \quad \text{for no} \quad \begin{bmatrix} \lambda \\ u \\ x \end{bmatrix} \geqq 0$$

$$\text{such that} \quad \begin{bmatrix} b' & -c' \\ 0 & A \\ -A' & 0 \end{bmatrix}' \begin{bmatrix} \lambda \\ u \\ x \end{bmatrix} \geqq 0.$$

So, by Lemma 2,

$$\begin{bmatrix} b' & -c' \\ 0 & A \\ -A' & 0 \end{bmatrix} \begin{bmatrix} u_0 \\ x_0 \end{bmatrix} \leqq \begin{bmatrix} 0 \\ b \\ -c \end{bmatrix} \quad \text{for some} \quad \begin{bmatrix} u_0 \\ x_0 \end{bmatrix} \geqq 0.$$

Multiplying these out, we get

$$b'u_0 \leqq c'x_0,\ Ax_0 \leqq b,\ A'u_0 \geqq c \quad \text{for some} \quad u_0 \geqq 0,\ x_0 \geqq 0.$$

But $b'u_0 \geqq u_0'Ax_0 \geqq c'x_0$, so

$$(\delta) \qquad\qquad b'u_0 = u_0'Ax_0 = c'x_0.$$

That is, replacing b and c by By_0 and $C'v_0$, we have

$$u_0'By_0 = u_0'Ax_0 = v_0'Cx_0.$$

Let

$$D = \frac{Cx_0u_0'B}{u_0'Ax_0} \quad \text{or} \quad \frac{hu_0'B}{v_0'h} + \frac{Cx_0j'}{j'y_0} \quad \text{according as} \quad u_0'Ax_0 \neq 0 \text{ or } = 0,$$

h and j denoting vectors all of whose components are 1's. Then, in either case,

$$Dy_0 = Cx_0, \quad \text{and} \quad v_0'D = u_0'B.$$

This means that our D has properties (1) and (2) for the y_0, v_0 taken initially and the x_0, u_0 arising in the course of the argument (see remark below). Consequently, D is a solution for Problem 3—and so, by Theorem 3, for Problems 1 and 2 also.

Conversely, it is obvious that (3) and (4) must hold if there exists a D having properties (1) and (2). This completes the proof of Theorem 4.

Remark: It is to be noted that the gist of the above proof—namely, the part from conditions (3δ) and (4δ) to equation (δ)—amounts to showing that Problems 1δ and 2δ have a common solution,

$$\delta = b'u_0 = u_0'Ax_0 = c'x_0,$$

when (3δ) and (4δ) both hold.

THEOREM 5 (existence theorem): *A solution, D, exists for Problem 1 if, and only if, the following existence conditions both hold:*

(3) $Ax \leq By$ for some $x \geq 0, y > 0,$

(4*) $Cx \geq 0$ for no $x \geq 0$ such that $Ax \leq 0.$

Similarly, a solution, D, exists for Problem 2 if, and only if, the following existence conditions both hold:

(4) $A'u \geq C'v$ for some $u \geq 0, v > 0,$

(3*) $B'u \leq 0$ for no $u \geq 0$ such that $A'u \geq 0.$

PROOF: By Lemma 3, conditions (3*) and (3) are equivalent. Likewise, replacing A, B, u, x, y in Lemma 3 by $-A'$, $-C'$, x, u, v, we see that (4*) and (4) are equivalent. Hence (3) and (4*) or (4) and (3*) hold if, and only if, (3) and (4) hold. And, by Theorem 4, a solution, D, exists for Problems 1 or 2 if, and only if, (3) and (4) hold. This completes the proof of Theorem 5.

Remarks: It is to be noted that each of the four existence conditions (3), (4), (3*), (4*) is necessary and sufficient that there exist a matrix D having the corresponding one of the four properties (1), (2), (1*), (2*). Thus (3) or (4) is implied by the existence of a matrix D having property (1) or (2); and conversely, if (3) or (4) holds, we can construct a matrix D having property (1) or (2) merely by taking large enough negative or positive elements, respectively. The equivalence of (1) to (1*), etc., then shows that (3*) or (4*) is necessary and sufficient for the existence of a matrix D having property (1*) or (2*), respectively.

It is to be noted also that the existence conditions (3), (3*), (4), (4*) can be interpreted in terms of special "null" problems, $1d'$, $2d'$ and $2d$, $1d$, in which $c' = 0$ and $b = 0$, respectively. For, with $C = c' = 0$, property (1) or (1*) is held by $D = d' = 0$ if, and only if, condition (3) or (3*) holds, while property (2*) or (1) is held trivially; and, with $B = b = 0$, property (2) or (2*) is held by $D = d = 0$ if, and only if, condition (4) or (4*) holds, while property (1*) or (2) is held trivially. Hence the special "null" problem, $1d'$, $2d'$, $2d$, or $1d$, admits a null solution $(d' = 0 \text{ or } d = 0)$ if, and only if, the corresponding existence condition (3), (3*), (4), or (4*) holds.

5. Programming and Games

Let A be the "payoff" matrix of a zero-sum two-person game [von Neumann and Morgenstern, 1944, Chapter III]. Then, to solve the game, we must find the *value*, λ, of the game and *optimal* (or good) *mixed strategies*, u and x, characterized by the following relations:

$$A'u \geqq \lambda i, \qquad u \geqq 0, \qquad g'u = 1,$$

$$Ax \leqq \lambda g, \qquad x \geqq 0, \qquad i'x = 1,$$

where g and i are vectors whose components are all 1's. The fact that such λ, u, x always exist—the main theorem for zero-sum two-person games—can be established as a by-product of Theorem 4. To this end, assume that $A > 0$—not an essential restriction, since the same arbitrary constant κ can be added to all the elements of a game matrix without affecting the game (except to increase the value of the game by κ). Then λ must be positive (if it exists), and the relations above can be divided throughout by λ. The divided relations may be rewritten in reverse order, as follows:

(1a) $i'x = \delta$ for some $x \geqq 0$ such that $Ax \leqq g$,

(2a) $g'u = \delta$ for some $u \geqq 0$ such that $A'u \geqq i$;

where now δ, x, u replace the previous $1/\lambda$, x/λ, u/λ. This amounts to Problem 3 for the special scalar case $A > 0$, $B = g$, $C = i'$, $D = \delta$. (See remark preceding Theorem 4 concerning the use of equations involving δ rather than inequalities.) By Theorem 4 this scalar problem has a solution, δ, because the existence conditions,

$$Ax \leqq g \text{ for some } x \geqq 0; \quad A'u \geqq i \text{ for some } u \geqq 0,$$

are easily satisfied by taking $x = 0$ and u sufficiently large. We carry the solution back to the initial game relations by dividing (1a) and (2a) throughout by δ, which is clearly positive—and unique, by the argument of the corollary to Theorem 2. Hence we conclude that the game with payoff matrix A has a unique value, $\lambda = 1/\delta$, and at least one pair of optimal mixed strategies, u and x. Such reduction of games to programming problems is treated in this volume by Dantzig [XX] and Dorfman [XXII].

It will now be shown that Problems 1 and 2, in full generality, are related through Problem 3 to a zero-sum two-person game.

THEOREM 6: *A matrix D is a solution for Problem 1 or 2 if, and only if, the game with the payoff matrix*

$$\begin{bmatrix} A & -B \\ -C & D \end{bmatrix}$$

has value zero and optimal mixed strategies

$$\begin{bmatrix} u \\ v \end{bmatrix}, \begin{bmatrix} x \\ y \end{bmatrix}$$

such that v > 0 and y > 0.

PROOF: Substituting

$$\begin{bmatrix} A & -B \\ -C & D \end{bmatrix}, \begin{bmatrix} u \\ v \end{bmatrix}, \begin{bmatrix} x \\ y \end{bmatrix}, \begin{bmatrix} g \\ h \end{bmatrix}, \begin{bmatrix} i \\ j \end{bmatrix},$$

for A, u, x, g, i, respectively, in the basic relations for a zero-sum two-person game stated at the beginning of this section (g, h, i, j being vectors whose components are all 1's), and requiring $\lambda = 0$, $v > 0$, $y > 0$, we get

$$A'u \geqq C'v, \qquad B'u \leqq D'v, \qquad u \geqq 0, \qquad v > 0, \qquad g'u + h'v = 1;$$

$$Ax \leqq By, \qquad Cx \geqq Dy, \qquad x \geqq 0, \qquad y > 0, \qquad i'x + j'y = 1.$$

But these amount to properties (2) and (1) of Problem 3, coupled with the "normalizations" $g'u + h'v = 1$ and $i'x + j'y = 1$, which can always be achieved in Problem 3, because the inequalities $v > 0$ and $y > 0$ assure that (2) and (1) can be divided by $g'u + h'v$ and $i'x + j'y$, respectively.   Therefore Theorem 6 is a direct consequence of Theorem 3. This completes the proof.

One further theorem relating linear programming to games is stated below.   It follows out an ingenious idea of Dantzig [XX] and Brown [XXIV].   There does not seem to be any natural generalization for Problems 1 and 2.

THEOREM 7: *A solution, δ, exists for Problems 1δ or 2δ if, and only if, the symmetric game with the payoff matrix*

$$\begin{bmatrix} 0 & A & -b \\ -A' & 0 & c \\ b' & -c' & 0 \end{bmatrix}$$

has an optimal mixed strategy whose last component is positive.

PROOF: We will not give the proof explicitly, but it is contained in the proof of Theorem 4. (See the remark at the end of Theorem 4.)

Remark: Theorems 6 and 7 do not exclude necessarily the possibility that there also exist optimal mixed strategies lacking the specified positiveness. Thus the symmetric game above may also possess an optimal mixed strategy,

$$\begin{bmatrix} u \\ x \\ 0 \end{bmatrix},$$

even when Problems 1δ and 2δ have a solution, δ. In this particular event, $b'u = c'x = 0$ due to conditions $(3\delta^*)$ and $(4\delta^*)$.

6. PROBLEMS WITH CONSTRAINT EQUATIONS

The following dual problems present themselves when a system of *equations,*

$$Ex = Fy,$$

is added to the constraints $Ax \leq By$, $x \geq 0$, $y > 0$ in Problem 1.

PROBLEM 4: *To find a* maximal *matrix D having the property that Cx $\geq$ Dy for some x $\geq$ 0, y > 0 such that Ax $\leq$ By, Ex = Fy.*

PROBLEM 5: *To find a* minimal *matrix D having the property that B'u + F'w $\leq$ D'v for some u $\geq$ 0, v > 0, w, such that A'u + E'w $\leq$ C'v, the vector w being unrestricted in sign.*

These problems can be regarded as arising from Problems 1 and 2 by

substituting $\begin{bmatrix} A \\ E \\ -E \end{bmatrix}$ for A, $\begin{bmatrix} B \\ F \\ -F \end{bmatrix}$ for B, and $\begin{bmatrix} u \\ w_1 \\ w_2 \end{bmatrix}$ for u. Then $w =$

$w_1 - w_2$ is a vector whose components take all values, unrestricted in sign, as the vectors w_1 and w_2 vary subject to the constraints $w_1 \geq 0$ and $w_2 \geq 0$. Conversely, any vector w can be expressed as the difference $w_1 - w_2$ of two vectors ≥ 0, say, by taking $2w_1 = |w| + w$, and $2w_2 = |w| - w$, where $|w|$ is the vector whose components are the absolute values of the components of w.

There are exact analogues of Theorems 1–7 for these two problems, which the reader may easily formulate for himself.

If the matrices B and F consist of single columns, b and f, then D becomes a vector d, and y becomes a scalar that may be eliminated by division.   In this case the general problems, 4 and 5, reduce to vector problems that bear on Koopmans' treatment of "efficient points" in the presence of *intermediate* commodities [III].   To cover this extension the following line should be added to the table of corresponding notations near the end of Section 2:

$$E = \pm A_{\text{int}}, \qquad f = 0, \qquad w = p_{\text{int}}.$$

CHAPTER XX

A PROOF OF THE EQUIVALENCE OF THE PROGRAMMING
PROBLEM AND THE GAME PROBLEM [1]

BY GEORGE B. DANTZIG

J. von Neumann first pointed out that a game problem can be reduced
to a program problem.[2] He was also the first to point out that a problem
concerning the maximizing of a linear form whose variables are subject
to a system of linear inequalities could be replaced by a solution to an
extended system of linear inequalities. This result depends on the use
of an important lemma on inequalities stated in the last section of this
chapter.

George W. Brown demonstrated that the technique of reducing the
game problem to a program problem could not be readily reversed.
Gale, Kuhn, and Tucker at Princeton showed that a program was
equivalent to a game in which the maximum value of the linear form
occurs as an unknown element in the game matrix. When the program
is suitably combined with its dual, there results a linear form with upper
bound zero. This forms the basis of the present proof. Tucker is
responsible for the skew symmetric form of the game matrix as it appears
here in the solution of the program problem. Brown independently
arrived at the same result.

1. Consider a zero-sum two-person game with the payoff matrix A,
where $A = [a_{ij}]$ $(i = 1, \cdots, m; j = 1, \cdots, n)$. The expected payoff
for player 1, if he engages in a mixed strategy, $x_1, \cdots, x_n$, is given by

$$M = \min \sum_{j=1}^{n} a_{ij}x_j,$$

where $\sum x_j = 1$, $x_j \geq 0$. It is well known [see, e.g., von Neumann,
1948, Theorem IV] that the optimal mixed strategy is given by determining the x_j that maximize the value of M. We are thus looking for

[1] The author wishes to acknowledge the assistance of Major Dalton H. Wright
in the preparation of a previous version of this chapter.

[2] He further conjectured that the converse reduction was possible.

the largest M for which there exists a solution to the system of inequalities

(1) $\qquad Ax \geqq M$, or $\begin{bmatrix} a_{11} & \cdots & a_{1n} \\ \cdot & \cdot \cdot \cdot \cdot \cdot & \cdot \\ a_{m1} & \cdots & a_{mn} \end{bmatrix} \begin{bmatrix} x_1 \\ \vdots \\ x_n \end{bmatrix} \geqq \begin{bmatrix} M \\ \vdots \\ M \end{bmatrix}$,

where $M = $ maximum, $\sum_{j=1}^{n} x_j = 1$, and $x_j \geqq 0$.

We may rewrite (1) in the completely equivalent form

(2)
$$x_1 a_{11} + x_2 a_{12} + \cdots + x_n a_{1n} - v_1 = M,$$
$$\cdot \cdot \cdot \cdot \cdot \cdot \cdot \cdot \cdot \cdot \cdot \cdot \cdot \cdot \cdot$$
$$x_1 a_{m1} + x_2 a_{m2} + \cdots + x_n a_{mn} - v_m = M,$$
$$x_1 + x_2 + \cdots + x_n = 1,$$

where $v_i \geqq 0$, $x_j \geqq 0$.

By subtracting the first equation of (2) from the second, third, etc., the resulting system is equivalent to the linear programming problem of maximizing a linear form of nonnegative variables subject to a system of linear restrictions, that is,

(3)
$$x_1 a_{11} + \cdots + x_n a_{1n} - v_1 = M = \max,$$
$$x_1(a_{21} - a_{11}) + \cdots + x_n(a_{2n} - a_{1n}) - (v_2 - v_1) = 0,$$
$$\cdot \cdot \cdot \cdot \cdot \cdot \cdot \cdot \cdot \cdot \cdot \cdot \cdot \cdot \cdot \cdot \cdot \cdot \cdot \cdot \cdot$$
$$x_1(a_{m1} - a_{11}) + \cdots + x_n(a_{mn} - a_{1n}) - (v_m - v_1) = 0,$$
$$x_1 + \cdots + x_n = 1,$$

where $v_i \geqq 0$, $x_j \geqq 0$ $(j = 1, \cdots, n)$.

It is obvious that solutions to (3) exist and that max M of (3) is equal to max M of (1). Thus a game problem can be "reduced" to a program problem.

Another, more symmetric way of effecting the "reduction" to a program problem is obtained by substituting $\bar{x}_j M = x_j$ in (1), thus obtaining the system

$$\bar{x}_1 a_{11} + \cdots + \bar{x}_n a_{1m} \geqq 1,$$
$$\cdot \cdot \cdot \cdot \cdot \cdot \cdot \cdot \cdot \cdot \cdot$$
$$\bar{x}_1 a_{m1} + \cdots + \bar{x}_n a_{mn} \geqq 1,$$
$$\bar{x}_1 + \cdots + \bar{x}_n = (1/M) = \min,$$

where $\bar{x}_j \geqq 0$.

This substitution is valid only if the value of the game, M, is known to be positive. However, since all the elements of the payoff matrix can be made positive by adding a suitable constant without affecting the mixed strategy, the restriction $M > 0$ presents no difficulties.

2. Conversely, a linear program problem can be expressed in terms of a solution to an associated game problem. In fact, we shall transform a linear program problem into a skew symmetric game problem and show that the solution of the former, if any, is equivalent (except for one side condition) to the solution of the latter. Consider a program problem in the form

$$a_{11}x_1 + \cdots + a_{1n}x_n \geqq b_1,$$

(4)   . . . .

$$a_{m1}x_1 + \cdots + a_{mn}x_n \geqq b_m,$$

(5) $$c_1x_1 + \cdots + c_nx_n \geqq M,$$

where $x_i \geqq 0$, and $M =$ minimum of the linear form (5). The set of all n-tuples, $x_1, \cdots, x_n$, satisfying (4) constitute the set of so-called feasible solutions to the program problem. The one which minimizes the linear expression (5) is termed an optimum feasible solution and is the one sought.

The close relationship between (4) and (5) and the dual system (6) and (7) below, obtained by interchanging the role of rows and columns and reversing the inequalities, will now be considered. We have

$$a_{11}y_1 + \cdots + a_{m1}y_m \leqq c_1,$$

(6)   . . . .

$$a_{1n}y_1 + \cdots + a_{mn}y_m \leqq c_n,$$

(7) $$b_1y_1 + \cdots + b_my_m \leqq M',$$

where $y_i \geqq 0$, $M' =$ maximum of the linear form (7).

It will be assumed that solutions to (4) exist and that the greatest lower bound, M, of the linear form (5) for x_j satisfying (4) is finite. There exists in this case at least one set of x_i satisfying (4) which attains the lower bound M. By the lemma which appears at the end of this paper it follows that there exists also y_i satisfying the dual system (6) and that M', the least upper bound of (7), is also finite. The value M' is attained for at least one set of y_i satisfying the dual system.

Letting $(x_1, x_2, \cdots, x_n)$ be *any* solution to (4) and $(y_1, y_2, \cdots, y_m)$ *any* solution to (6), then, by weighting the first inequality of (4) by y_1, the second by $y_2, \cdots$, the last by y_m, and summing the inequalities, we have

$$(8) \qquad b_1 y_1 + \cdots + b_m y_m \leqq \left(\sum_{i=1}^{m} a_{i1} y_i \right) x_1 + \cdots + \left(\sum_{i=1}^{m} a_{in} y_i \right) x_n,$$

where, applying (6),

$$(9) \qquad b_1 y_1 + \cdots + b_m y_m \leqq c_1 x_1 + c_2 x_2 + \cdots + c_n x_n,$$

from which it follows by the observations made in the above paragraph that $M' \leqq M$.

The relationship between M and M', by the lemma on linear inequalities to be discussed in the last section of this chapter, is, however, stronger than this indicates, namely, one of strict equality,

$$(10) \qquad\qquad M' = M.$$

This lemma is a fundamental property of homogeneous linear inequalities, proved by J. Farkas [1901] and H. Weyl [1935, 1950]. An equivalent proof is given by M. Gerstenhaber [XVIII, Theorem 11].

Consider now the *reverse* inequality to (9), written in the form

$$(11) \qquad -(c_1 x_1 + c_2 x_2 + \cdots + c_n x_n) + (b_1 y_1 + \cdots + b_m y_m) \geqq 0.$$

A simultaneous solution to the system of inequalities (4), (6), and (11) will, because of relation (9), be an optimizing solution. We may rewrite the system (4), (6), and (11) in homogeneous form by setting $b_i = b_i z$, $c_j = c_j z$. It is desired to solve this system for $x_i \geqq 0$, $y_j \geqq 0$, $z = 1$. To transform the system into a game problem, we shall look for a solution to the homogeneous system under the assumption

$$(12) \qquad\qquad \sum_{j=1}^{n} x_j + \sum_{i=1}^{m} y_i + z = 1,$$

with the additional restriction that $z > 0$. By dividing through by z a solution to the original system is obtained.

Consider now the game problem given by the equations

$$a_{11} x_1 + \cdots + a_{1n} x_n - b_1 z \geqq M,$$

$$\cdots \cdots \cdots \cdots \cdots \cdots \cdots \cdots \cdots$$

$$a_{m1} x_1 + \cdots + a_{mn} x_n - b_m z \geqq M,$$

$$(13) \qquad \cdots \cdots \cdots \cdots \cdots \cdots \cdots \cdots \cdots$$

$$-(a_{11} y_1 + \cdots + a_{m1} y_m - c_1 z) \geqq M,$$

$$\cdots \cdots \cdots \cdots \cdots \cdots \cdots \cdots \cdots$$

$$-(a_{1n} y_1 + \cdots + a_{mn} y_m - c_n z) \geqq M,$$

$$-(c_1 x_1 + \cdots + c_n x_n) + (b_1 y_1 + \cdots + b_m y_m) \geqq M,$$

where M = maximum. A solution to (13) with $M = 0$ is equivalent to (4), (6), and (11) in homogeneous form.

The payoff matrix associated with (13) is skew symmetric and may be written

(14)
$$\begin{bmatrix} 0 & A & -b \\ -A' & 0 & c \\ b' & -c' & 0 \end{bmatrix},$$

where A' is the transpose of A, and b' and c' are the row vectors obtained by transposing the column vectors b and c.

The value of a game with a skew symmetric payoff matrix is always zero. If a solution to (4) and (5) exists, a solution to (13) with $M = 0$ can be obtained. Thus an optimum mixed strategy exists for (14) with $z \geq 0$. It is also clear that a solution to the game matrix (14) always exists, but not necessarily with $z > 0$. If one exists with $z > 0$, a solution is obtained to the system (4), (6), (11). Hence a program problem can be "reduced" to a game problem with a skew symmetric payoff matrix.

The following lemma was used to justify (10). No proof will be given, but its relation to the dual will be discussed presently.

LEMMA: *If there exists one or more solutions to a system of N linear inequalities, $L_i \geq c_i$, where $i = 1, 2, \cdots, N$, and if, whenever the system $L_i \geq c_i$ is satisfied, a linear inequality $L_0 \geq c_0$ is satisfied, then L_0 can be formed as a positive linear combination of L_i; that is,*

(15)
$$L_0 = \sum \lambda_i L_i \geq c_0.$$

COROLLARY: $\min L_0 = \sum \lambda_i c_i \geq c_0.$

We now rewrite (4) and (5) in proper form to apply the lemma:

(16)
$$x_i \geq 0 \qquad (i = 1, \cdots, n),$$

$$a_{11}x_1 + a_{12}x_2 + \cdots + a_{1n}x_n \geq b_1,$$

(17)
$$\cdot \quad \cdot \quad \cdot \quad \cdot \quad \cdot \quad \cdot \quad \cdot \quad \cdot \quad \cdot \quad \cdot \quad \cdot \quad \cdot \quad \cdot \quad \cdot$$

$$a_{m1}x_1 + a_{m2}x_2 + \cdots + a_{mn}x_n \geq b_m,$$

(18)
$$c_1x_1 + c_2x_2 + \cdots + c_nx_n \geq M,$$

where M = minimum of the linear form (18).

It is clear that, if there exist solutions to (16) and (17), they will always satisfy (18). Hence, by the lemma and corollary, (18) is a positive linear combination of (16) and (17) provided $M \neq -\infty$. Let

$u_1 \geqq 0$, $u_2 \geqq 0$, $\cdots$, $u_n \geqq 0$ be weights applied to inequalities (16), and $y_1 \geqq 0$, $y_2 \geqq 0$, $\cdots$, $y_m \geqq 0$ weights applied to (17); then

$$a_{11}y_1 + \cdots + a_{m1}y_m - u_1 = c_1,$$

(19) $\cdot \quad \cdot \quad \cdot \quad \cdot \quad \cdot \quad \cdot \quad \cdot \quad \cdot \quad \cdot \quad \cdot \quad \cdot \quad \cdot \quad \cdot$

$$a_{1n}y_1 + \cdots + a_{mn}y_m - u_n = c_n,$$

(20) $$b_1 y_1 + \cdots + b_m y_m = M.$$

By dropping $u_i \geqq 0$ from (19) we obtain (6). Relation (9) may be used with (20) to obtain (7) and $M' = M$, where it should be noted that y_i satisfying (19) and (20) are optimum y_i, while any $y_i \geqq 0$ satisfying (7) and (9) were considered initially. This completes the setting up of the dual.

PART FOUR

PROBLEMS OF COMPUTATION

MAXIMIZATION OF A LINEAR FUNCTION OF VARIABLES SUBJECT TO LINEAR INEQUALITIES [1]

By George B. Dantzig

The general problem indicated in the title is easily transformed, by any one of several methods, to one which maximizes a linear form of non-negative variables subject to a system of linear equalities. For example, consider the linear inequality $ax + by + c > 0$. The linear inequality can be replaced by a linear equality in nonnegative variables by writing, instead, $a(x_1 - x_2) + b(y_1 - y_2) + c - z = 0$, where $x_1 \geqq 0$, $x_2 \geqq 0, y_1 \geqq 0, y_2 \geqq 0, z \geqq 0$. The basic problem throughout this chapter will be considered in the following form:

PROBLEM: *Find the values of* $\lambda_1, \lambda_2, \cdots, \lambda_n$ *which maximize the linear form*

$$(1) \qquad \lambda_1 c_1 + \lambda_2 c_2 + \cdots + \lambda_n c_n$$

subject to the conditions that

$$(2) \qquad\qquad \lambda_j \geqq 0 \qquad\qquad (j = 1, 2, \cdots, n)$$

and

$$(3) \qquad
\begin{aligned}
\lambda_1 a_{11} + \lambda_2 a_{12} + \cdots + \lambda_n a_{1n} &= b_1, \\
\lambda_1 a_{21} + \lambda_2 a_{22} + \cdots + \lambda_n a_{2n} &= b_2, \\
&\cdots \\
\lambda_1 a_{m1} + \lambda_2 a_{m2} + \cdots + \lambda_n a_{mn} &= b_m,
\end{aligned}$$

where a_{ij}, b_i, c_j *are constants* $(i = 1, 2, \cdots, m; j = 1, 2, \cdots, n)$.

[1] The author wishes to acknowledge that his work on this subject stemmed from discussions in the spring of 1947 with Marshall K. Wood, in connection with Air Force programming methods. The general nature of the "simplex" approach (as the method discussed here is known) was stimulated by discussions with Leonid Hurwicz.

The author is indebted to T. C. Koopmans, whose constructive observations regarding properties of the simplex led directly to a proof of the method in the early fall of 1947. Emil D. Schell assisted in the preparation of various versions of this chapter. Jack Laderman has written a set of detailed working instructions and has tested this and other proposed techniques on several examples.

Each column of coefficients in (3) may be viewed as representing the coordinates of a point in Euclidean R_m space. Let P_j denote the jth column of coefficients and P_0 the constants on the right-hand side, i.e., by definition,

$$(4) \qquad [P_1, P_2, \cdots, P_n; P_0] = \begin{bmatrix} a_{11} & a_{12} & \cdots & a_{1n} & b_1 \\ a_{21} & a_{22} & \cdots & a_{2n} & b_2 \\ \cdot & \cdot & \cdot & \cdot & \cdot \\ a_{m1} & a_{m2} & \cdots & a_{mn} & b_m \end{bmatrix}.$$

The basic problem then is to determine nonnegative $\lambda_j \geqq 0$ such that

$$(5) \qquad \lambda_1 P_1 + \lambda_2 P_2 + \cdots + \lambda_n P_n = P_0,$$

$$(6) \qquad \lambda_1 c_1 + \lambda_2 c_2 + \cdots + \lambda_n c_n = z = \text{max}.$$

A set of λ_j which satisfy (5) without necessarily yielding the maximum in (6) will be termed a *feasible* solution; one which maximizes (6) will be called a *maximum feasible* solution. The purpose of this chapter is to discuss the so-called "simplex" technique, which consists in constructing first a feasible, and then a maximum feasible, solution. In many applications, of course, feasible solutions are easily obtained by inspection. For this reason, and because an arbitrary feasible solution can be obtained in a manner analogous to the construction of a maximum feasible solution, we shall consider first the construction of a maximum feasible solution from a given feasible solution.

ASSUMPTION (nondegeneracy): *Every subset of m points from the set $(P_0; P_1, P_2, \cdots, P_n)$ is linearly independent.*[2]

The theorems given in Sections 1 and 2 below come about naturally in the construction of a feasible and a maximum feasible solution to (5)

---

[2] The nondegeneracy assumption has been made to simplify the development that follows. There are obvious ways in which this assumption could be weakened. For example, the m equations implied in (5) may not all be linearly independent, in which case $k < m$ independent equations could be chosen and the remainder dropped. When this is done it may still be true that P_0 is linearly dependent on less than k of the P_i. One way to avoid this type of "degeneracy" is to alter slightly the values of the components of P_0. This method is extensively employed in the transportation problem [XXIII]. Recently a workable numerical procedure has been developed for the general case as well. The procedure augments the original set of points, P_j, by a set of unit vectors V_i where the c_i for maximizing form (1) associated with the points V_i are assumed "small." By choosing either V_i or $-V_i$, a feasible solution can be obtained by inspection rather than through the method of Section 2 of this paper. This cuts the computations in half. Moreover, the rank of the system is automatically m, i.e., $k = m$, so that by this approach all problems connected with degeneracy are solved.

and (6). They may be used to prove the following important propositions (actually, the proofs of Theorems A and B do not require the nondegeneracy assumption):

THEOREM A: *If one feasible solution exists, then there exists a feasible
solution (called a basic feasible solution) with, at most, m points P_i with
positive weights λ_i and $n - m$, or more, points P_i with $\lambda_i = 0$.*

THEOREM B: *If the values of z for the class of feasible solutions have a
finite upper bound, then a maximum feasible solution exists which is a basic
feasible solution.*

1. CONSTRUCTION OF A MAXIMUM FEASIBLE SOLUTION

Assume as given a feasible solution consisting of exactly m points,
P_i, with nonzero weights; that is,

$$(7) \qquad \lambda_1 P_1 + \lambda_2 P_2 + \cdots + \lambda_m P_m = P_0, \qquad \lambda_i > 0.$$

$$(8) \qquad \lambda_1 c_1 + \lambda_2 c_2 + \cdots + \lambda_m c_m = z_0.$$

In establishing the conditions for and the construction of a maximum
feasible solution, it will be necessary first to express all points, P_j, in
terms of a *basis* consisting of m points which form the above feasible
solution; that is,

$$(9) \qquad x_{1j} P_1 + x_{2j} P_2 + \cdots + x_{mj} P_m = P_j \quad (j = 1, 2, \cdots, n).$$

We now define z_j by

$$(10) \qquad x_{1j} c_1 + x_{2j} c_2 + \cdots + x_{mj} c_m = z_j \quad (j = 1, 2, \cdots, n).$$

THEOREM 1: *If, for any fixed j, the condition*

$$(11) \qquad c_j > z_j$$

holds, then a set of feasible solutions can be constructed such that

$$(12) \qquad z > z_0$$

*for any member of the set, where the upper bound of z is either finite or
infinite.*

CASE I: *If finite, a feasible solution consisting of exactly m points with
positive weights can be constructed.*

CASE II: *If infinite, a class of feasible solutions consisting of exactly
$m + 1$ points with positive weights can be constructed such that the upper
bound of $z = +\infty$.*

PROOF: Multiplying (9) by θ and subtracting from (7), and similarly multiplying (10) by θ and subtracting from (8), we get

$$(13) \quad (\lambda_1 - \theta x_{1j})P_1 + (\lambda_2 - \theta x_{2j})P_2 + \cdots + (\lambda_m - \theta x_{mj})P_m + \theta P_j = P_0,$$

$$(14) \quad (\lambda_1 - \theta x_{1j})c_1 + (\lambda_2 - \theta x_{2j})c_2 + \cdots + (\lambda_m - \theta x_{mj})c_m + \theta c_j$$

$$= z_0 + \theta(c_j - z_j),$$

where the term θc_j has been added to both sides of (14).

Since $\lambda_i > 0$ for all i in (13), it is clear that there is, for $\theta \geqq 0$, either a finite range of values $\theta_0 > \theta \geqq 0$ or an infinite range of values such that the coefficients of P_i remain positive. It is clear from (14) that the z of this set of feasible solutions is a strictly monotonically increasing function of θ,

$$(15) \qquad z = z_0 + \theta(c_j - z_j) > z_0, \qquad \theta > 0,$$

since $c_j > z_j$ by hypothesis (11), thus establishing (12).

CASE I: If $x_{ij} > 0$ for at least one $i = 1, 2, \cdots, m$ in (13) or (9), the largest value of θ for which all coefficients in (13) remain nonnegative is given by

$$(16) \qquad \theta_0 = \min_i (\lambda_i/x_{ij}), \qquad x_{ij} > 0.$$

If $i = i_0$ yields θ_0 in (16), it is clear that the coefficient corresponding to i_0 in (13) and (14) will vanish, hence *a feasible solution, given by $\theta = \theta_0$, has been constructed with exactly m positive weights; moreover, $z > z_0$.* It will be noted that this new set of m points consists of the new point, P_j, and $(m - 1)$ of the m points previously used. This, then, is a desired solution for Case I of Theorem 1.

The new set of m points may be used as a *new basis*, and again, as in (9) and (10), all points may be expressed in terms of the new basis and the values of c_j compared with newly computed z_j's. If any $c_j > z_j$, the value of z can be increased. If at least one $x_{ij} > 0$, another new basis can be formed. We shall assume that the process is iterated until it is not possible to form a new basis. This must occur in a *finite* number of steps because, of course, there are at most $\binom{n}{m}$ bases and none of these bases can recur, for in that case their z-values would also recur, whereas the process gives strictly increasing values of z. Thus it is clear that the iteration must eventually terminate, either because at some stage

(17) $x_{ij} \leq 0$ for all $i = 1, 2, \cdots, m$

and some fixed j, or because

(18) $c_j \leq z_j$ for all $j = 1, 2, \cdots, n.$

CASE II: If (17) holds (i.e., for all i, $x_{ij} \leq 0$), then it is clear that θ has no finite upper bound and that a class of feasible solutions has been constructed consisting of $m + 1$ points with nonzero weights such that the upper bound of $z = +\infty$.

In all problems in which there is a finite upper bound to z, the iterative process must necessarily lead to condition (18).   We shall prove, however, that the feasible solution associated with the final basis, which has the property $c_j \leq z_j$ for all $j = 1, 2, \cdots, m$, is also a maximum feasible solution (Theorem 2).   Hence, *in all problems in which there is no finite upper bound to z, the iterative process must necessarily lead to condition* (17); moreover, by rewriting (9) as

(19) $P_j + (-x_{1j})P_1 + (-x_{2j})P_2 + \cdots + (-x_{mj})P_m = 0$, $x_{ij} \leq 0$,

for the fixed j of (17), we have shown that *a nonnegative linear combination of* $(m + 1)$ *points vanishes if the upper bound of z is* $+\infty$.   In many practical problems physical considerations will dictate the impossibility of (19).

As a practical computing matter the iterative procedure of shifting from one basis to the next is not as laborious as would first appear because the basis, except for the deletion of one point and the insertion of a new point, is the same as before.   In fact, a shift of a basis involves less than mn multiplications and an equal number of additions.   It has been observed *empirically* that the number of shifts of basis can be greatly reduced not by arbitrarily selecting any point, P_j, satisfying $c_j > z_j$, but by selecting the one which gives the greatest immediate increase in z; from (15) the criterion for choice of j is such that

(20) $\theta_0(c_j - z_j) = \max_{j},$

where θ_0 is given by (16) and is a function of j.   A criterion that involves considerably less computation and apparently yields just as satisfactory results is to choose j such that

(21) $(c_j - z_j) = \max_{j}.$

By the use of either (20) or (21) approximately m changes in basis are encountered in practice, so that about m^2n multiplications are involved in getting a maximum feasible solution from a feasible solution. However, to obtain a feasible solution will also require about m^2n multiplications if one such solution is not readily available, and the selection of an original basis will require m^3 more—hence the method involves about $2m^2n$ multiplications.[3] When a large number of coefficients a_{ij} are zero it is often possible to reduce the number of multiplications by performing algebraically equivalent computations.

THEOREM 2: *If, for all $j = 1, 2, \cdots, n$, the condition $c_j \leq z_j$ holds, then (7) and (8) constitute a maximum feasible solution.*

PROOF: Let

$$(22) \qquad \mu_1 P_1 + \mu_2 P_2 + \cdots + \mu_n P_n = P_0, \qquad \mu_j \geq 0,$$

$$(23) \qquad \mu_1 c_1 + \mu_2 c_2 + \cdots + \mu_n c_n = z^*,$$

constitute any other feasible solution. We shall show that $z_0 \geq z^*$.

By hypothesis, $c_j \leq z_j$, so that replacing c_j by z_j in (23) yields

$$(24) \qquad \mu_1 z_1 + \mu_2 z_2 + \cdots + \mu_n z_n \geq z^*.$$

Substituting the value of P_j given by (9) into (22) and the value of z_j given by (10) into (24), we obtain

$$(25) \quad \left(\sum_{j=1}^{n} \mu_j x_{1j} \right) P_1 + \left(\sum_{j=1}^{n} \mu_j x_{2j} \right) P_2 + \cdots + \left(\sum_{j=1}^{n} \mu_j x_{mj} \right) P_m = P_0,$$

$$(26) \quad \left(\sum_{j=1}^{n} \mu_j x_{1j} \right) c_1 + \left(\sum_{j=1}^{n} \mu_j x_{2j} \right) c_2 + \cdots + \left(\sum_{j=1}^{n} \mu_j x_{mj} \right) c_m \geq z^*.$$

According to our assumption of nondegeneracy, the corresponding coefficients of P_i in (7) and (25) must be equal; hence (26) becomes

$$(27) \qquad \lambda_1 c_1 + \lambda_2 c_2 + \cdots + \lambda_m c_m \geq z^*;$$

or, by (8),

$$(28) \qquad z_0 \geq z^*.$$

In order that another maximum feasible solution exist it is necessary that $c_j = z_j$ for some P_j (not in the final basis). It will be noted, however, that in this case the extended matrix

$$(29) \qquad \begin{bmatrix} P_1 & P_2 & \cdots & P_n \\ c_1 & c_2 & \cdots & c_n \end{bmatrix}$$

[3] See footnote 2 on page 340.

[see (4) above] has at least one set of $m + 1$ columns which are linearly dependent. *Thus a sufficient condition that the maximum feasible solution constructed from the given feasible solution be unique is that every set of $(m + 1)$ points, defined by columns in (29), be linearly independent.*

2. Construction of a Feasible Solution [4]

We begin by selecting an arbitrary basis of $(m - 1)$ points, P_j, and P_0. Denote this set by $(P_0; P_1, \cdots, P_{m-1})$. Any P_j can be expressed in terms of this basis by

$$(30) \qquad y_{0j}P_0 + y_{1j}P_1 + \cdots + y_{(m-1)j}P_{m-1} = P_j \quad (j = 1, 2, \cdots, n).$$

Theorem 3: *A sufficient condition that there exist no feasible solution is that $y_{0j} \leq 0$ for all j.*

Proof: Assume on the contrary that there exists a feasible solution,

$$(31) \qquad \lambda_1 P_1 + \lambda_2 P_2 + \cdots + \lambda_n P_n = P_0, \qquad \lambda_j \geq 0.$$

Substitute the expressions for P_j given by (30) into (31):

$$(32) \quad P_0\left(\sum_1^n \lambda_j y_{0j} - 1\right) + P_1\left(\sum_1^n \lambda_j y_{ij}\right) + \cdots$$
$$+ P_{m-1}\left(\sum_1^n \lambda_j y_{(m-1)j}\right) = 0.$$

In view of the assumed independence of $(P_0; P_1, \cdots, P_{m-1})$ it is clear that each coefficient in (32) must vanish; in particular,

$$(33) \qquad \sum_1^n \lambda_j y_{0j} - 1 = 0.$$

This is impossible if simultaneously $\lambda_j \geq 0$ and $y_{0j} \leq 0$ for all j.

To construct a feasible solution we first define a fixed reference point, G, given by

$$(34) \qquad G = w_1 P_1 + w_2 P_2 + \cdots + w_{m-1}P_{m-1} - \rho_0 P_0,$$

where $w_i > 0$ $(i = 1, \cdots, m - 1)$ and $\rho_0 > 0$ are arbitrarily chosen. For convenience we rewrite (34) in the form

$$(35) \qquad G + \rho_0 P_0 = w_1 P_1 + w_2 P_2 + \cdots + w_{m-1}P_{m-1}.$$

In the development that follows, ρ_0 will play a role analogous to z_0.

[4] See footnote 2 on page 340.

By Theorem 3, if there exists a feasible solution, there exists at least one j (which we shall consider fixed) such that

$$(36) \qquad\qquad y_{0j} > 0.$$

Multiplying (30) by θ and subtracting from (35), we obtain

$$(37) \quad G + (\rho_0 + \theta y_{0j})P_0$$
$$= \theta P_j + (w_1 - \theta y_{1j})P_1 + \cdots + (w_{m-1} - \theta y_{(m-1)j})P_{m-1}.$$

For a range of $\theta_0 > \theta > 0$ we can construct, in a manner analogous to (13) and (14), a set of points of the form $G + \rho P_0$, each given by a positive linear combination of points P_j. Since ρ will play a role analogous to z, we are interested in the highest value of ρ for which this is possible. It will be noted that

$$(38) \qquad\qquad \rho = \rho_0 + \theta y_{0j} > \rho_0$$

since $y_{0j} > 0$ has been assumed.

If, in the representation of P_j in (30), all $y_{ij} \leq 0$ $(i = 1, \cdots, m - 1)$, the coefficients of P_j will be positive and $\rho \to +\infty$ as $\theta \to +\infty$. At the same time it will be seen, by solving (30) for P_0,

$$(39) \quad P_0 = (1/y_{0j})P_j + (-y_{1j}/y_{0j})P_1 + \cdots + (-y_{(m-1)j}/y_{0j})P_{m-1},$$

that a feasible solution has been obtained (i.e., P_0 has been expressed as a positive linear combination of $P_1, P_2, \cdots, P_{m-1}$ and P_j). If at least one $y_{ij} > 0$ $(i = 1, \cdots, m - 1)$, the largest value of θ is given by

$$(40) \qquad\qquad \theta_0 = \min_i (w_i/y_{ij}), \qquad y_{ij} > 0.$$

Setting $\theta = \theta_0$, the coefficient of at least one point, P_i, will vanish and a new point,

$$G + \rho_1 P_0,$$

will be formed from (34) which is expressed as a positive linear combination of just $m - 1$ points, P_i, where

$$(41) \qquad\qquad \rho_1 = \rho_0 + \theta_0 y_{0j} > \rho_0.$$

Expressing all points P_j in terms of the new basis, the process may be repeated, each time obtaining a higher value of ρ (or an infinite value, i.e., a feasible solution). The process must terminate in a finite number of steps. For, otherwise, since there is only a finite number of bases, the same combination of $(m-1)$ points P_i would appear a second time; that is,

$$(42) \qquad G + \rho' P_0 = w_1' P_1 + w_2' P_2 + \cdots + w_{m-1}' P_{m-1},$$

$$(43) \qquad G + \rho'' P_0 = w_1'' P_1 + w_2'' P_2 + \cdots + w_{m-1}'' P_{m-1},$$

where $\rho'' > \rho'$. Subtracting (42) from (43), we obtain a nonvanishing expression giving P_0 in terms of $(m-1)$ points P_i, contradicting the nondegeneracy assumption.

There are, however, only two conditions which will terminate the process; i.e., after a finite number of iterations either

$$(44) \qquad\qquad y_{0j} \leqq 0 \quad \text{for all} \quad j = 1, \cdots, n,$$

in which case, by Theorem 3, no feasible solution exists; or, for some fixed j,

$$(45) \qquad\qquad y_{ij} \leqq 0 \quad \text{for all} \quad i = 1, \cdots, m,$$

in which case, by solving (30) for P_0, as was done in (40), we obtain the desired feasible solution.

The term "simplex" technique arose in a geometric version of this development which assumes that one of the m equations (3) is of the form

$$(46) \qquad\qquad \lambda_1 + \lambda_2 + \cdots + \lambda_n = 1.$$

A point, P_j, is defined by the remaining coordinates in a column including c_j from (1) as an additional "z"-coordinate. We may interpret (1) and (3) as defining the center of gravity of a system of points P_j with weights λ_j. The problem consists, then, in finding weights λ_j so that the center of gravity lies on a line L defined by $m-1$ of the relationships $x_1 = b_1,\ x_2 = b_2,\ \cdots,\ x_m = b_m$, such that the z-coordinate is maximum. A basis, $P_1, P_2, \cdots, P_m$, may be considered one of the faces of a simplex formed by $P_1, P_2, \cdots, P_m$ and P_j. The z-coordinate of P_j is c_j; the z-coordinate of the projection parallel to the z-axis of the point P_j on the plane of the face formed by the basis is z_j. Because $c_j > z_j$ by (11), all points in the simplex lie "above" the plane of this face. The line L cuts the base in an interior point whose z-value is z_0, hence it must intersect another face of the simplex in a "higher" point (i.e., a point whose z-value is greater than z_0).

CHAPTER XXII

APPLICATION OF THE SIMPLEX METHOD TO A GAME THEORY PROBLEM [1]

BY ROBERT DORFMAN

This chapter was presented at the Conference on Linear Programming because there seems to be a shortage of small scale examples of the calculations involved in computing an optimum program. The chapter is concerned, to be sure, with working out the optimum strategies of two opponents in accordance with the principles of game theory. But, as is shown in the first section, such a problem in game theory is equivalent to a problem in linear programming, and the transformation from game form to programming form is easy to make. Another demonstration of the equivalence of game and programming problems is given by Dantzig [XX].

It will be noted that when a game is reduced to linear programming form there results a special type of matrix, part of whose columns form a negative identity matrix. Such special matrices are also characteristic of some genuine linear programming problems. They arise whenever disposal activities are used.

In problems of game theory there is never any difficulty in finding a feasible solution from which to begin the optimizing process. Such difficulties may be encountered in a genuine linear programming problem, however, and this is the principal difference between the two as far as computational problems are concerned.

The first part of this chapter will show how any game situation may be put in proper form for the simplex method. In the second part the calculations involved in solving a specific game will be outlined and explained.

1. REDUCTION OF A GAME TO SIMPLEX FORM

Consider a constant-sum two-person game where X, the maximizing player, has m strategies, 1, 2, $\cdots$, m; Y, the minimizing player, has

[1] The assistance of George B. Dantzig in the preparation of this chapter is gratefully acknowledged. Thanks are due also to M. L. Slater for a number of helpful suggestions.

n strategies, $1, 2, \cdots, n$; and a_{ij} is the value of the game to X if he plays his ith strategy and Y plays his jth.   The payoff matrix is then

$$A = \begin{bmatrix} a_{11} & a_{21} & \cdots & a_{m1} \\ a_{12} & a_{22} & \cdots & a_{m2} \\ \cdot & \cdot \cdot \cdot \cdot \cdot \cdot & \cdot & \cdot \\ a_{1n} & a_{2n} & \cdots & a_{mn} \end{bmatrix}.$$

Without loss of generality it can be assumed that every element of this matrix is greater than zero.   If this is not true of the game as originally formulated, a sufficiently large constant can be added to the elements of the matrix to make them all positive.   The addition of such a constant will leave the optimum strategies unchanged.

Suppose that X plays the mixed strategy defined by giving weight x_i to the ith pure strategy, $\sum_i^m x_i = 1$.   Then the value of the game will be

$$v = \sum_{j=1}^{n} y_j(a_{1j}x_1 + a_{2j}x_2 + \cdots + a_{mj}x_m),$$

where y_j is the weight given to the jth strategy open to Y.   Let

$$B_j(x) = a_{1j}x_1 + a_{2j}x_2 + \cdots + a_{mj}x_m,$$

and let

$$B_{j_0}(x) = \min_j B_j(x).$$

Then X can anticipate that, if his strategy is found out, Y will choose $y_{j_0} = 1$, $y_j = 0$ $(j \neq j_0)$, so that the value of the game to X is $v = \min_j B_j(x) = B_{j_0}(x)$.   Thus X must endeavor to select $x_1, x_2, \cdots, x_m$ so that $\min_j B_j(x)$ is as great as possible, subject to the condition $\sum_i^m x_i = 1$.

The linear programming problem equivalent to this will now be constructed.   Consider any set, x, of weights, and let $B_{j_0}(x) = \min_j B_j(x)$.   Also let

(1)
$$u_i = x_i/B_{j_0}(x).$$

Since we have assumed that all the elements of the matrix are positive, $B_{j_0}(x)$ must also be positive, and then

(2)
$$B_j(u) = B_j(x)/\min_j B_j(x) \geqq 1,$$

(3)
$$S = \sum_{i=1}^{m} u_i = \sum_{i=1}^{m} x_i/B_{j_0}(x) = 1/B_{j_0}(x).$$

Each set of weights, x, determines a game-value, $B_{j_0}(x)$, a set of u defined by equation (1), and a sum S defined by equation (3). By virtue of equation (3), the set of x which determines the smallest S will also determine the largest $B_{j_0}(x)$. This set of x can be found in two steps:

(a) Find a set of values, $u_1, u_2, \cdots, u_m, u_{m+1}, \cdots, u_{m+n}$, satisfying

(4) $$u_k \geqq 0 \qquad (k = 1, 2, \cdots, m + n),$$

(5) $$B_j(u) - u_{m+j} = 1 \qquad (j = 1, 2, \cdots, n),$$

(6) $$S = u_1 + u_2 + \cdots + u_m = \text{minimum}.$$

This is the problem in the form for the simplex method.

(b) Compute x_i from

(7) $$x_i = u_i/S \qquad (i = 1, 2, \cdots, m).$$

2. APPLICATION TO A SPECIFIC GAME

This method of computation will be illustrated by solving the game specified by the payoff matrix of Table I.

TABLE I. PAYOFF MATRIX

Player B's Strategy *	Player A's Strategy *				
	1	2	3	4	5
1	5.31	8.52	12.05	16.00	20.00
2	2.70	3.77	6.30	9.70	13.40
3	3.64	2.70	3.60	5.91	8.99
4	5.91	3.60	2.70	3.64	6.02
5	9.70	6.30	3.77	2.70	4.04
6	16.00	12.05	8.52	5.31	2.70

* A is the maximizing player, B the minimizing player.

The matrix for determining the u is obtained by appending to this matrix the negative of the identity matrix and prefixing a column-vector of 1's, as in Table II. Appending the negative identity matrix amounts to introducing n "dummy strategies" for the maximizing player. Each of these dummy strategies corresponds to one of the real strategies of the minimizing player, the one in whose row the nonzero element occurs.

Each of the columns in this matrix is regarded as a point in six-dimensional Euclidean space. The simplex method makes use of the fact that any point in an n-dimensional space can be expressed as a sum of n linearly independent points.

TABLE II. MATRIX FOR DETERMINING u

P_0	P_1	P_2	P_3	P_4	P_5	P_6	P_7	P_8	P_9	P_{10}	P_{11}
1	5.31	8.52	12.05	16.00	20.00	-1	0	0	0	0	0
1	2.70	3.77	6.30	9.70	13.40	0	-1	0	0	0	0
1	3.64	2.70	3.60	5.91	8.99	0	0	-1	0	0	0
1	5.91	3.60	2.70	3.64	6.02	0	0	0	-1	0	0
1	9.70	6.30	3.77	2.70	4.04	0	0	0	0	-1	0
1	16.00	12.05	8.52	5.31	2.70	0	0	0	0	0	-1

The first step in the solution is to select six points on the basis of which all twelve points can be expressed. The only requirement on this set is that P_0, the point with unit coordinates, should be expressible as a linear combination in which the points in the set appear with positive weights. We note that all the elements in the P_1 column are greater than unity. Hence a selection such as P_1, P_6, P_8, P_9, P_{10}, P_{11} will satisfy the requirement. This is the original basis which was, somewhat arbitrarily, selected. The result is shown in Table III. For example, the P_0 line in Table III is equivalent to

$$P_0 = 0.370P_1 + 0.967P_6 + 0.348P_8 + 1.189P_9 + 2.583P_{10} + 4.926P_{11}.$$

TABLE III. THE TWELVE POINTS ON THE ORIGINAL BASIS

Basis	P_0	P_1	P_2	P_3	P_4	P_5	P_6	P_7	P_8	P_9	P_{10}	P_{11}
P_1	0.370	1	1.396	2.333	3.592	4.962	0	-0.370	0	0	0	0
P_6	0.967	0	-1.107	0.338	3.073	6.348	1	-1.965	0	0	0	0
P_8	0.348	0	2.382	4.892	7.164	9.071	0	-1.347	1	0	0	0
P_9	1.189	0	4.650	11.088	17.588	23.305	0	-2.187	0	1	0	0
P_{10}	2.593	0	7.241	18.860	32.142	44.091	0	-3.589	0	0	1	0
P_{11}	4.926	0	10.286	28.808	52.162	76.692	0	-5.920	0	0	0	1
S	0.370	1	1.396	2.333	3.592	4.962	0	-0.370	0	0	0	0

In matrix notation, this may be written

$$P_0 = [P_1\ P_6\ P_8\ P_9\ P_{10}\ P_{11}] \begin{bmatrix} 0.370 \\ 0.967 \\ 0.348 \\ 1.189 \\ 2.593 \\ 4.926 \end{bmatrix},$$

or

$$P_0 = \begin{bmatrix} 5.31 & -1 & 0 & 0 & 0 & 0 \\ 2.70 & 0 & 0 & 0 & 0 & 0 \\ 3.64 & 0 & -1 & 0 & 0 & 0 \\ 5.91 & 0 & 0 & -1 & 0 & 0 \\ 9.70 & 0 & 0 & 0 & -1 & 0 \\ 16.00 & 0 & 0 & 0 & 0 & -1 \end{bmatrix} \begin{bmatrix} 0.370 \\ 0.967 \\ 0.348 \\ 1.189 \\ 2.593 \\ 4.926 \end{bmatrix} = \begin{bmatrix} 1 \\ 1 \\ 1 \\ 1 \\ 1 \\ 1 \end{bmatrix}.$$

This checks with the P_0 column of Table II. Similarly, from Table III,

$$P_2 = 1.396P_1 - 1.107P_6 + 2.382P_8 + 4.650P_9 + 7.241P_{10} + 10.286P_{11}.$$

In matrix notation,

$$P_2 = [P_1\ P_6\ P_8\ P_9\ P_{10}\ P_{11}] \begin{bmatrix} 1.396 \\ -1.107 \\ 2.382 \\ 4.650 \\ 7.241 \\ 10.286 \end{bmatrix},$$

or

$$P_2 = \begin{bmatrix} 5.31 & -1 & 0 & 0 & 0 & 0 \\ 2.70 & 0 & 0 & 0 & 0 & 0 \\ 3.64 & 0 & -1 & 0 & 0 & 0 \\ 5.91 & 0 & 0 & -1 & 0 & 0 \\ 9.70 & 0 & 0 & 0 & -1 & 0 \\ 16.00 & 0 & 0 & 0 & 0 & -1 \end{bmatrix} \begin{bmatrix} 1.396 \\ -1.107 \\ 2.382 \\ 4.650 \\ 7.241 \\ 10.286 \end{bmatrix} = \begin{bmatrix} 8.52 \\ 3.77 \\ 2.70 \\ 3.60 \\ 6.30 \\ 12.05 \end{bmatrix}.$$

This checks with the P_2 column of Table II.

In this manner, each column of Table III shows one of the twelve "points" of Table II as a weighted sum of the six selected points which form the "basis."

In Table III each of the twelve points under consideration has been expressed as a linear function of six of them. Two aspects of this table should be noticed. First, all the coefficients in the P_0 column, which corresponds to the right-hand side of equation (5), are positive. This shows that a set of u satisfying equation (4) has been found. A basis which fulfills this requirement is known as a feasible solution.

It should be remarked that in a matrix of this sort there is never any difficulty in finding a feasible solution. All that is necessary is to find a column all of whose elements are at least equal to unity. If no such column exists, the situation can be remedied by adding unity to each of the elements of the game matrix. This will not alter the solutions obtained, though it does increase by unity the value of the game.

Secondly, attention should be drawn to the S-line at the foot of Table III, which is related to the S of equation (6). This line is defined to be the sum of the entries on the lines corresponding to points P_1, P_2, $\cdots$, P_5 in each of the columns. In the present instance, since only P_1 and points beyond P_5 occur in the basis, it is simply the entry on the P_1 line. We shall denote by S_i the entry on the S-line of the point P_i. The entry in the P_0 column of this line is the S of equation (6). The use of the other entries on this line will be explained below.

Now, to each set of six points constituting a feasible basis, there will correspond a certain value of S, which will appear at the bottom of the P_0 column. The problem, as set forth in equation (6), is to find the feasible basis to which corresponds the smallest possible value of S. This is done by starting with the basis already found and substituting one of the excluded points for one of the points in the original basis, thus obtaining a new basis which has five points in common with the old one. The formula for shifting the basis is given in the Appendix to this chapter.

Naturally, the point to be deleted and the point to be added must be selected in such a way that the revised basis satisfies two requirements, namely (i) it is a feasible basis, and (ii) it corresponds to a smaller value of S than the original basis. This is accomplished by the following procedure: [2]

(a) Introduce into the basis the point selected as follows:

    (1) For points P_1, $\cdots$, P_5 compute $S_i' = S_i - 1$ ($i = 1, \cdots, 5$).

    (2) For points P_5, $\cdots$, P_{11} take $S_i' = S_i$ ($i = 6, \cdots, 11$).

    (3) Introduce the point with the largest value of S', provided that it is positive. If there is no positive value of S', the basis at

[2] The mathematical justification of this procedure has been given by Dantzig [XXI].

hand is the best possible one and constitutes the desired solution. In the case under discussion, point P_5 is to be introduced.

(b) Delete from the basis the point selected as follows:

    (1) Divide the values in column P_5 (the point to be introduced) by the values on the corresponding lines of column P_0.

    (2) Find the row that has the largest ratio. The point corresponding to this row is the one to be dropped. In this case it is the point P_8.

(c) Calculate the change of basis by the formula given in the Appendix to this chapter.

(d) Repeat the process of changing the basis one point at a time until there are no positive values of S'.

(e) The weights of the points in the P_0 column are then the desired values of u, and the S-value of the P_0 column is the minimum possible value of S.

The work in the present instance required four changes of basis. Each change of basis required $n(m + 1) = 6(5 + 1) = 36$ multiplications and a corresponding number of subtractions. Thus the total computation required 144 of these basic operations, finally resulting in the weighting shown in Table IV.

TABLE IV. THE TWELVE POINTS ON THE FINAL BASIS

Basis	P_0	P_1	P_2	P_3	P_4	P_5	P_6	P_7	P_8	P_9	P_{10}	P_{11}
P_1	0.057	1	0.677	0.339	0.045	0	0	0	0	0.115	−0.174	0
P_5	0.109	0	−0.066	0.115	0.562	1	0	0	0	−0.279	0.170	0
P_6	1.495	0	−6.257	−7.938	−4.533	0	1	0	0	−4.959	2.478	0
P_7	0.645	0	−2.838	−3.842	−2.058	0	0	1	0	−3.426	1.811	0
P_8	0.191	0	−0.829	−1.314	−0.692	0	0	0	1	−2.074	0.891	0
P_{11}	0.215	0	−1.393	−2.756	−3.083	0	0	0	0	1.106	−2.324	1
S	0.166	1	0.611	0.454	0.607	1	0	0	0	−0.164	−0.004	0

This table indicates that strategies 1 and 5 are the only ones which occur in the optimum mixed strategy for player x, and they occur with weights

$$x_1 = 0.057/0.166 = 0.343, \qquad x_5 = 0.109/0.166 = 0.657.$$

This application of the simplex method rests on two assumptions. To discuss the first, let n represent the number of strategies available to the minimizing player. Each of the maximizing player's strategies may then be represented by a vector of $n + 1$ components. The first of these components would be unity if the strategy being represented were real, and zero for a dummy strategy. The remaining elements of the vector would be the entries in a column of the payoff matrix, such as the one illustrated in Table II. In these terms, the simplex method assumes that every set of $n + 1$ of such vectors constitutes a linearly independent set. The procedure is valid even if this assumption is not satisfied, but then the optimum solution is not necessarily unique. In fact, there may be an infinite number of mixed strategies all yielding the maximum value of the game if the vectors are not linearly independent.

The second assumption is more critical. It states that the first column of Table II, the column consisting of 1's, is linearly independent of every set of $n - 1$ of the following columns. If this assumption is violated, the line of reasoning behind the simplex method fails. It appears, nevertheless, that, if the simplex method is applied in such a case, it will lead to the correct solution. A satisfactory proof of this assertion, however, remains to be found.

3. THE MINIMIZING PLAYER

At the Linear Programming Conference, Herman Rubin pointed out that this calculation, which is made from the viewpoint of the maximizing player, yields simultaneously an optimum strategy for the minimizing player. In fact, the entries on the S-line of Table IV are proportional to the probability weights in the minimizing player's optimum mixed strategy.

This becomes evident once it is noticed that the essence of the simplex calculation is to select the set of "good" strategies for the maximizing player and to attach probability weights to those good strategies in such a way that, no matter which pure strategy the minimizing player uses, the value of the game will be at least equal to a certain amount. The good strategies are the real strategies which appear in the final basis. The real strategies which do not appear in the final basis are not good strategies and, of course, receive zero weight in the optimum mixed strategy.

The computation at the same time reveals the good strategies for the minimizing player. This can be seen as follows: Let us assume that the maximizing player has k good strategies (in the example, $k = 2$), and for convenience let us assume that the strategies have been numbered in such a way that the first k are the good ones. Then all the maximizing player's strategies beyond the first k may be disregarded; they will never be used. The simplex computation has produced a k-component vector of weights, u_1, u_2, $\cdots$, u_k such that

$$
\begin{bmatrix}
a_{11} & a_{21} & \cdots & a_{k1} \\
a_{12} & a_{22} & \cdots & a_{k2} \\
\cdot & \cdot & \cdot & \cdot \\
a_{1n} & a_{2n} & \cdots & a_{kn}
\end{bmatrix}
\begin{bmatrix}
u_1 \\
u_2 \\
\cdots \\
u_k
\end{bmatrix}
\geqq
\begin{bmatrix}
1 \\
1 \\
\cdots \\
1
\end{bmatrix}.
$$

The result of the multiplication on the left side of this expression is a column vector. The first element of this vector is proportional to the value of the game if the maximizing player uses his optimum mixed strategy and the minimizing player uses his first pure strategy. The second element is proportional to the value of the game if the maximizing player uses his optimum mixed strategy and the minimizing player uses his second strategy. Each line of the inequality thus gives a value proportional to the value of the game for one of the minimizing player's strategies. The set of good strategies for the minimizing player consists of those of his strategies for which the element in this vector is as small as possible, namely equal to unity. Now, the final basis found in the simplex calculation included n strategies, real and dummy together, of which we assume that k are real and $n - k$ are dummy. Since there was a total of n dummy strategies, k of them were excluded from the final basis. But the exclusion of a dummy strategy from the final basis requires that the equality, rather than the inequality, hold on the line in which its nonzero element occurs. Thus the equality holds on k lines of the expression just given. This indicates that the minimizing player has k good strategies, and these are the ones for which the corresponding dummy vectors are excluded from the final basis.

In the example under consideration the excluded dummy vectors are P_9 and P_{10}. The nonzero element of P_9 occurs on the line corresponding to the minimizing player's strategy 4, and the nonzero element of P_{10} occurs on the line corresponding to the minimizing player's strategy 5. These are the two strategies which make up the minimizing player's set of good strategies.

Now, just as the maximizing player uses only good strategies in his optimum mixed strategy, so does the minimizing player. And just as only columns of the basic payoff matrix which correspond to good strategies for the maximizing player occur in the final solution, so only do rows which correspond to good strategies for the minimizing player. It will be assumed also, for convenience, that the good strategies for the minimizing player constitute his first k. Since the equality sign holds for all rows corresponding to the minimizing player's good strategies, the requirement on the u-vector may now be written

$$
\begin{bmatrix}
a_{11} & a_{21} & \cdots & a_{k1} \\
a_{12} & a_{22} & \cdots & a_{k2} \\
\cdot & \cdot & \cdots & \cdot \\
a_{1k} & a_{2k} & \cdots & a_{kk}
\end{bmatrix}
\begin{bmatrix}
u_1 \\
u_2 \\
\cdots \\
u_k
\end{bmatrix}
=
\begin{bmatrix}
1 \\
1 \\
\cdots \\
1
\end{bmatrix}.
$$

The pure strategies which enter into the minimizing player's optimum mixed strategy have now been identified. They are the ones corresponding to dummy strategies excluded from the maximizing player's final basis. But the probability weights to be assigned to these strategies remain to be determined. These weights are determined from the following condition: If the minimizing player adopts his optimum mixed strategy, the expected value of the game must be independent of which pure strategy the maximizing player selects from his set of good strategies. This can be expressed algebraically. Let $W = (w_1, w_2, \cdots, w_k)'$ be a vector proportional to the minimizing player's optimal mixed strategy, and let A^* denote the k by k submatrix of A which corresponds to the sets of good strategies for both players. Then the requirement is that $W'A^* = 1_k'$, where 1_k is a column vector of k elements all equal to 1.

It will now be shown that the line S of Table IV satisfies the requirement on the vector W. The simplex solution consisted in expressing the strategies excluded from the final basis in terms of those strategies included in that basis. In so far as the real strategies included in the basis and the dummy strategies excluded from it (there are k of each) are concerned, it consisted in solving $A^*Q = -I_k$, where I_k is the k-rowed identity matrix. Evidently $Q = -A^{*-1}$, and the S-line of Table IV is simply $S' = 1_k'Q$, whence

$$
-S' = 1_k'A^{*-1}.
$$

If $-S$ be substituted for the W-vector it is seen that the requirement is satisfied. Thus the negatives of the entries on the S-line of Table IV in the columns corresponding to the dummy strategies excluded from the final basis are proportional to the weights in the minimizing player's optimal strategy. In the example the entry at the foot of the P_9 column is -0.164 and the entry at the foot of the P_{10} column is -0.004. Thus the probability weights for the minimizing player are

$$
y_4 = 0.164/0.168 = 0.976, \qquad y_5 = 0.004/0.168 = 0.024,
$$

since $0.164 + 0.004 = 0.168$.

APPENDIX

Formula for changing basis. Suppose that there are S points expressed on the basis of n of them, $n < S$, and suppose, for simplicity of notation, that the n points in the basis are those numbered $1, 2, \cdots, n$. Then each point is expressed in the form

$$P_i = C_{1i}P_1 + C_{2i}P_2 + \cdots + C_{ni}P_n \qquad (i = 1, 2, \cdots, S).$$

Now let it be desired to delete the point P_j from the basis, $j \leqq n$, and substitute the point P_k, $n < k \leqq S$. The calculation is as follows:

(1) $\qquad P_i = C_{1i}P_1 + \cdots + C_{ji}P_j + \cdots + C_{ni}P_n \qquad (i = 1, 2, \cdots, S),$

(2) $\qquad 0 = C_{1k}P_1 + \cdots + C_{jk}P_j + \cdots + C_{nk}P_n - P_k.$

Multiplying equation (2) by C_{ji}/C_{jk}, we get

(3) $\qquad 0 = C_{1k}\dfrac{C_{ji}}{C_{jk}}P_1 + \cdots + C_{ji}P_j + \cdots + C_{nk}\dfrac{C_{ji}}{C_{jk}}P_n - \dfrac{C_{ji}}{C_{jk}}P_k.$

Subtracting this from equation (1) gives

(4) $\quad P = \left(C_{1i} - C_{1k}\dfrac{C_{ji}}{C_{jk}}\right)P_1 + \cdots + 0 \cdot P_j + \cdots + \left(C_{ni} - C_{nk}\dfrac{C_{ji}}{C_{jk}}\right)P_n + \dfrac{C_{ji}}{C_{jk}}P_k,$

Equation (4) is the formula for the n points on the new basis, $1, 2, \cdots, j-1$, $j+1, \cdots, n, k$.

CHAPTER XXIII

APPLICATION OF THE SIMPLEX METHOD TO A TRANSPORTATION PROBLEM [1]

BY GEORGE B. DANTZIG

A number of years before the Air Force generalized the work of Leontief to make it applicable to highly dynamic situations, Hitchcock [1941] and Koopmans [XIV, 1947] independently considered an interesting special case: A homogeneous product is to be shipped in the amounts $a_1, a_2, \cdots, a_m$, respectively, from each of m shipping *origins* and received in amounts $b_1, b_2, \cdots, b_n$, respectively, by each of n shipping *destinations*. The cost of shipping a unit amount from the ith origin to jth destination is c_{ij} and is known for all combinations (i, j). The problem is to determine the amounts x_{ij} to be shipped over all routes (i, j) so as to minimize the total cost of transportation. In Table I it is clear that x_{ij} must be chosen so that the rows sum to the marginal

TABLE I. PROGRAM OF SHIPMENTS

		Destinations				Total
	$\overset{j}{\underset{i}{\diagdown}}$	(1)	(2)	$\cdots$	(n)	
Origins	(1)	x_{11}	x_{12}	$\cdots$	x_{1n}	a_1
	(2)	x_{21}	x_{22}	$\cdots$	x_{2n}	a_2
	$\cdots$	$\cdots$	$\cdots$	$\cdots$	$\cdots$	$\cdots$
	(m)	x_{m1}	x_{m2}	$\cdots$	x_{mn}	a_m
Total		b_1	b_2	$\cdots$	b_n	$\displaystyle\sum_{i=1}^{m} a_i = \sum_{j=1}^{n} b_j$

[1] The author is indebted to Emil D. Schell for assistance in preparing earlier versions of this chapter.

totals a_i and the columns to b_j. The basic relations that must be satisfied are

(1)
$$\sum_{j=1}^{n} x_{ij} = a_i \qquad (i = 1, 2, \cdots, m),$$

(2)
$$\sum_{i=1}^{m} x_{ij} = b_j \qquad (j = 1, 2, \cdots, n),$$

(3)
$$x_{ij} \geqq 0,$$

(4)
$$\sum_{i=1}^{m} \sum_{j=1}^{n} c_{ij} x_{ij} = \min.$$

The linear programming problem concerns itself with minimization (maximization) of a linear form whose variables satisfy a system of linear inequalities. Usually in practice this problem is encountered in the above standard form, namely, as the minimization of a linear form of *nonnegative* variables subject to a system of linear *equalities*.

1. APPLICATION OF THE SIMPLEX METHOD

According to the general theory [XXI], if there are k independent equations in l variables, a solution (provided one exists) which minimizes the linear form can be obtained that involves at most k variables with positive value while the remaining $l - k$ variables vanish. Chapter XXI establishes this under the condition that every determinant of kth order is nonvanishing. This condition is not satisfied in the transportation case; however, an earlier version of this chapter contains a direct proof of this theorem which can be slightly altered to remove this restriction [XXI, Theorem A; see also XV]. The method of proof is to show that, if any feasible solution involves more than k variables with positive values, the number can be reduced.

It is not difficult to show that the $m + n$ equations (1) and (2) constitute $m + n - 1$ independent equations in mn unknowns. Thus the minimizing solution requires at most $m + n - 1$ routes with positive shipments.

It is useful to reformulate the transportation problem in terms of a system of activities that have various items in common. The activity of shipping the homogeneous product from i to j will be denoted by A_{ij}. To sustain a *unit level* of this activity, one unit of the product at the ith origin is required as input, and one unit at the jth destination will be made available as output. We shall by convention use $+$ to indicate flow toward an activity and $-$ to indicate flow away from an activity of an item. Thus, if m "origin" items and n "destination" items are defined, a unit of activity A_{ij} is characterized by a vector with $+1$ (input) for origin item i, -1 (output) for destination item j, and 0 for all other items. We shall use the same symbol to denote an activity A_{ij} and the vector associated with unit amounts of the activity A_{ij}. The elements of the vector A_{ij} are shown in Table II.

TABLE II. ELEMENTS OF A_{ij}

Item	$(A_{ij}) = (\xi_i) + (\eta_j)$			B_0
Origin				
1	0	0	0	a_1
2	0	0	0	a_2
...	...	...	...	...
i	$+1$	$+1$	0	a_i
...	...	...	...	...
m	0	0	0	a_m
Destination				
1	0	0	0	$-b_1$
2	0	0	0	$-b_2$
...	...	...	...	...
j	-1	0	-1	$-b_j$
...	...	...	...	...
n	0	0	0	$-b_n$

It will be noted that, if a dummy activity, ξ_i, is defined with $+1$ for origin item i and 0 elsewhere, and similarly η_j is defined with -1 for destination item j and 0 elsewhere, all mn activities have a simple representation in terms of this basic set of $m + n$ dummy activities:

$$(5) \qquad A_{ij} = \xi_i + \eta_j.$$

A feasible solution consisting of $m + n - 1$ combinations is easily obtained provided only $a_i \geqq 0$, $b_j \geqq 0$, and $\sum a_i = \sum b_j$. For example, A_{11} can be chosen first and x_{11} units of this activity performed, where $x_{11} = \min(a_1, b_1)$. If $a_1 \leqq b_1$, then obviously all other x_{ij} in the first row of Table I vanish, and the corresponding $n - 1$ activities are excluded from the feasible solution. Deleting the row and replacing b_1 by $b_1 - a_1$ reduces the rectangular array in Table I by one row. (If $a_1 > b_1$, the other elements in the column would be deleted.) Continuing this process, a row or column will be deleted and one activity selected at each step until only one row or column is left.   Thus, if, for example, in k steps $m - 1$ rows and $k - (m - 1)$ columns have been determined, the remaining $n - [k - (m - 1)]$ activities in the last row will be used to complete the set of activities in the feasible solution.   Accordingly, $k + n - [k - (m - 1)] = m + n - 1$ activities have been chosen. The possibility of one or more $x_{ij} = 0$ in the set of $m + n - 1$ activities is not excluded.

Moreover, A_{11} is followed by A_{12} (or A_{21}) and A_{12} followed by A_{13} (or A_{22}), etc.   In general, A_{ij} is followed by $A_{i(j+1)}$ or $A_{(i+1)j}$.   It is thus a simple matter to express the dummy activities in terms of the activities of the feasible solution.   If $A_{11}, A_{12}, A_{22}, A_{32}, A_{33}$, etc., appear in the solution, then we obtain, by taking differences of activities as they are generated,

$$\eta_2 - \eta_1 = A_{12} - A_{11},$$

$$\xi_2 - \xi_1 = A_{22} - A_{12},$$

(6)

$$\xi_3 - \xi_2 = A_{32} - A_{22},$$

$$\eta_3 - \eta_2 = A_{33} - A_{32},$$

so that $\xi_2 - \xi_1, \xi_3 - \xi_2, \cdots, \xi_m - \xi_{m-1}$ will be determined in turn, as well as $\eta_2 - \eta_1, \cdots, \eta_n - \eta_{n-1}$.   We may thus directly express any ξ_i and η_j in terms of the activities of the feasible solution.   Denoting the activities of the feasible solution by $B_1, B_2, \cdots, B_{m+n-1}$, and making use of the relation $\eta_1 = B_1 - \xi_1$, it is a straightforward matter of summing differences on either ξ_i or η_j to obtain a solution of ξ_i or η_j as a linear combination of the vectors $B_1, B_2, \cdots, B_{m+n-1}$ and ξ_1:

$$\xi_i = \xi_1 + \sum_{k=1}^{m+n-1} \lambda_{ik}B_k \qquad (i = 1, 2, \cdots, m),$$

(7)

$$\eta_j = -\xi_1 + \sum_{k=1}^{m+n-1} \mu_{jk}B_k \qquad (j = 1, 2, \cdots, n),$$

where λ_{ik} and μ_{jk} are constants.   Moreover, from (5) any A_{ij} is given by

(8)
$$A_{ij} = \sum_{k=1}^{m+n-1} (\lambda_{ik} + \mu_{jk})B_k.$$

The fundamental approach of the simplex technique is to express all activities in the system in terms of a basic set of activities constituting a feasible solution.   This has just been done.   There are thus two ways to accomplish an activity A_{ij}, either directly or indirectly as a linear combination of activities B_k.   In (8), however, the coefficients can be positive or negative. This is interpreted to mean that one unit of A_{ij} can be done by doing $(\lambda_{i1} + \mu_{j1})$ units of B_1, $(\lambda_{i2} + \mu_{j2})$ units of B_2, etc. When the coefficient of B_1 is negative, it means to decrease the number of units of B_1 by this amount, *if possible*, in some system in which $B_1, B_2, \cdots, B_{m+n-1}$ are being performed at some positive number of units.

The next step of the method is to "cost" the direct versus the indirect way of doing one unit of A_{ij}. The direct cost of one unit of A_{ij} is c_{ij}, the direct costs of $B_1, B_2, \cdots, B_{m+n-1}$ will be denoted by $c_1, c_2, \cdots, c_{m+n-1}$; i.e., if $B_1 = A_{11}$, then $c_1 = c_{11}$. The indirect cost of A_{ij} will be denoted by $\bar{c}_{ij}$,

$$(9) \qquad \bar{c}_{ij} = \sum_{k=1}^{m+n-1} (\lambda_{ik} + \mu_{jk})c_k = u_i + v_j,$$

where u_i and v_j "cost" the dummy activities ξ_i and η_j,

$$(10) \qquad \begin{aligned} u_i &= \lambda_{i1}c_1 + \cdots, + \lambda_{i,\,m+n-1}c_{m+n-1} \quad (i = 1, 2, \cdots, m), \\ v_j &= \mu_{j1}c_1 + \cdots, + \mu_{j,\,m+n-1}c_{m+n-1} \quad (j = 1, 2, \cdots, n). \end{aligned}$$

The general theory states that if

$$(11) \qquad c_{ij} < \bar{c}_{ij}$$

it pays to introduce A_{ij} and to drop one of the activities $B_1, B_2, \cdots, B_{m+n-1}$ from the feasible solution. Which one to drop will now be discussed.

Let $x_1, x_2, \cdots, x_{m+n-1}$ be the number of units of $B_1, B_2, \cdots, B_{m+n-1}$ in the feasible solution; then

$$(12) \qquad x_1 B_1 + x_2 B_2 + \cdots + x_{m+n-1} B_{m+n-1} = B_0 \qquad (x_i > 0),$$

where B_0 is the column vector $a_1, \cdots, a_m, -b_1, \cdots, -b_n$ (see Table II). It will be noted that x_i is *assumed positive*. The case where one or more $x_i = 0$ will be considered degenerate and will be discussed later. The total cost of the solution given by (12) will be denoted by z_0;

$$(13) \qquad x_1 c_1 + x_2 c_2 + \cdots, + x_{m+n-1} c_{m+n-1} = z_0.$$

Assume $c_{ij} < \bar{c}_{ij}$ for some A_{ij}, and rewrite (8) and (9) as

$$(14) \qquad A_{ij} - (\nu_1 B_1 + \nu_2 B_2 + \cdots + \nu_{m+n-1} B_{m+n-1}) = 0,$$

$$(15) \qquad c_{ij} - (\nu_1 c_1 + \nu_2 c_2 + \cdots + \nu_{m+n-1} c_{m+n-1}) = -(\bar{c}_{ij} - c_{ij}),$$

where

$$(16) \qquad \nu_k = \lambda_{ik} + \mu_{jk}.$$

By multiplying equation (14) by θ and adding this to (12), other feasible solutions are obtained provided $\theta > 0$ and θ is not so large that any coefficient of B_i is negative. By multiplying (15) by θ and adding this to (13), the corresponding cost, z_1, of the new feasible solution is obtained;

$$(17) \qquad\qquad z_1 = z_0 - \theta(\bar{c}_{ij} - c_{ij}),$$

which by (11) is clearly *less* than z_0.

Now there is a very simple rule for evaluating the largest value of θ. Referring back to (6), (7), and (8) it will now be shown that the values of λ_{ik} and μ_{jk} are either 0, $+1$, or -1. If $\lambda_{ik} = +1$ for any B_k, then $\mu_{jk} = 0$ or -1, because in (6) the A_{ij} does not appear with the same sign for differences involving ξ and η. To put it another way, coefficients in (8) are either 0, $+1$, or -1. Moreover, if (8) is used to eliminate any B_k from (7) in order to express ξ_i and η_j in terms of the remaining B_k and the new A_{ij}, it is clear from the structure of A_{ij} that the same properties will hold after the elimination. Thus all coefficients in (14) are $+1$, -1, or 0. Any $\nu_i = +1$ in (14) will automatically place a restriction on the size of θ. The maximum θ is thus the minimum x_i in (12) whose corresponding $\nu_i = +1$ in (14). Therefore

$$(18) \qquad\qquad \theta = \min x_i, \qquad \nu_i = +1.$$

If the minimum occurs for $i = k$, then B_k will be eliminated, and the new solution consists again of $m + n - 1$ activities.

The new feasible solution has x_i increased by θ for $\nu_i = -1$, decreased by θ for $\nu_i = +1$, untouched for $\nu_i = 0$. There will be θ units of A_{ij} introduced. The cost of the new solution is given by (17). The "cost" of the dummy activities ξ_i and η_j given by (10) will be decreased or increased by $+(\bar{c}_{ij} - c_{ij})$, or remain unchanged accordingly as the coefficients of B_k in (7) or of c_k in (10) appear equal to $+1$, -1, or 0, respectively. It should be noted that, if any u_i is increased, no v_j can be increased and conversely.

The selection of A_{ij} to improve the feasible solution depended on $c_{ij} < \bar{c}_{ij}$. The improvement in z, however, may be small or large depending on which A_{ij} is chosen. It has been found empirically that selection of A_{ij} such that

$$(19) \qquad\qquad c_{ij} - \bar{c}_{ij} = \max \quad (i = 1, \cdots, m; j = 1, \cdots, n)$$

will seldom introduce or eliminate an activity that is not in the final solution. Other criteria for selection of A_{ij} are discussed in Chapter XXI.

The process described is iterated, each iteration producing a new feasible solution involving $m + n - 1$ activities. For each iteration the value of z, the total cost, is decreased. In a finite number of steps an optimum solution is obtained, since the solution at each iteration is unique, and there is only a finite number of ways to choose a basic set of $m + n - 1$ activities.

2. The Case of Degeneracy

If for any iteration several B_k are eliminated, the general rule is to treat only one as eliminated and leave the others formally in the solution even though they appear with zero weight. A criterion will now be developed for the determination of the B_k with zero weight to be dropped from the basic solution. This is necessary, because it is not known whether an *arbitrary* selection will lead to a decrease in total cost in a finite number of iterations. In empirical examples *arbitrary* selection has proved to be a good working rule. However, for a slight amount of additional effort, one can protect oneself against possible failure of the method in degenerate cases. The fundamental idea is that by slight modifications of the marginal totals, a_i and b_j, in Table I, degeneracy can be avoided in a family of equations whose marginal totals differ uniformly from the corresponding a_i and b_j by less than any desired ϵ.[2]

Any basic solution consists of $m + n - 1$ combinations, and, in case of degeneracy, it involves one or more combinations with zero weights. When this occurs, it implies that a partial sum of the a_i's equals a partial sum of the b_j's. The proof can be argued as follows:

Let $m \geq n$; then there is at least one row in Table I which contains exactly one B_k from the basic solution (there must always, of course, be one or more for each column or row). Otherwise the number of A_{ij} in the basic solution would be at least $2m$, which would require $2m \leq m + n - 1$, or $m \leq n - 1$, i.e., a contradiction. Thus one of the rows yields $x_{ij} = a_i$. Deleting the ith row and replacing b_j by $b_j - a_i$, the process may be repeated with the reduced array. With each iteration the new row or column totals differ from the previous ones by one difference, $a_i - b_j$ or $b_j - a_i$; in terms of the original a_i and b_j's the new a_i and b_j are differences of partial sums of the original a_i and b_j. Thus, if at any stage an $x_{ij} = 0$, this implies the vanishing of both the new a_i and b_j.

[2] The *specific* way to alter the marginal totals by ϵ to avoid "degeneracy" problems has been introduced in this version, although it was indicated as possible in earlier papers. This extension was stimulated by Robert Dorfman and Merrill Flood, as well as by Tjalling C. Koopmans and M. L. Slater, the referees of this manuscript, who have insisted that the status of degeneracy be clarified.

Thus degeneracy can be avoided if we can prevent any partial sum of the a_i's equaling a partial sum of the b_j's. Consider a class of problems with unspecified ϵ in which

$$\bar{a}_i = a_i + \epsilon \qquad\qquad (i = 1, 2, \cdots, m),$$

(20)
$$\bar{b}_j = \begin{cases} b_j & (j = 1, 2, \cdots, n-1), \\ b_j + m\epsilon & (j = n). \end{cases}$$

Assume $\epsilon > 0$. It will be shown that there exists an ϵ_0 such that for any ϵ in the range $0 < \epsilon < \epsilon_0$ there can be no partial sum of $\bar{a}_i$'s equal to a partial sum of $\bar{b}_j$'s. There are a finite number of possible equalities of partial sums of $\bar{a}_i$'s to partial sums of $\bar{b}_j$'s. Consider the kth of these possibilities; it will be shown that there exists a range $0 < \epsilon < \epsilon_k$ in which $\sum_k \bar{a}_i \neq \sum_k \bar{b}_j$, where ϵ_k depends on the partial sums in question. The sum of the coefficients of ϵ associated with the $\bar{a}_i$ cannot be equal to the sum of the coefficients of ϵ associated with the $\bar{b}_j$, for the sum on the $\bar{a}$ side has a minimum of 1 and a maximum of $m-1$, while the sum on the $\bar{b}$ side is either 0 or m. Since the coefficients of ϵ are not equal, by setting $\sum_k \bar{a}_i = \sum_k \bar{b}_j$ we can solve for ϵ. If $\epsilon \leqq 0$, set $\epsilon_k = +\infty$, and if $\epsilon > 0$, set $\epsilon_k = \epsilon$. There are a finite number of ϵ_k's. Let ϵ_0 be the smallest of them; then for $0 < \epsilon < \epsilon_0$, there is no partial sum of $\bar{a}_i$'s equal to a partial sum of $\bar{b}_j$'s.

For any basis, the general solution $\{\bar{x}_k\}$ to $(\bar{a}_1, \bar{a}_2, \cdots, \bar{a}_m; \bar{b}_1, \bar{b}_2, \cdots, \bar{b}_n)$ can be represented as the sum of two special solutions; the first, $\{x_k\}$, for $(a_1, a_2, \cdots, a_m; b_1, b_2, \cdots, b_n)$, the second, $\{x'_k\}$, for the coefficients of ϵ, where $k = 1, 2, \cdots, m+n-1$. Thus

(21)
$$\bar{x}_k = x_k + x'_k\epsilon \qquad (k = 1, 2, \cdots, m+n-1).$$

In the shift from one basis to the next, the use of $\bar{x}_k$ constitutes a small additional effort over just working with x_k alone. This device may now be used to resolve all ties (i.e., equalities, that give rise to degeneracy). Suppose, for example, that in (18) $\theta = x_k = x_l$; then the min $[\bar{x}_k, \bar{x}_l]$ is chosen by comparing the value of x'_k with x'_l.[3]

---

[3] It has been proved by A. Orden that the following procedure for assigning a fixed value to ϵ removes degeneracy and is convenient for computation. Let δ equal the least significant digit in the shipments a_i and b_j. Take ϵ equal to the largest significant digit in $\delta/2m$. This ϵ used in (20) permits no equalities of partial sums. All computations are done on the basis of $\bar{a}_i$ and $\bar{b}_j$. These artificial shipments have more significant digits than the original problem. Upon completion of the computations, the final $\bar{x}_{ij}$ values are rounded off to the same number of significant digits as in the original a_i and b_j, and the results are then an exact minimum cost solution to the problem.

A solution which minimizes the total cost will be reached in a finite number of iterative steps because the removal of degeneracy by the ϵ technique makes it impossible for a basis to appear more than once. With degeneracy removed, the total cost must decrease at each stage of iteration, which would not be true if a basis were to recur. Since the number of possible bases is finite, a minimum cost solution must be reached in a finite number of iterations.

3. RULES FOR COMPUTING AN OPTIMUM SOLUTION

(a) Construct a unit cost table giving the cost, c_{ij}, to ship a unit amount from shipping origin i to shipping destination j. In the example (Table III), the cost to ship from origin (2) to destination (1) is 5; from

TABLE III.   DIRECT UNIT COSTS, c_{ij}

		Destinations				
	$\diagdown\, j$ i	(1)	(2)	(3)	(4)	(5)
Origins	(1)	3	2	1	2	3
	(2)	5	4	3	−1	1
	(3)	0	2	3	4	5

origin (2) to destination (4) is −1. No interpretation is given to negative cost, except to show that there is no restriction on the sign of c_{ij}. A constant amount may be added or subtracted uniformly from all c_{ij} without affecting the values of x_{ij} appearing in the solution. In Table IV the total amount to be shipped is 13. If all c_{ij} were increased by 2, the total cost of transportation would be increased by $2 \cdot 13 = 26$.

TABLE IV.   AMOUNTS TO BE SHIPPED

		Destinations					Total
	$\diagdown\, j$ i	(1)	(2)	(3)	(4)	(5)	$\bar{a}_i$
Origins	(1)	x_{11}	x_{12}	x_{13}	x_{14}	x_{15}	$1 + \epsilon$
	(2)	x_{21}	x_{22}	x_{23}	x_{24}	x_{25}	$5 + \epsilon$
	(3)	x_{31}	x_{32}	x_{33}	x_{34}	x_{35}	$7 + \epsilon$
Total	$\bar{b}_j$	3	3	3	2	$2 + 3\epsilon$	$13 + 3\epsilon$

(b) The basic problem is illustrated in the shipping table of the example (Table IV). Unknown values, $x_{ij} \geqq 0$, are to be selected so that the row totals sum to $a_1 = 1$, $a_2 = 5$, $a_3 = 7$, and the column totals to $b_1 = b_2 = b_3 = 3$, $b_4 = b_5 = 2$ in such a manner that $\sum_{i=1}^{n} \sum_{j=1}^{m} c_{ij} x_{ij}$ is a minimum. For computation purposes Table IV should be set up leaving the boxes for x_{ij} blank. To avoid degeneracy, a_i and b_j are considered the limits of $\bar{a}_i$ and $\bar{b}_j$ as $\epsilon \to +0$, where (1) $\bar{a}_i = a_i + \epsilon$ for $i = 1, 2, \cdots, m$, and (2) $\bar{b}_j = b_j$ for $j = 1, 2, \cdots, n - 1$ and $\bar{b}_j = b_j + m\epsilon$ for $j = n$.

(c) An arbitrary basic solution is obtained (Table V) by assigning a

TABLE V. ARBITRARY BASIC SOLUTION, $\bar{x}_{ij}$

		Destinations					Total
	$\begin{smallmatrix}j\\i\end{smallmatrix}$	(1)	(2)	(3)	(4)	(5)	$\bar{a}_i$
Origins	(1)	$1 + \epsilon$					$1 + \epsilon$
	(2)	$2 - \epsilon$	$3 + 0\epsilon$	$0 + 2\epsilon$			$5 + \epsilon$
	(3)			$3 - 2\epsilon$	$2 + 0\epsilon$	$2 + 3\epsilon$	$7 + \epsilon$
Total	$\bar{b}_j$	3	3	3	2	$2 + 3\epsilon$	$13 + 3\epsilon$

value, $\bar{x}_{11} = \min (\bar{a}_1, \bar{b}_1)$ as $\epsilon \to +0$. In the example $3 + 0\epsilon > 1 + \epsilon$. If $\bar{a}_1$ is minimum, all other $\bar{x}_{ij}$ in the first row are zero; if $\bar{b}_1$ is minimum, all other $\bar{x}_{ij}$ in the first column are zero. Deleting then, the evaluated row or column, the procedure is now repeated with the remaining rows or columns where the marginal totals are reduced by the evaluated part.

Actually there is no need to carry along the ϵ part of this solution unless at some stage there is an equality when taking a minimum. In the example such an equality took place in the third stage in evaluating $x_{22} = 3$. Thus there appears to be a choice whether to have (2, 3) or (3, 2) included as next point in the basis. However, by going back and including the ϵ part of the solution, it is clear that (2, 3) is the next combination to be introduced into the basis.

(d) Step 1, part I of the iterative process, consists in determining the indirect unit cost table, $\bar{c}_{ij}$, associated with the basis. For any (i, j) appearing in the basis, $\bar{c}_{ij} = c_{ij}$. Any other $\bar{c}_{ij}$ is obtained through the relation $\bar{c}_{ij} = u_i + v_j$. In the example, start with any c_{ij} from a basis (e.g., $c_{ij} = c_{34}$). Arbitrarily set $u_i = c_{ij}$ and $v_j = 0$; thus

$$u_3 = c_{34}, \qquad v_4 = 0.$$

Consider next all c_{kl} from the basis that have a subscript in common with c_{34}; these are c_{33} and c_{35}. From this v_3 and v_5 can be evaluated by

$$v_3 - v_4 = c_{33} - c_{34},$$

$$v_5 - v_4 = c_{35} - c_{34}.$$

Consider next all c_{kl} that have subscripts in common with c_{33} and c_{35}; this set consists only of c_{23}, whence

$$u_2 - u_3 = c_{23} - c_{33}.$$

Consider next the c_{kl} with subscripts in common with c_{23}; these are c_{21} and c_{22}, whence

$$v_1 - v_3 = c_{21} - c_{23},$$

$$v_2 - v_3 = c_{22} - c_{23}.$$

Finally, the only c_{kl} with subscripts in common with c_{21} and c_{22} is c_{11}, whence

$$u_1 - u_2 = c_{11} - c_{21}.$$

The indirect unit cost table, $\bar{c}_{ij} = u_i + v_j$, may now be formed. In Table VI, step 1, the (i, j) combinations occurring in the basis are given in bold-face type; for these, $\bar{c}_{ij} = c_{ij}$.

(e) Compare the indirect cost table, $\bar{c}_{ij} = u_i + v_j$, with the direct costs, c_{ij}, in Table III, and form

$$M = \max (\bar{c}_{ij} - c_{ij}) = \bar{c}_{kl} - c_{kl}.$$

There are two possibilities: $M > 0$ or $M = 0$. If $M > 0$, select any combination (k, l) such that $\bar{c}_{kl} - c_{kl} = M$. This means that as many units as possible, $\theta = \theta_1$, of combination (k, l) are to be introduced into the transportation schedule, and the remainder is to be made up from combinations in the basis. If $M = 0$, it means that the basis represents the final solution, and no units of any other combination are to be introduced. In Table VI, step 1, the element $\bar{c}_{24}$ is boxed to indicate $M = \bar{c}_{24} - c_{24} = 5$. This is an arbitrary selection since, also, $M = \bar{c}_{31} - c_{31} = 5$.

(f) Step 1, part II of the iterative process, consists in determining the solution of the transportation problem in terms of the combinations occurring in the basis under one of two assumptions: If $M = \bar{c}_{kl} - c_{kl} > 0$, an unknown number of units $\theta = \theta_1$, of combination (k, l), will be assumed to occur (if $M = 0$, no units of any other combination will be assumed to occur). The shipping table is solved in terms of the basis by seeking a row or column in which only one element appears in the

TABLE VI. ITERATIVE PROCESS OF COST MINIMIZATION

Step 1

$\bar{c}_{ij}$

3	2	1	2	3
5	4	3	$\boxed{4}$	5
5	4	3	4	5

x_{ij}

1					1
2	3	$\boxed{0-\theta_1}$	θ_1		5
		$3+\theta_1$	$2-\theta_1$	2	7
3	3	3	2	2	13

Step 2

$\bar{c}_{ij}$

3	2	-4	-3	-2
5	4	-2	-1	0
$\boxed{10}$	9	3	4	5

$\bar{x}_{ij}$

$1\ +\epsilon$					$1+\ \epsilon$
$2-\theta_2-\epsilon$	3		$0+\theta_2+2\epsilon$		$5+\ \epsilon$
θ_2		3	$2-\theta_2-2\epsilon$	$2+3\epsilon$	$7+\ \epsilon$
3	3	3	2	$2+3\epsilon$	$13+3\epsilon$

Step 3

$\bar{c}_{ij}$

3	2	6	-3	8
5	4	8	-1	$\boxed{10}$
0	-1	3	-6	5

x_{ij}

1					1
$\boxed{0-\theta_3}$	3		2	$+\theta_3$	5
$2+\theta_3$		3		$2-\theta_3$	7
3	3	3	2	2	

Step 4

$\bar{c}_{ij}$

3	$\boxed{11}$	6	6	8
-4	4	-1	-1	1
0	8	3	3	5

x_{ij}

$\boxed{1-\theta_4}$	$+\theta_4$				1
	$3-\theta_4$		2	$0+\theta_4$	5
$2+\theta_4$		3		$2-\theta_4$	7
3	3	3	2	2	

TABLE VI (*Continued*)

Step 5

$\bar{c}_{ij}$

6	2	-3	-3	-1
-4	4	-1	-1	1
0	[8]	3	3	5

x_{ij}

	1				1
	$2-\theta_5$		2	$1+\theta_5$	5
3	$+\theta_5$	3		$\boxed{1-\theta_5}$	7
3	3	3	2	2	

Step 6

$\bar{c}_{ij}$

0	2	3	-3	-1
2	4	[5]	-1	+1
0	2	3	-3	-1

x_{ij}

	1				1
	$\boxed{1-\theta_6}$	$+\theta_6$	2	2	5
3	$1+\theta_6$	$3-\theta_6$			7
3	3	3	2	2	

Step 7

$\bar{c}_{ij}$

0	2	[3]	-1	+1
0	2	3	-1	+1
0	2	3	-1	+1

x_{ij}

	$\boxed{1-\theta_7}$	$+\theta_7$			1
		1	2	2	5
3	$2+\theta_7$	$2-\theta_7$			7
3	3	3	2	2	

Step 8

$\bar{c}_{ij}$

-2	0	1	-3	-1
0	2	3	-1	+1
0	2	3	-1	+1

x_{ij}

		1			1
		1	2	2	5
3	3	1			7
3	3	3	2	2	

basis (there is always one such in the larger dimension). Thus $x_{11} = 1$, $x_{22} = 3$, $x_{34} = 2 - \theta_1$, $x_{44} = 2$. These variables are eliminated, and the process is repeated with the remainder. The maximum value for θ_1 that can be introduced equals the minimum x_{ij} in which a term $x_{ij} - \theta_1$ occurs. In the example, min $x_{ij} = x_{23} = 0 = \theta_1$. Thus shipping combination (2, 3) is to be dropped; this combination is the one boxed in the right-hand table. The case where there is a multiple choice of combinations to be dropped is discussed in (g) below.

(g) If $M > 0$ in any step k, the process (d), (e), (f) is repeated for step $k + 1$. A new basis, consisting of all the combinations occurring in the basis for step k, is formed by deleting the boxed combination in the x_{ij}-table and introducing the boxed combination occurring in the c_{ij}-table. In step 2 there was ambiguity as to the combination (i, j) in our example to be dropped. Thus min $x_{ij} = x_{21} = x_{34} = 2 = \theta_2$. *In this case the ϵ component of $\bar{a}_i$ and $\bar{b}_j$ must be adjoined and a solution in terms of ϵ obtained.* It is not possible with this component to have any ambiguity. Thus $\bar{x}_{34} < \bar{x}_{21}$ for $\epsilon > 0$, and combination (3, 4) is the one to be dropped in step 3. If $M = 0$ in step k, the x_{ij}-table represents the final shipping table.

(h) The total cost of any solution is given by $\sum c_{ij} x_{ij}$. A simple formula for evaluating z from one step to the next is given in Table VII.

TABLE VII. EVALUATING TOTAL COST, z

Step	$z_{t+1} = z_t - M_t \theta_t$	$M = \max \bar{c}_{ij} - c_{ij}$	θ
1	$z_1 = 52$ *	$M_1 = 5$	$\theta_1 = 0$
2	$z_2 = 52$	$M_2 = 10$	$\theta_2 = 2$
3	$z_3 = 32$	$M_3 = 9$	$\theta_3 = 0$
4	$z_4 = 32$	$M_4 = 9$	$\theta_4 = 1$
5	$z_5 = 23$	$M_5 = 6$	$\theta_5 = 1$
6	$z_6 = 17$	$M_6 = 2$	$\theta_6 = 1$
7	$z_7 = 15$	$M_7 = 2$	$\theta_7 = 1$
8	$z_8 = 13$	$M_8 = 0$	

* Evaluated directly, $z = \sum c_{ij} x_{ij}$.

Chapter XXV

COMPUTATIONAL SUGGESTIONS FOR MAXIMIZING A LINEAR FUNCTION SUBJECT TO LINEAR INEQUALITIES

By George W. Brown and Tjalling C. Koopmans

It is the purpose of this chapter to record suggestions that arose from discussions between the authors and G. B. Dantzig regarding iterative computational procedures for maximizing a linear function,

$$(1) \qquad\qquad y = c'x$$

(y scalar, c and x vectors), subject to linear inequalities,

$$(2) \qquad\qquad \alpha_k + a_k'x \geqq 0 \quad (k = 1, \cdots, K, \alpha_k \text{ scalar}, a_k \text{ vector}).$$

We distinguish two main cases (1 and 2) and record in each case two suggestions. At present, insufficient experience or theoretical knowledge is available to assess the possible usefulness of these suggestions. No proofs of convergence are offered. The general idea underlying the suggestions is an attempt to make big jumps rather than "crawling along the edges" of the convex set (2), as in the simplex method. It depends on the set (2) whether in fact faster convergence is obtained. In comparing two different methods, it is usually possible to construct sets (2) so as to favor one method as compared with the other. All methods indicated are based on some idea of steepest ascent and thus depend on the units of measurement of the variables x.

1. The Case in which an Initial Point x_0 Satisfying (2) Is Known

1.1. *Traversal method.* Find the largest value θ_0 of the scalar θ such that

$$(3) \qquad\qquad x = x_0 + \theta c$$

satisfies (2), and write

$$(4) \qquad\qquad \bar{x}_0 = x_0 + \theta_0 c.$$

Then, if we insert $\bar{x}_0$ for x in (2), we must for at least one value, k_0, say, of k, have an equality

(5) $$\alpha_{k_0} + a'_{k_0}\bar{x}_0 = 0$$

because otherwise values $\theta > \theta_0$ could be found for which x satisfies (2). If (5) is true for only one value of k, determine scalars λ_0, μ_0, such that

(6) $$c'(\lambda_0 a_{k_0} + \mu_0 c) = 0.$$

This is impossible only if $c = -\nu a_{k_0}$, ν a positive scalar, in which case $\bar{x}_0$ already maximizes y. Determine $\bar{\theta}_0$ as the largest value of θ for which

(7) $$x = \bar{x}_0 + \theta(\lambda_0 a_{k_0} + \mu_0 c)$$

satisfies (2), and write

(8) $$x_1 = \bar{x}_0 + \tfrac{1}{2}\bar{\theta}_0(\lambda_0 a_{k_0} + \mu_0 c).$$

Proceed with x_1 as previously with x_0. If at the nth step more than one value of k_n of k satisfies, or nearly satisfies, an equation like (5), select one arbitrarily, or use an average of all a_{k_n} that satisfy (5) exactly, or within a small amount ϵ, under some rule of normalization used for the vectors a_k.

1.2. *Plane intersection method.* Having obtained the point (4) above, intersect the plane

(9) $$x = \bar{x}_0 + \lambda a_{k_0} + \mu c$$

(λ and μ freely variable scalar parameters) successively with each of the hyperplanes

(10) $$\alpha_k + a'_k x = 0.$$

The intersections consist of K straight lines inside (9). The segments of these lines on which (2) is satisfied form a convex polygon. On the polygon select a point on which y reaches its maximum. Generally there is just one such point, for which write $\bar{x}_1$. Now there are two variants.

1.2a. *Plane determined by normal to the convex set* (2). If x_1 is unique, there are at least two values of k for which (10) is satisfied. Take any one of these, or take their average, as a_{k_1} and proceed as in (9) with $\bar{x}_0$ replaced by $\bar{x}_1$.

1.2b. *Plane determined by normal within boundary of the convex set* (2). Having arrived close to the maximum, it may be desirable to attempt not to lose any of the equalities (10) once they are satisfied.   Let $\bar{x}_n$ be such that

(11) $$\alpha_k + a_k'\bar{x}_n = 0 \qquad (k = k_1, k_2, \cdots, k_{r_n}).$$

In the space of the vectors d such that

(12) $$d'a_{k_r} = 0 \qquad\qquad (r = 1, \cdots, r_n),$$

choose the vector of steepest ascent, i.e., the vector d satisfying

(13) $$d'd = 1, \qquad d'c = \text{maximum},$$

and use that vector as a_{k_n} in (9).   This will have been wasted effort if the resulting $\bar{x}_{n+1}$ fails to satisfy (11).   Since iterations on this principle become computationally more expensive as r_n grows, the present variant should only be employed toward the end of a sequence of iterations.

2. How to Obtain an Initial Point Satisfying (2)

2.1. *Successive penetration method.*   Take an arbitrary initial point, x_0. This point partitions the set S of inequalities (2) into two subsets, S_0 and S_0', those of S_0 being satisfied by x_0, those of S_0' not being satisfied by x_0. If S_0' is empty, the goal has been achieved.   If it is not, select arbitrarily an inequality of S_0', numbered k_0, say.   Use a_{k_0} as the vector c in (1) indicating the "desired direction."   Use the inequalities of S_0 instead of the full set of conditions (2), and apply any variant of the method in Section 1 until a point is reached in which the inequality number k_0 is satisfied.   Call that point x_1 and proceed with a new subset S_1 of the inequalities (2).   Obviously

(14) $$S_0 \subset S_1 \subset S_2 \cdots.$$

If for any n a maximum x_n of $a_{k_n}'x$ subject to the inequalities of S_n fails to satisfy (2) for $k = k_n$, no point satisfying (2) exists.

2.2. *Guided penetration method.*   Instead of selecting an arbitrary a_k of S_0' to be the c in (1), take

(15) $$c = \sum_{k\,\epsilon\,S_0'} (\alpha_k + a_k'x_0) \frac{a_k}{a_k'a_k}.$$

This is the vector sum of the normals dropped from x_0 onto the planes

(16) $$(\alpha_k + a_kx) = 0 \qquad\qquad (k\,\epsilon\,S').$$

Two alternative modes of proceeding from here are worth considering.

2.2a. Keep the c so selected constant while making a number of iterative improvements to x_0 by method A, always requiring that the inequalities S_0 be preserved.

2.2b. Be willing to sacrifice some inequalities of S_0 if thereby a larger number of inequalities of S_0' can be satisfied. In this case determine θ_0 in (4) in such a way as to minimize the number of inequalities in S_1'.

For neither of these variants certain attainment of the objective (if attainable) has been proved. They might, however, work faster than the successive penetration method. The second alternative is suspect if the convex set (2) is not bounded.

REFERENCES

ARROW, KENNETH J., 1951, *Social Choice and Individual Values*, Cowles Commission Monograph No. 12, New York: John Wiley & Sons, Inc., 1951, 99 pp.

——, 1950, "Homogeneous Systems in Mathematical Economics: A Comment," *Econometrica*, Vol. 18, January, 1950, pp. 60–62.

BARONE, ENRICO, "The Ministry of Production in the Collectivist State," in *Collectivist Economic Planning*, F. A. von Hayek, ed., London: George Routledge and Sons, Ltd., 1935, pp. 245–290.

BELL, F. G., *see* G. M. Browning, R. A. Norton, A. G. McCall, and F. G. Bell.

BERGSON (BURK), ABRAM, "A Reformulation of Certain Aspects of Welfare Economics," *Quarterly Journal of Economics*, Vol. 52, February, 1938, pp. 310–334.

BONNESEN, T., AND W. FENCHEL, *Theorie der konvexen Körper*, Ergebnisse der Mathematik und ihrer Grenzgebiete, Vol. 3, No. 1, Berlin: Julius Springer, 1934; New York: Chelsea Publishing Company, 1948, 164 pp.

BROWN, D. W., *see* John von Neumann and G. W. Brown.

BROWNING, G. M., R. A. NORTON, A. G. McCALL AND F. C. BELL, "Investigation in Erosion Control and the Reclamation of Eroded Land," *Technical Bulletin of the United States Department of Agriculture, Soil Conservation Service*, No. 959, October, 1948, pp. 1–88.

CAHN, A. S., "The Warehouse Problem" (abstract), *Bulletin of the American Mathematical Society*, Vol. 54, October, 1948, p. 1073.

CHAMPERNOWNE, D. G., "A Note on J. von Neumann's Article," *Review of Economic Studies*, Vol. 13, No. 1, 1945–46, pp. 10–18.

CORNFIELD, J., W. D. EVANS, AND M. HOFFENBERG, "Full Employment Patterns, 1950," Parts I and II, *Monthly Labor Review*, Vol. 64, February and March, 1947, pp. 163–190, 420–432.

DANTZIG, GEORGE B., "Programming of Interdependent Activities: II. Mathematical Model," *Econometrica*, Vol. 17, July–October, 1949, pp. 200–211. (Reprinted in revised form as Chapter II of this volume.)

——, *see* Marshall K. Wood and George B. Dantzig.

DINES, L. L., "Convex Extension and Linear Inequalities," *Bulletin of the American Mathematical Society*, Vol. 42, June, 1936, pp. 353–365.

DUESENBERRY, JAMES S., "Income-Consumption Relations and Their Implications," in *Income, Employment and Public Policy: Essays in Honor of Alvin H. Hansen*, New York: W. W. Norton and Co., 1948, pp. 54–81.

Electric Circuits, by members of the staff of the Department of Electrical Engineering, Massachusetts Institute of Technology, New York: John Wiley & Sons, Inc., 1943, 782 pp.

EVANS, W. D., *see* J. Cornfield, W. D. Evans, and M. Hoffenberg.

FARKAS, J., "Über die Theorie der einfachen Ungleichungen," *Journal für reine und angewandte Mathematik*, Vol. 124, 1901, pp. 1–27.

FENCHEL, W., *see* T. Bonnesen and W. Fenchel.

GEORGESCU-ROEGEN, N., "Fixed Coefficients of Production and the Marginal Productivity Theory," *Review of Economic Studies*, Vol. 3, October, 1935, pp. 40–49.

HALMOS, PAUL R., *Finite Dimensional Vector Spaces*, Annals of Mathematics Studies, No. 7, Princeton: Princeton University Press, 1948.

382   REFERENCES

HAWKINS, DAVID, AND HERBERT SIMON, "Some Conditions of Macro-Economic Stability," *Econometrica*, Vol. 17, July–October, 1949, pp. 245–248.

HICKS, J. R., "The Foundations of Welfare Economics," *Economic Journal*, Vol. 49, December, 1939, pp. 696–712.

HITCHCOCK, FRANK L., "The Distribution of a Product from Several Sources to Numerous Localities," *Journal of Mathematics and Physics*, Massachusetts Institute of Technology, Vol. 20, 1941, pp. 224–230.

HOFFENBERG, MARVIN, see J. Cornfield, W. D. Evans, and M. Hoffenberg.

HOTELLING, HAROLD, "The General Welfare in Relation to Problems of Taxation and of Railway and Utility Rates," *Econometrica*, Vol. 6, July, 1938, pp. 242–269.

KALDOR, NICHOLAS, "Welfare Propositions of Economics and Interpersonal Comparisons of Utility," *Economic Journal*, Vol. 49, September, 1939, pp. 549–552.

KIRCHHOFF, G., "Über die Auflösung der Gleichungen, auf welche man bei der Untersuchung der linearen Verteilung galvanischer Ströme geführt wird," *Annalen der Physik und Chemie*, Vol. 72, 1847, pp. 497–508 (also in *Gesammelte Abhandlungen*, Leipzig: J. A. Barth, 1882, pp. 22–33).

KÖNIG, DENES, *Theorie der endlichen und unendlichen Graphen; Kombinatorische Topologie der Streckenkomplexe*, Leipzig: Akademische Verlagsgesellschaft M.B.H., 1936, 258 pp.

KOOPMANS, TJALLING C., 1947, "Optimum Utilization of the Transportation System," in *Proceedings of the International Statistical Conferences, 1947*, Washington, D. C., Vol. 5 (Vol. 5 reprinted as Supplement to *Econometrica*, Vol. 17, 1949; article to be reprinted as Cowles Commission Paper, New Series, No. 34; abstract in *Econometrica*, Vol. 16, January, 1948, pp. 66–68).

———, 1951, "Efficient Allocation of Resources," *Econometrica* (forthcoming).

KUHN, H. W., AND A. W. TUCKER, eds., *Contributions to the Theory of Games*, Annals of Mathematics Studies, No. 24, Princeton: Princeton University Press, 1950, 217 pp.

LANGE, OSKAR, 1938, "On the Economic Theory of Socialism," in F. Taylor and O. Lange, *On the Economic Theory of Socialism*, Benjamin E. Lippincott, ed., Minneapolis: The University of Minnesota Press, 1938, pp. 57–142.

———, 1942, "The Foundations of Welfare Economics," *Econometrica*, Vol. 10, July–October, 1942, pp. 215–228.

———, 1944, *Price Flexibility and Employment*, Cowles Commission Monograph No. 8, Bloomington, Ind.: The Principia Press, Inc., 1944, 114 pp.

LE CORBEILLER, PH., 1931, *Les systèmes autoentretenus et les oscillations de relaxation*, Conférences d'actualités scientifiques et industrielles, No. 27, Paris: Hermann et Cie., 1931, 46 pp.

———, 1933, "Les oscillations de relaxation," *Econometrica*, Vol. 1, July, 1933, pp. 328–332.

LEFSCHETZ, SOLOMON, *Introduction to Topology*, Princeton Mathematical Series, No. 11, Princeton: Princeton University Press, 1949, 218 pp.

LEONTIEF, WASSILY W., 1928, "Die Wirtschaft als Kreislauf," *Archiv für Sozialwissenschaft und Sozialpolitik*, Vol. 60, No. 3, 1928.

———, 1936, "Quantitative Input and Output Relations in the Economic System of the United States," *Review of Economic Statistics*, Vol. 18, August, 1936, pp. 105–125.

———, 1937, "Interrelations of Prices, Output, Savings, and Investment," *Review of Economic Statistics*, Vol. 19, August, 1937, pp. 109–132.

LEONTIEF, WASSILY W., 1941, *The Structure of the American Economy, 1919–1929*, Cambridge, Mass.: Harvard University Press, 1941, 181 pp. (new, enlarged edition, New York: Oxford University Press, 1951).

———, 1944, "Output, Employment, Consumption, and Investment," *Quarterly Journal of Economics*, Vol. 48, February, 1944, pp. 290–314.

———, 1946a, "Exports, Imports, Domestic Output, and Employment," *Quarterly Journal of Economics*, Vol. 60, February 1946, pp., 171–193.

———, 1946b, "Wages, Profit, and Prices," *Quarterly Journal of Economics*, Vol. 61, November, 1946, pp. 26–39.

———, 1948a, "Econometrics," in *A Survey of Contemporary Economics*, H. S. Ellis, ed., Philadelphia: The Blakiston Co., 1948, pp. 388–411.

———, 1948b, "Computational Problems Arising in Connection with Economic Analysis of Industrial Relationships," *Proceedings of a Symposium on Large-Scale Digital Calculating Machinery*, Cambridge, Mass.: Harvard University Press, 1948, pp. 169–175.

———, 1949, "Recent Developments in the Study of Interindustrial Relationships," in *Papers and Proceedings of the Sixty-first Annual Meeting of the American Economic Association, American Economic Review*, Vol. 39, May, 1949, pp. 211–225 (with discussion by Solomon Fabricant, Irvin Friend and Walter Jacobs, Marvin Hoffenberg, Tjalling C. Koopmans, Raymond W. Goldsmith, and Oskar Morgenstern, pp. 226–240).

LERNER, ABBA P., *The Economics of Control*, New York: The Macmillan Co., 1944, 428 pp.

McCALL, A. G., see G. M. Browning, R. A. Norton, A. G. McCall, and F. G. Bell.

MINKOWSKI, HERMAN, *Geometrie der Zahlen*, Leipzig and Berlin: B. Teubner, 1896, 1910, 256 pp.

MISES, LUDWIG VON, 1922, *Die Gemeinwirtschaft*, Vienna: 1922 (revised edition, 1932; English edition, *Socialism*, London: Jonathan Cape, Ltd., 1936, 521 pp.).

———, 1935, "Economic Calculation in the Socialist Commonwealth," *Collectivist Economic Planning*, F. A. von Hayek, ed., London: George Routledge, 1935, pp. 87–130.

MODIGLIANI, FRANCO, "Fluctuations in the Saving-Income Ratio: A Problem in Economic Forecasting," in *Studies in Income and Wealth*, Vol. XI, New York: National Bureau of Economic Research, 1949, pp. 371–441.

MORGENSTERN, OSKAR, *On the Accuracy of Economic Observations*, Princeton: Princeton University Press, 1950, 101 pp.

———, see also John von Neumann and Oskar Morgenstern.

NEISSER, HANS, "Lohnhöhe und Beschäftigungsgrad im Marktgleichgewicht," *Weltwirtschaftliches Archiv*, Vol. 36, 1932, pp. 413–455.

NEUMANN, JOHN VON, 1937, 1945, "Über ein ökonomisches Gleichungssystem und eine Verallgemeinerung des Brouwerschen Fixpunktsatzes," *Ergebnisse eines mathematischen Kolloquiums*, No. 8, 1935–36, pp. 73–83, Leipzig and Vienna: Franz Deuticke, 1937 (English translation, "A Model of General Economic Equilibrium," *Review of Economic Studies*, Vol. 13, No. 1, 1945–46, pp. 1–9).

———, 1947, *Discussion of a Maximum Problem* (manuscript), Princeton: Institute for Advanced Study, 1947.

———, 1948, *A Numerical Method for Determination of the Value and Best Strategies of a Zero-Sum, Two-Person Game* (manuscript), Princeton: Institute for Advanced Study, 1948.

NEUMANN, JOHN VON, AND G. W. BROWN, "Solutions of Games by Differential Equations," in *Contributions to the Theory of Games*, H. W. Kuhn and A. W. Tucker, eds., Annals of Mathematics Studies, No. 24, Princeton: Princeton University Press, 1950, pp. 73–79.

NEUMANN, JOHN VON, AND OSKAR MORGENSTERN, *Theory of Games and Economic Behavior*, Princeton: Princeton University Press, 1944 (second edition, 1947, 640 pp.).

NORTON, R. A., *see* G. M. Browning, R. A. Norton, A. G. McCall, and F. G. Bell.

PARETO, VILFREDO, *Manuel d'économie politique*, Paris: V. Giard et E. Brière, 1909, 695 pp.

POL, BALTH. VAN DER, "On 'Relaxation Oscillations,' " *London, Edinburgh and Dublin Philosophical Magazine and Journal of Science*, Seventh Series, Vol. 2, November, 1926, pp. 978–992.

REDER, MELVIN WARREN, *Studies in the Theory of Welfare Economics*, New York: Columbia University Press, 1947, 208 pp.

REMAK, ROBERT, "Kann die Volkswirtschaftslehre eine exakte Wissenschaft werden?" *Jahrbücher für Nationalökonomie und Statistik*, 1929, 131 Band, III Folge, Band 76, pp. 703–735.

SAKS, STANISLAW, *Theory of the Integral*, Warszawa-Lwow, New York: G. H. E. Stechert and Co., 1937 (second edition), 347 pp.

SAMUELSON, PAUL A., 1939, "Interactions between the Multiplier Analysis and the Principle of Acceleration," *Review of Economic Statistics*, Vol. 21, May, 1939, pp. 75–78.

———, 1947, *Foundations of Economic Analysis*, Cambridge, Mass.: Harvard University Press, 1947, 448 pp.

———, 1948, "The Simple Mathematics of Income Determination," in *Income, Employment and Public Policy: Essays in Honor of Alvin H. Hansen*, New York: W. W. Norton and Co., 1948, pp. 133–155.

———, 1949, *Market Mechanisms and Maximization* (manuscript), Santa Monica: The RAND Corporation, 1949, 78 pp.

SCHLESINGER, KARL, "Über die Produktionsgleichungen der ökonomischen Wertlehre," *Ergebnisse eines mathematischen Kolloquiums*, No. 6, 1933–34, Leipzig and Vienna: Franz Deuticke, 1935, pp. 10–11.

SCHNEIDER, ERICH, "Bemerkungen zur Grenzproduktivitätstheorie," *Zeitschrift für Nationalökonomie*, Vol. 4, No. 5, 1933, pp. 604–624.

SIERPINSKI, WACLAW, *Introduction to General Topology*, Toronto: University of Toronto Press, 1934, 283 pp.

SIMON, HERBERT, *see* David Hawkins and Herbert Simon.

STACKELBERG, HEINRICH VON, "Zwei kritische Bemerkungen zur Preistheorie Gustav Cassels," *Zeitschrift für Nationalökonomie*, Vol. 4, No. 4, 1933, pp. 456–472.

STIGLER, GEORGE F., "The Cost of Subsistence," *Journal of Farm Economics*, Vol. 27, May, 1945, pp. 303–314.

TOMPKINS, C. B., *Projection Methods in Calculation of Some Linear Problems* (mimeographed), Engineering Research Associates, Logistic Papers, Issue No. IV.

TUCKER, A. W., AND H. W. KUHN, *see* H. W. Kuhn and A. W. Tucker.

VILLE, JEAN, "Sur la théorie des jeux ou intervient l'habileté des joueurs," in *Traité du calcul des probabilités et de ses applications*, Emil Borel, ed., Vol. IV, Part 2, Paris: Gauthiers-Villars, 1938, pp. 105–113.

WALD, ABRAHAM, 1935, "Über die eindeutige positive Lösbarkeit der neuen Produktionsgleichungen," *Ergebnisse eines mathematischen Kolloquiums*, No. 6, 1933–34, Leipzig and Vienna: Franz Deuticke, 1935, pp. 12–20.

WALD, ABRAHAM, 1936a, "Über die Produktionsgleichungen der ökonomischen Wertlehre," *Ergebnisse eines mathematischen Kolloquiums*, No. 7, 1934–35, Leipzig and Vienna: Franz Deuticke, 1936, pp. 1–6.

———, 1936b, "Über einige Gleichungsysteme der mathematischen Ökonomie," *Zeitschrift für Nationalökonomie*, 1936, Vol. 7, No. 5, pp. 637–670.

WEYL, HERMANN, "Elementare Theorie der konvexen Polyeder," *Commentarii Mathematici Helvetici*, Vol. 7, 1934–35, pp. 290–306 (English translation, "The Elementary Theory of Convex Polyhedra," in *Contributions to the Theory of Games*, H. W. Kuhn and A. W. Tucker, eds., Annals of Mathematics Studies, No. 24, Princeton: Princeton University Press, 1950, pp. 3–18).

WOOD, MARSHALL K., AND GEORGE B. DANTZIG, "Programming of Interdependent Activities: I. General Discussion," *Econometrica*, Vol. 17, July–October, 1949, pp. 193–199. (Reprinted in revised form as Chapter I of this volume.)

ZEUTHEN, F., "Das Prinzip der Knappheit, technische Kombination und ökonomische Qualität," *Zeitschrift für Nationalökonomie*, Vol. 7, No. 1, 1933, pp. 1–24.

INDEX OF NAMES

387

SUBJECT INDEX